STUDIES IN APPLIED MECHANICS 8

Probabilistic Approach to Mechanisms

STUDIES IN APPLIED MECHANICS

1. Mechanics and Strength of Materials (Skalmierski)

2. Nonlinear Differential Equations (Fučík and Kufner)

3. Mathematical Theory of Elastic and Elastico-Plastic Bodies
   An Introduction (Nečas and Hlaváček)

4. Variational, Incremental and Energy Methods
   in Solid Mechanics and Shell Theory (Mason)

5. Mechanics of Structured Media, Parts A and B (Selvadurai, Editor)

6. Mechanics of Material Behavior (Dvorak and Shield, Editors)

7. Mechanics of Granular Materials: New Models and Constitutive
   Relations (Jenkins and Satake, Editors)

8. Probabilistic Approach to Mechanisms (Sandler)

STUDIES IN APPLIED MECHANICS 8

Probabilistic Approach to Mechanisms

B. Z. Sandler

Mechanical Engineering Department, Ben-Gurion University of the Negev, Beer-Sheva, Israel

ELSEVIER
Amsterdam – Oxford – New York – Tokyo 1984

ELSEVIER SCIENCE PUBLISHERS B.V.
Molenwerf 1
P.O. Box 211, 1000 AE Amsterdam, The Netherlands

Distributors for the United States and Canada:

ELSEVIER SCIENCE PUBLISHING COMPANY INC.
52, Vanderbilt Avenue
New York, NY 10017

ISBN 0-444-42306-0 (Vol. 8)
ISBN 0-444-41758-3 (Series)

Printed in The Netherlands

ACKNOWLEDGEMENT

I express my deep gratitude and appreciation to my colleagues at the Mechanical Engineering Department of the Ben Gurion University of the Negev for their spiritual support and efficient cooperation in accumulating the material for this book and assistance in writing it.

I express especially sincere gratitude and thanks to those who transformed my poor Russian English into something readable, who edited, typed and helped through their useful advice in manuscript writing. My thanks to Mrs. Inez Muerinik, Mrs. Marion Milner and Mrs. Tzila Barneis. And, of course, many, many thanks to my wonderful family and my wife whose warmth and humor helps me in all aspects of my life.

PREFACE

Probabilistics is a powerful tool for the processing of experimental and computational data. As such, it has been in use for more than a century for estimating the reliability of experimental and computational results in many scientific and technological fields.

During the past 30-40 years, classical probabilistics have been reinforced by the development of random function theory, particularly by Norbert Wiener and Andrey Kolmogorov. Random function theory which is the very heart of cybernetics was originally created to meet the needs of automatic control theory and optimization. Later, especially in the 60s, the beginning of the era of missiles and space investigation, random function theory was applied to problems connected with mechanical vibrations of bodies and shells.

At that stage, probabilistics was almost never used in the investigation of the kinematics and dynamics of mechanisms: on the contrary, situations in which random factors were inherent were largely dealt with by deterministic means. For instance, accuracy problems in linkages, cams, or gears were often reduced to the common classical forms by making determined assumptions about the shape, frequency, or nature of the errors. Classical deterministic analyses and synthesis methods are attractive because of their ability, at least in principle, to provide complete numerical solutions. On the other hand, a statistical approach may in some cases shorten the computation process because this technique inherently requires less complete information.

Although a great deal of work has been devoted to perfecting deterministic computation techniques, and brilliant results have been achieved, there is a certain sphere of problems for which the probabilistic approach can be fruitfully applied. These problems include, firstly, the estimation of the influence of random factors on the action of a particular mechanism. Secondly, the spectral theory of random processes can be effectively applied for estimating the dynamic behavior of mechanical systems. Thirdly, the use of probabilities can sometimes obviate the need for a master pattern. Lastly, the higher-order kinematic pairs to which cam and gear mechanisms belong can be effectively investigated by means of a probabilistic approach where conventional deterministic methods are practically useless (this book shows, for example, how random function theory can be applied to the problems caused by random errors in cam profiles and gear pitch). In summary, application of random function and probabilistic theory deal with the concept of kinematic and dynamic accuracy of mechanisms.

This book also deals with some other technical applications of probabilistic theory, including those relating to pneumatic and hydraulic mechanisms and rolling bearings. Kinematic and dynamic treatments are presented for both linear and nonlinear cases. The text discusses both the analysis and synthesis aspects of the mechanisms described. (Synthesis problems imply the optimization of the system in line with fixed criteria.) The approach presented illustrates that the spectral concept of random function theory is a powerful tool for the optimal synthesis procedure even when the excitation is determined.

Optimization problems led the author to consider the possibility of the creation of adaptive mechanisms, i.e. to the possibility of automatically adapting the transform function of a mechanical system to the variations of a randomly changing excitation. Some examples of automatic vibration control are discussed and illustrated.

The possibility of obtaining reliable results for mass phenomena has facilitated the development of a measurement technique which differs in essence from classical measuring methods in that it does not require a master part. Results are obtained by processing the statistical characteristics gathered by comparison of the measured elements. Some examples of the application of this probabilistic technique are given in the book.

This book consists of seven chapters, the material being divided as follows. In Chapter I the main concepts of probability theory (sections 1-24) and random function theory (sections 25-37) are discussed. This chapter may be omitted by those readers who are familiar with the subject. Chapter II introduces the general concepts of kinematics and dynamics of mechanisms and shows the major general dependences and error transformations. Chapter III and IV are devoted to the problems of kinematic and dynamic accuracy of cam and gear mechanisms, respectively. In Chapter V we consider nonlinear kinematic and dynamic problems, with emphasis on the influence of the backlash on the action of mechanisms. Chapter VI is devoted to some special applications of statistics to pneumatic, hydraulic, and belt-drive mechanisms. Finally, Chapter VII deals with the automatic vibration control aspect of the creation of adaptive mechanisms.

B.Z. Sandler

CONTENTS

CONTENTS (cont'd) Page

CONTENTS (cont'd) Page

CHAPTER I
CONCEPTS OF PROBABILITY

1. INTRODUCTION

This chapter is devoted to describing the main concepts and definitions in probability theory that the reader of this book will encounter. It does not aspire to replace first-hand basic acquaintance with probability theory but is aimed at helping the reader to become familiar with the designations and formulas used consistently by the author. The intention is to refresh the memory rather than to teach. Logical sequence is not always strictly observed: in order to keep the listing brief, concepts are sometimes discussed before their definition is given.

The chapter covers two main topics:

(1) Random variables (sections 2 to 24)

(2) Random functions (sections 25 to 37).

2. RANDOM VARIABLES

A variable - a quantity of unpredicted value - is generally defined as random. In practice, a random variable changes within a specific range, and a definite probability is associated with each value (for discrete variables) or with a definite set of values (for continuous variables).

For example:

(1) Deviation of the real size of a machine part from the nominal value denoted in the designer's working drawings.

(2) Deviation of the acceleration of a cam follower at some specific moment from the designed value.

We will now give a number of definitions, each of which will be illustrated with an example:

(1) *Random events (RE)*

e.g., whether or not a part will break in the course of a specific period of time.

(2) *Discrete random variables (DRV)*

e.g., the number of rebounds of a relay contact during the process of closing.

(3) *Continuous random variables (CRV)*

e.g., the thickness of a tooth of a gear wheel.

(4) *Random functions (RF)*

e.g., the profile of a cam; the trace of a ball bearing.

(5) *A function of a random variable (FRV)*

e.g., the movement of a cam follower as a function of the rotation angle of the cam.

3. EVENTS

Random variables and probability are closely connected with the concept of an "event".

Mechanical examples of events are:

(1) acceleration exceeding some specified allowed value;

(2) breakage or nonbreakage of a machine part;

(3) a specific ball in a ball bearing coming into contact with the upper ring of a thrust bearing;

(4) occurrence of a crack in a tooth of a wheel.

An event is a fact which as a result of an experiment may or may not occur. For instance, the appearance of a part with a size bigger than predicted is an event. We can express an "event" in terms of numbers.

We will now list the following group of definitions:

Impossible events - those which can never occur:

The probability of the occurrence of an impossible event P=0.

Trustworthy or sure events - those which always occur:

The probability of the occurrence of a trustworthy event P=1.

A complete whole group of events - a group of events, one of which always takes place as a result of an experiment:

The probability of the occurrence of one of these events is P=1.

Mutually exclusive (incompatible) events - events which cannot occur simultaneously:

Thus, if $P_1, P_2, P_3, \ldots, P_n$ are separate probabilities of such events, the probability P that one of these events will occur is

$$P = P_1 + P_2 + \ldots + P_n$$

It should be emphasized that the sum of all probabilities of all possible outcomes always equals 1.

Events not mutually exclusive - those which can occur separately and simultaneously:

In this case, the probability of obtaining event A or B is given as

$$P(A + B) = P(A) + P(B) - P(AB)$$

where AB - the appearance of both events.

Independent events - events the occurrence of which does not depend on the others:
If $P_1, P_2, P_3, \ldots, P_n$ are the probabilities of independent events, the probability P that all of these events will occur in a trial is

$$P = P_1 \cdot P_2 \cdot P_3 \cdot \ldots \cdot P_n$$

Dependent events - events the occurrence of each of which depends on the situation of one vis-a-vis the others:
Here, the concept of conditional probability has to be introduced. If P_1 is the probability of the occurrence of the first event and $P'_2, P'_3, \ldots, P'_n$ are the conditional probabilities of the occurrences of the subsequent events 2, 3,...,n the probability P that all subsequent events will occur in the specified order is

$$P = P'_1 \cdot P'_2 \cdot P'_3 \cdot \ldots \cdot P'_n$$

4. PROBABILITY

In practice, we define probability as the ratio of successful outcomes to all possible outcomes in an experiment or measurement:

$$P = \frac{N_S}{N_T}$$

where N_S is the number of successes and N_T is the number of outcomes of all kinds or number of trials. As was stated above, the probability of an impossible event equals 0; the probability of a trustworthy event equals 1.

Hence, it is true that:

$$0 \leq P(A) \leq 1,$$

where P(A) is the probability of a certain outcome A.

5. DISTRIBUTION

The distribution of a random variable describes its behavior: it connects the values of the variable with their respective probabilities.

6. DISTRIBUTION OF A DISCRETE VARIABLE

The random variable is better described by a cumulative distribution function (CDF). This function F(x) describes the probability that X is equal or less than a stated value x:

$$F(x) = P(X \leq x)$$

If the random variable X changes over a range from x_1 to x_2 then

$F(x) = 0$ for $X < x_1$

$F(x) = 1$ for $X > x_2$

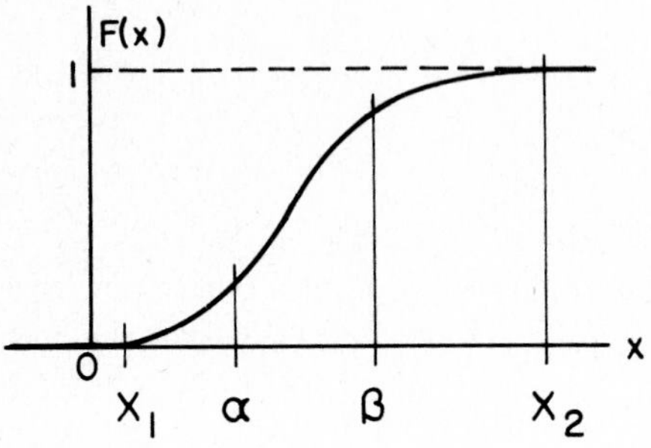

Fig. 1. A typical cumulative distribution function.

Figure 1 shows a typical CDF. Practical problems often demand a solution to the question: "What is the probability that the random value falls within an interval between α and β?"

$\alpha \leq X < \beta$

i.e., we seek the probability $P(\alpha \leq X < \beta)$.

With regard to the following events, we can state that:

for event A $X < \beta$

for event B $X < \alpha$

for event C $\alpha \leq X < \beta$

Taking into account that A = B + C, we can write

$$P(X < \beta) = P(X < \alpha) + P(\alpha \leq X < \beta)$$

or (I.6.1)

$$P(\alpha \leq X < \beta) = F(\beta) - F(\alpha)$$

The probability that the random value falls within the given interval equals the increment of the distribution function on this interval.

If $\alpha \to \beta$ we find the probability $P(X = \beta)$. From equation (I.6.1) it follows that only in the case that F has a jump at point β do we obtain a result which equals the jump of the distribution function at this point.

Obviously, if the distribution function is continuous at point β then $P(X = \beta) = 0$. The probability of the occurrence of any separate fixed value of a continuous random variable equals 0.

7. DISTRIBUTION OF A CONTINUOUS VARIABLE

To calculate the probability $P(x \leq X < x + \Delta x)$ we write, in accordance with equation (I.6.1),

$$P(x \leq X < x + \Delta x) = F(x + \Delta x) - F(x)$$

Then, we express the derivative of the distribution function

$$F'(x) = \lim_{\Delta x \to 0} \frac{F(x + \Delta x) - F(x)}{\Delta x} = f(x)$$

This new function is called the probability density function (PDF). To calculate the value

$$P(x_1 \leq X < x_2)$$

we write:

$$P(x_1 \leq X < x_2) = \int_{x_1}^{x_2} f(x)dx \qquad (I.7.1)$$

The main properties of f(x) are:

(1) when $f(x) \geq 0$ - PDF is always non-negative

(2) when $\int_{-\infty}^{\infty} f(x)dx = 1$ - the area below the function restricted by the x-axis equals 1.

8. EXPECTED, AVERAGE OR MEAN VALUES

The average value of a particular measured physical quantity is obtained by summing up a number of measured values and dividing the sum by the number of measurements n. Assuming a set of $N_1 \ldots N_n$ measured values, we obtain:

$$E(N) = E_N = \bar{N} = \frac{\sum_1^n N_i}{n} \qquad (I.8.1)$$

where E is the expectation.

1. For a discrete variable x_i $(i = 1, \ldots, n)$ with a distribution function F(x) which defines probabilities P_i corresponding to every x_i, the average becomes

$$E(X) = \bar{X} = \sum_{i=1}^{n} x_i P_i \qquad (I.8.2)$$

2. For a continuous variable X with a density function f(x) in the range α, β, the expectation takes the form:

$$E(X) = \bar{X} = \int_{\alpha}^{\beta} xf(x)dx \tag{I.8.3}$$

Expectation may be defined as the first-order moment of a random variable. While an s-order moment is defined as:

$$M_s(X) = \sum_{i=1}^{n} x_i^s P_i \qquad \text{for a discrete variable}$$

and

$$M_s(X) = \int_{-\infty}^{\infty} x^s f(x)dx \qquad \text{for a continuous variable}$$

for a random function X(t) (see Chapter I, sections 25-37) the average or expectation may also be expressed in the following way:

$$E(X) = \bar{x} = \frac{1}{T}\int_{0}^{T} x(t)dt \tag{I.8.4}$$

where t - time.

Obviously, if the variable is a parameter other than time, the expression does not change. For instance, for a random function Y(x) we have

$$E(Y) = \bar{y} = \frac{1}{x}\int_{0}^{x} y(u)du \tag{I.8.5}$$

In our discussion, we will use both E and " - " to describe the expectation (or average or mean value) of a random variable. The main properties of the expectation are:

(1) linearity, i.e., the expectation of a sum equals the sum of expectations: thus,

$$E[\sum_{i=1}^{n} x_i] = \sum_{i=1}^{n} E(x_i) \tag{I.8.6}$$

and

$$E(aX) = aE(X) \tag{I.8.7}$$

where a = const

(2) that the expectation of a constant value equals the value

$$E(C) = C \quad \text{and} \quad E(\bar{x}) = \bar{x} \tag{I.8.8}$$

A random variable is said to be centered if its average equals 0. Thus,

$$\overset{\circ}{X} = X - \bar{x} \tag{I.8.9}$$

where $\overset{\circ}{X}$ - centered random variable,

X - random variable,

$\bar{x}$ - average of random variable x

Obviously, $E(\overset{\circ}{X}) = 0$. (I.8.10)

9. VARIANCE

This characteristic describing the deviation of the random variable from mean (average) value is called variance (or dispersion), and we will denote it by D or σ^2. The positive square root of the variance is known as the standard deviation σ. Thus, variance is defined as:

$$\sigma^2 = E[(X - \bar{x})^2] = [\overline{(X - \bar{x})}^2] \qquad (I.9.1)$$

From equation (I.9.1) we obtain:

$$\sigma^2 = E(X^2 - 2X\bar{x} + \bar{x}^2) \qquad (I.9.2)$$

From equations (I.9.2) and (I.8.7):

$$\sigma^2 = E(X^2) - 2E(X\bar{x}) + E(\bar{x}^2) = E(X^2) - \bar{x}^2 \qquad (I.9.3)$$

or

$$\sigma^2 = \frac{\sum_{i=1}^{n} (\overset{\circ}{X}_i)^2}{n} \qquad (I.9.4)$$

From equation (I.9.3) the standard deviation

$$\sigma = \sqrt{E(X^2) - \bar{x}^2} \qquad (I.9.5)$$

Variance may also be defined by:

$$\sigma^2 = \int_{-\infty}^{\infty} \overset{\circ}{X}{}^2 f(x)dx \qquad (I.9.6)$$

Obviously, variance is a second-order moment.

As follows from the definition, the variance of a random variable multiplied by a constant, equals the product of the square of this constant and the variance of the random variable.

Thus,

$$E\{[a(X - \bar{x})]^2\} = a^2E[(X - \bar{x})^2] = a^2\sigma_x^2 \qquad (I.9.7)$$

and

$$\sigma_{ax} = |a|\sigma_x \qquad (I.9.8)$$

The importance of the concept of standard deviation in practical applications follows from Chebyshev's inequality:

$$P[|X - \bar{x}| \geq n\sigma] \leq \frac{1}{n^2} \qquad \text{for } n = 1,2,3,4,5...$$

Thus, we have for n=2 $\quad P[|X - \bar{x}| \geq 2\sigma] \leq 0.25$

n=3 $\quad P[|X - \bar{x}| \geq 3\sigma] \leq 0.111$

n=4 $\quad P[|X - \bar{x}| \geq 4\sigma] \leq 0.0625$

n=5 $\quad P[|X - \bar{x}| \geq 5\sigma] \leq 0.040$

Chebyshev's inequality guarantees that the probability of a random variable exceeding the $\pm 3\sigma$ range from its mean is no more than 0.111... for any distribution law. This statement is illustrated in Figure 2.

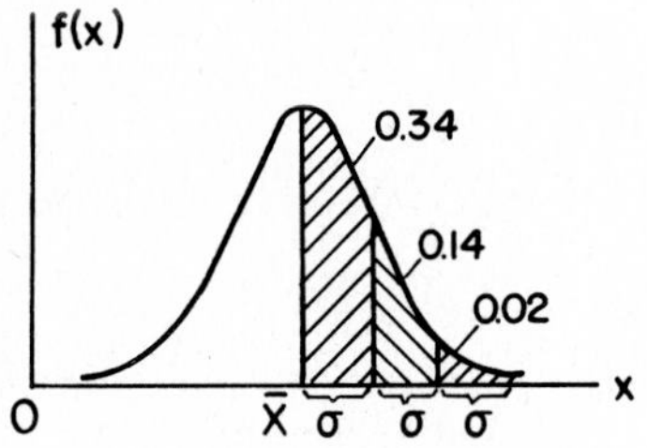

Fig. 2 Illustration of Chebyshev's inequality for a normal density distribution.

10. UNIFORM DISTRIBUTION

In some practical problems we meet continuous random variables which change within some definite range, and the probability density of the variable within this range is constant. A fly-wheel rotating on a vertical axis can serve as an example. When the wheel stops, there is no specific preferred angle between any fixed radius and any particular direction.

Let us consider a random variable X. The range is restricted by boundaries α and β, and within these ranges the density function is constant

$$f(x) = c \qquad \alpha \leq x < \beta$$

$$f(x) = 0 \qquad x < \alpha \quad \text{and} \quad x \geq \beta$$

Since the area limited by the function f(x) equals 1, we have

$$c(\beta - \alpha) = 1$$

and

$$c = \frac{1}{\beta - \alpha}$$

Thus,

$$f(x) = \frac{1}{\beta - \alpha} \qquad \alpha \leq x < \beta$$

$$f(x) = 0 \qquad x < \alpha \quad \text{and} \quad x \geq \beta \tag{I.10.1}$$

In this case, the distribution function F(x) obviously takes the following form:

$$F(x) = \begin{cases} 0 & \text{for} \quad x < \alpha \\ \dfrac{x - \alpha}{\beta - \alpha} & \text{for} \quad \alpha \leq x < \beta \\ 1 & \text{for} \quad x \geq \beta \end{cases} \tag{I.10.2}$$

The functions f(x) and F(x) are presented graphically in Figure 3.

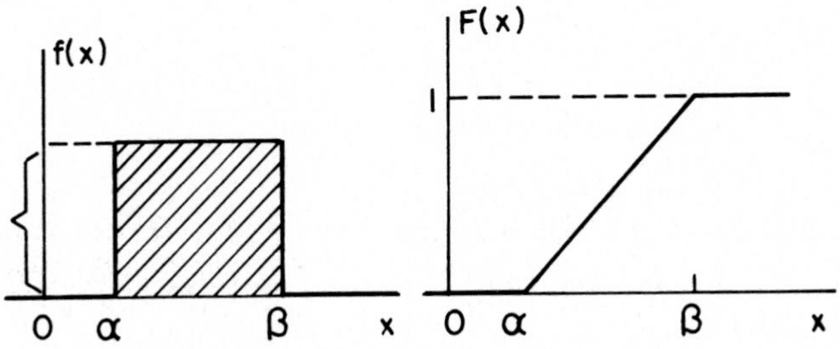

Fig. 3 Graphic representation of a uniform distribution.

For the expectation:

$$\bar{x} = \int_{\alpha}^{\beta} \frac{x}{\beta - \alpha} dx = \frac{\alpha + \beta}{2} \tag{I.10.3}$$

and for the variance:

$$\sigma_x^2 = \frac{1}{\beta - \alpha} \int_{\alpha}^{\beta} (x - \frac{\alpha + \beta}{2})^2 dx = \frac{(\beta - \alpha)^2}{12} \tag{I.10.4}$$

and

$$\sigma_x = \frac{\beta - \alpha}{2\sqrt{3}} \tag{I.10.5}$$

To find the probability that X falls within a range a, b

$$P(a < X < b) = \frac{b - a}{\beta - \alpha} \tag{I.10.6}$$

The graphical interpretation of this expression is shown in Figure 4.

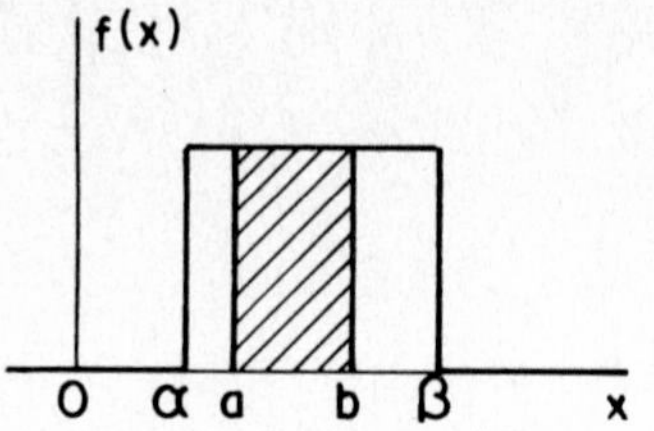

Fig. 4 Graphical interpretation of the probability $P(a < X < b)$.

11. NORMAL DISTRIBUTION

This well-known distribution was discovered by the French mathematician, DeMoivre, in 1730. It is, however, known as Gaussian distribution, after the German Scientist, Gauss, who derived it some years later. The main particularity of normal distributions is that under certain conditions it is a limit distribution to which all other distributions tend. It can be proved that the sum of a large enough number of independent differently distributed random variables is approximately (when certain conditions are observed) described by normal distribution. The bigger the number of variables the more accurate this rule.

This distribution can be described analytically as follows:

$$f(x) = \frac{1}{\sigma\sqrt{2\pi}} \exp\left[-\frac{(x-\bar{x})^2}{2\sigma^2}\right] \qquad (I.11.1)$$

See Figure 5.

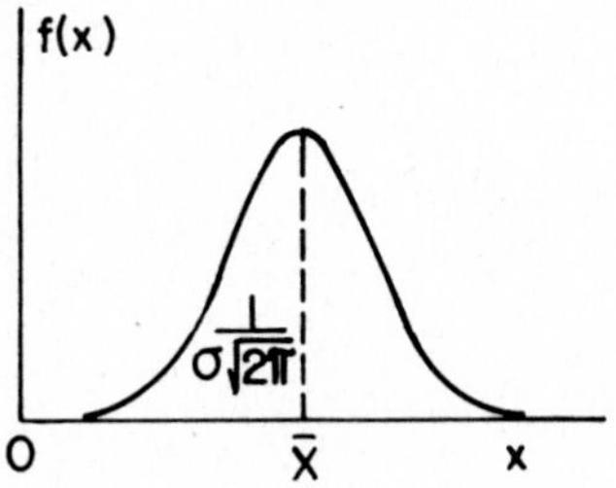

Fig. 5 Normal distribution.

The expectation is calculated in the usual manner:

$$\bar{x} = \frac{1}{\sigma\sqrt{2\pi}} \int_{-\infty}^{\infty} x\exp\left[-\frac{(x-\bar{x})^2}{2\sigma^2}\right]dx$$

This integral can be solved by substituting

$$\frac{x - \bar{x}}{\sigma\sqrt{2}} = t$$

Thus,

$$\bar{x} = \frac{\sigma\sqrt{2}}{\sqrt{\pi}} \int_{-\infty}^{\infty} te^{-t^2}\, dt + \frac{\bar{x}}{\sqrt{\pi}} \int_{-\infty}^{\infty} e^{-t^2} dt = \bar{x}$$

The variance in the case of normal distribution is calculated in the following manner:

$$D(X) = \frac{1}{\sigma\sqrt{2\pi}} \int_{-\infty}^{\infty} (x - \bar{x})^2 \exp\left[- \frac{(x-\bar{x})^2}{2\sigma^2}\right] dx \qquad (I.11.2)$$

Using the same variable $t = \frac{x-\bar{x}}{\sigma\sqrt{2}}$, we can rewrite equation (I.11.2) in the form:

$$D(X) = \frac{2\sigma^2}{\sqrt{\pi}} \int_{-\infty}^{\infty} t^2 e^{-t^2} dt = \frac{\sigma^2}{\sqrt{\pi}} \left\{-te^{-t^2}\Big|_{-\infty}^{\infty} + \int_{-\infty}^{\infty} e^{-t^2} dt\right\} = \sigma^2$$

The meaning of $\bar{x}$ and σ in this particular case of the normal distribution is illustrated in Figure 6 a and b. This distribution is symmetrical relative to the $\bar{x}$ coordinate. For a centered random variable $\bar{x} = 0$, and the curve is symmetrical with respect to zero. The bigger σ, the more gentle the slope of the curve and the lower the maximal value of f(x). The dimensions of $\bar{x}$ and are obviously the same as the dimension of X.

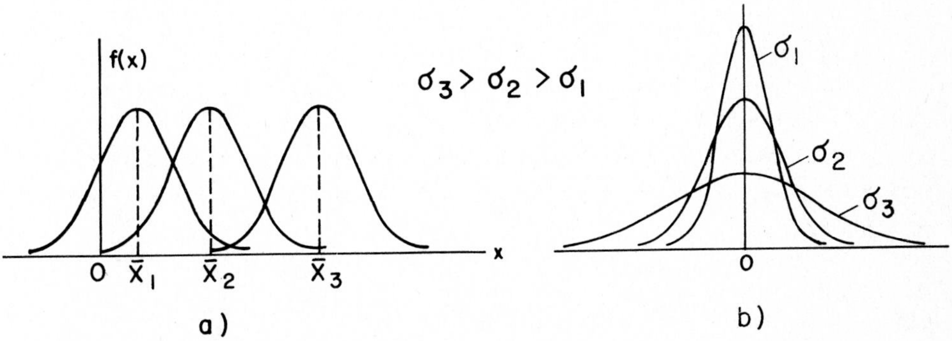

Fig. 6 (a) Normal distribution for different average values $\bar{x}$;
(b) Normal distribution for different root mean square values.

The probability of a normally distributed random variable falling within an interval x_1, x_2 is usually expressed in the following way:

$$P(x_1 < X < x_2) = \int_{x_1}^{x_2} f(x)dx = \frac{1}{\sigma\sqrt{2\pi}} \int_{x_1}^{x_2} \exp\left[- \frac{(x-\bar{x})^2}{2\sigma^2}\right] dx \qquad (I.11.3)$$

Substituting $t = \frac{x-\bar{x}}{\sigma\sqrt{2}}$

we obtain

$$P(x_1 < X < x_2) = \frac{1}{2\pi} \int_{\frac{x_1-\bar{x}}{\sigma\sqrt{2}}}^{\frac{x_2-\bar{x}}{\sigma\sqrt{2}}} e^{-t^2} dt$$

The integral $\int e^{-t^2} dt$ cannot be expressed by elementary functions. To calculate this integral, special tables (called Laplace function tables) are used.

Designating

$$\phi(x) = \frac{2}{\sqrt{\pi}} \int_0^x e^{-t^2} dt \qquad (I.11.4)$$

we obtain

$$P(x_1 < X < x_2) = \frac{1}{2} [\phi(\frac{x_2-\bar{x}}{\sigma\sqrt{2}}) - \phi(\frac{x_1-\bar{x}}{\sigma\sqrt{2}})] \qquad (I.11.5)$$

Here, we should note:

(1) $\phi(0) = 0$

(2) $\phi(\infty) = 1$ (I.11.6)

(3) $\phi(-x) = -\phi(x)$

12. FUNCTIONS OF RANDOM VARIABLES

In dealing with mechanisms, we sometimes handle functions of different kinds where the variables are of a random nature. The problem arising here is to define the average values of these functions as well as the standard deviation. Later, for some specific problems we will need to find the distribution for such functions.

13. PARTIAL DERIVATIVE METHODS

Let $\psi = \psi(X,Y)$, where X and Y are random. For any x_i and y_i which are the specific outcomes of X and Y we obtain:

$$\psi_i = \psi(x_i, y_i) \qquad (I.13.1)$$

Let us define

$$\bar{\psi} = \psi(\bar{x}, \bar{y}) \qquad (I.13.2)$$

rather than as

$$\bar{\psi} = \frac{\sum_{i=1}^{n} \psi_i}{n}$$

These two definitions of $\bar{\psi}$ are essentially the same if the deviations moderate.

The function ψ is assumed to be continuous and differentiable. The variables X and Y have the deviations:

$\Delta y_i = x_i - \bar{x}$ and $\Delta y_i = y_1 - \bar{y}$

which are assumed to be relatively small. The deviation of the ψ function is

$$\Delta\psi_i = \psi_i - \bar{\psi} \simeq \left.\frac{\partial\psi}{\partial x}\right|_{\substack{x=\bar{x}\\ y=\bar{y}}} \Delta x_i + \left.\frac{\partial\psi}{\partial y}\right|_{\substack{x=\bar{x}\\ y=\bar{y}}} \Delta y_i \qquad \text{(I.13.3)}$$

which follows from Taylor expansion if second-order (or higher) terms are neglected. The partial derivatives in equation (I.13.3) are taken at $x = \bar{x}$ and $y = \bar{y}$ and are thus constants.

The variance estimator σ_ψ^2 is given by

$$\sigma_\psi^2 = \frac{\sum_{i=1}^{n} (\Delta\psi_i)^2}{n} \qquad \text{(I.13.4)}$$

or

$$\sigma_\psi^2 = E\{[\psi - E(\psi)]^2\} \simeq E[(\psi - \bar{\psi})^2]$$

Squaring equation (I.13.3) and substituting it into equation (I.13.4) yields:

$$\sigma_\psi^2 = \frac{\left(\frac{\partial\psi}{\partial x}\right)^2 \sum(\Delta x_i)^2 + 2\frac{\partial\psi}{\partial x}\frac{\partial\psi}{\partial y}\sum(\Delta x_i \Delta y_i) + \left(\frac{\partial\psi}{\partial y}\right)^2 \sum(\Delta y_i)^2}{n} \qquad \text{(I.13.5)}$$

The sum $\Sigma(\Delta y_i \Delta y_i) \to 0$ if x_i and y_i are independent (see Chapter I, section 21). Then, since equation (I.9.4)

$$\sigma_x^2 = \frac{\sum(\Delta x_i)^2}{n}$$

and

$$\sigma_y^2 = \frac{\sum(\Delta y_i)^2}{n}$$

the expression for σ_ψ is

$$\sigma_\psi \simeq \sqrt{(\partial\psi/\partial y)^2_{\substack{x=\bar{x}\\y=\bar{y}}} \sigma_x^2 + (\partial\psi/\partial y)^2_{\substack{x=\bar{x}\\y=\bar{y}}} \sigma_y^2} \tag{I.13.6}$$

Obviously, the result obtained can be generalized for a function of more than two variables. Thus, if

$\psi = \psi(x,y,\ldots,u,z)$ then

$\bar{\psi} = \psi(\bar{x},\bar{y},\ldots,\bar{u},\bar{z})$

and

$$\sigma_\psi^2 \simeq (\partial\psi/\partial x)^2_{\substack{x=\bar{x}\\ \vdots\\ z=\bar{z}}} \sigma_x^2 + (\partial\psi/\partial y)^2_{\substack{x=\bar{x}\\ \vdots\\ z=\bar{z}}} \sigma_y^2 + \ldots + (\partial\psi/\partial y)^2_{\substack{x=\bar{x}\\ \vdots\\ z=\bar{z}}} \sigma_u^2 + (\partial\psi/\partial z)^2_{\substack{x=\bar{x}\\ \vdots\\ z=\bar{z}}} \sigma_z^2 \tag{I.13.7}$$

14. ADDITION AND SUBTRACTION

If $Z = X \pm Y$ and $E(X) = \bar{x}$, $E(Y) = \bar{y}$ we obtain for $E(Z)$:

$$E(Z) = E(X\pm Y) = E(X) \pm E(Y) = \bar{x} \pm \bar{y} = \bar{z} \tag{I.13.8}$$

Similarly, for the variance of σ_z^2 from equation (I.9.1), we get

$$E[(Z - \bar{z})^2] = E\{[(X\pm Y) - (\bar{x}\pm\bar{y})]^2\} = E[(\mathring{X}\pm\mathring{Y})^2] =$$

$$= E(\mathring{X}^2) \pm 2E(\mathring{X}\mathring{Y}) + E(\mathring{Y}^2) = \sigma_x^2 + \sigma_y^2 \pm K_{xy}$$

where $K_{xy} = E(\mathring{X}\mathring{Y})$ is covariance between $\mathring{X}$ and $\mathring{Y}$ (see equations I.21.2 and I.21.5).

From equation (I.21.8) (see below) $K_{xy} = 0$ when X and Y are independent variables. $K_{xy} = \sigma_x\sigma_y$ when X = Y. In the general case of dependence between the variables

$$-1 \leq K_{xy}/\sigma_x\sigma_y \leq 1 \tag{I.13.10}$$

Thus, for independent variables

$$\sigma_z^2 = \sigma_x^2 + \sigma_y^2 \tag{I.13.11}$$

for suming and subtracting.

15. PRODUCTS

If Z = XY where X and Y are random variables, as in the previous case, we use the definition of covariance to obtain the expressions for the expectation.

Thus, for $E(X) = \bar{x}$, $E(Y) = \bar{y}$

$$K_{xy} = E(\overset{\circ}{X}\overset{\circ}{Y}) = E[(X - \bar{x})(Y - \bar{y})] =$$

$$= E(XY) - \bar{x}E(Y) - \bar{y}E(X) + \bar{x}\bar{y} = E(XY) - \bar{x}\bar{y}$$

or

$$E(Z) = E(XY) = \bar{x}\bar{y} + K_{xy} \tag{I.15.1}$$

For independent variables $K_{xy} = 0$ equation (I.15.1) becomes

$$\bar{z} = E(Z) = \bar{x}\bar{y} \tag{I.15.2}$$

For independent random multipliers this rule can be generalized and expressed as follows:

$$E[\prod_{i=1}^{n} x_i] = \prod_{i=1}^{n} E(x_i) \tag{I.15.3}$$

The variance of a product will be considered only for independent random variables. Thus:

$$\sigma_z^2 = E(\overset{\circ}{Z}^2) = E[(Z - \bar{z})^2]$$

The independence of X and Y gives $\bar{z} = \bar{x}\bar{y}$ and then

$$\sigma_z^2 = E[(XY - \bar{x}\bar{y})^2] = E(X^2Y^2) - 2\bar{x}\bar{y}E(XY) + \bar{x}^2\bar{y}^2 \tag{I.15.4}$$

It can be proved that if X, Y,..., Z are independent random variables and

$\phi_x(X)$, $\phi_y(Y)$, ..., $\phi_z(Z)$

are functions of these variables, then

ϕ_x, ϕ_y, ..., ϕ_z are independent.

Thus, we obtain

$$\sigma_z^2 = E(X^2)E(Y^2) - \bar{x}^2\bar{y}^2 \tag{I.15.5}$$

Remembering that $E(X^2) = \sigma_x^2 + \bar{x}^2$ and $E(Y^2) = \sigma_y^2 + \bar{y}^2$ from equation (I.16.1) we obtain

$$\sigma_z^2 = \sigma_x^2\sigma_y^2 + \bar{x}\sigma_y^2 + \bar{y}\sigma_x^2 \tag{I.15.6}$$

If we deal with centered random variables instead of equation (I.15.6) we obtain

$$\sigma_z^2 = \sigma_x^2 \sigma_y^2 \qquad \text{(I.15.7)}$$

(because $\bar{x} = 0$ $\bar{y} = 0$).

Assuming X and Y are normally distributed and applying the method of partial derivatives, we will obtain for $Z = XY$

$$\sigma_z^2 \simeq \bar{y}^2 \sigma_x^2 + \bar{x}^2 \sigma_y^2 \qquad \text{(I.15.8)}$$

which, for small σ_x and σ_y, is similar to equation (I.15.6).

16. MOMENTS OF A SQUARE $Z=X^2$

For the expectation, we write

$$\bar{z} = E(X^2) = E[(\mathring{X} + \bar{x})^2] = E(\mathring{X}^2) + 2E(\mathring{X}\bar{x}) + E(\bar{x}^2) = \sigma_x^2 + \bar{x}^2 \qquad \text{(I.16.1)}$$

The variance of the Z variable (omitting the deduction) is expressed as follows:

$$\sigma_z^2 = E(\mathring{Z}^2) = E[(Z - \bar{z})^2] = E[X^4 - 2X^2(\sigma_x^2 + \bar{x}^2) + (\sigma_x^2 + \bar{x}^2)^2] =$$

$$= 4\bar{x}^2 \sigma_x^2 + 2\sigma_x^4 \qquad \text{(I.16.2)}$$

17. MOMENTS OF A ROOT $Z = \sqrt{X}$

Let us consider $Z = \sqrt{X}$ (where Z is positive). If we square this expression, we obtain $Z^2 = X$. Now, we can refer to the previous case: from equation (I.16.1), we obtain

$$\bar{z} = \sqrt{\bar{x} - \sigma_z^2} \qquad \text{(I.17.1)}$$

and from equation (I.16.2) it follows that

$$\sigma_x^2 = 4\bar{z}^2 \sigma_z^2 - 2\sigma_z^4 \qquad \text{(I.17.2)}$$

If we substitute equation (I.17.1) into equation (I.17.2), this expression changes to

$$\sigma_x^2 = 4(\bar{x} - \sigma_z^2)\sigma_z^2 + 2\sigma_z^4 = 4\bar{x}\sigma_z^2 - 2\sigma_z^4$$

and

$$\sigma_z^4 - 2\bar{x}\sigma_z^2 + \frac{1}{2}\sigma_x^2 = 0 \qquad \text{(I.17.3)}$$

which gives for σ_z^2

$$\sigma_z^2 = \bar{x} + \sqrt{\bar{x}^2 - \frac{\sigma_x^2}{2}} \qquad \text{(I.17.4)}$$

Now, if we combine equation (I.17.1) with equation (I.17.4) it follows that

$$\bar{z}^2 = \bar{x} - \bar{x} + \sqrt{\bar{x}^2 - \sigma_x^2/2} = \sqrt{\bar{x}^2 - \sigma_x^2/2}$$

or

$$\bar{z} = \sqrt[4]{\bar{x}^2 - \sigma_x^2/2} \qquad \text{(I.17.5)}$$

because Z is positive.

18. MOMENTS OF QUOTIENTS Z = X/Y

For statistically independent X and Y variables, $\bar{z} = \bar{x}/\bar{y}$. To prove this equality let us put $1/Y = U$. Then $Z = XU$. Now, using equation (I.13.2) we obtain,

$$\bar{z} = \bar{x}\bar{u} \simeq \frac{\bar{x}}{\bar{y}} \qquad \text{(I.18.1)}$$

To find the variance of Z we use the partial derivative method; thus:

$$\sigma_z^2 \simeq \frac{\sigma_x^2}{\bar{y}^2} + \frac{\bar{x}^2}{\bar{y}^4}\sigma_y^2 \simeq \frac{\bar{y}^2\sigma_x^2 + \bar{x}^2\sigma_y^2}{\bar{y}^4} \qquad \text{(I.18.2)}$$

19. LAWS OF LARGE NUMBERS

When the number of independent experiments is large enough, the mean of the observed values of the random variable tends to the mathematical expectation of the variable. In mathematical terms, this statement can be written in the following form:

$$P\left(\left|\frac{\sum_{i=1}^{n} x_i}{n} - \bar{x}\right| < \varepsilon\right) > 1 - \delta \qquad \text{(I.19.1)}$$

where ε and δ are arbitrary small positive numbers.

To prove equation (I.19.1) we denote

$$y = \frac{\sum_{i=1}^{n} x_i}{n} \qquad \text{(I.19.2)}$$

Then

$$\bar{y} = E(y) = \frac{1}{n} \sum_{i=1}^{n} E(x_i) = \frac{1}{n} n\bar{x} = \bar{x} \tag{I.19.3}$$

and

$$D_y = \sigma_y^2 = \frac{1}{n^2} \sum_{i=1}^{n} E(x_i^2) = \frac{D_x}{n} = \frac{\sigma_x^2}{n} \tag{I.19.4}$$

Applying Chebyshev's inequality to (Y) where $\varepsilon < |x-\bar{x}|$

$$P(|Y - \bar{y}| \geq \varepsilon) \leq \frac{D_y}{\varepsilon^2} = \frac{D_x}{n\varepsilon^2}$$

The number n can always be determined to be large enough to fulfill the following inequality

$$\frac{D_x}{n\varepsilon^2} < \delta$$

Thus,

$$P(|\frac{\sum_{i=1}^{n} x_i}{n} - \bar{x}| \geq \varepsilon) < \delta$$

and, moving on to the opposite event:

$$P(|\frac{\sum_{i=1}^{n} x_i}{n} - \bar{x}| < \varepsilon) > 1 - \delta \tag{I.19.5}$$

This rule is known as the <u>law of large numbers</u>.

As a consequence of the law of large numbers, we can state Bernoulli's theorem. For an indefinitely increasing number of experiments the frequency P^* of an event A tends to its probability p.

In mathematical terms this theorem may be expressed in the following form:

$$P(|P^* - p| < \varepsilon) > 1 - \delta \tag{I.19.6}$$

where ε and δ are arbitrary small positive numbers.

20. SYSTEM OF TWO RANDOM VARIABLES

The concept of a system of two random variables, X and Y, can be interpreted by a vector (Figure 7) or a random point in a place (Figure 8).

In this case, the distribution function F(x,y) is defined as follows:

$$F(x,y) = P[(X< x)(Y < y)] \tag{I.20.1}$$

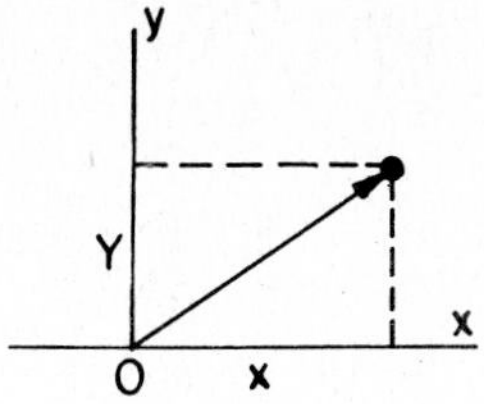

Fig. 7. Vectoral representation of two random variables.

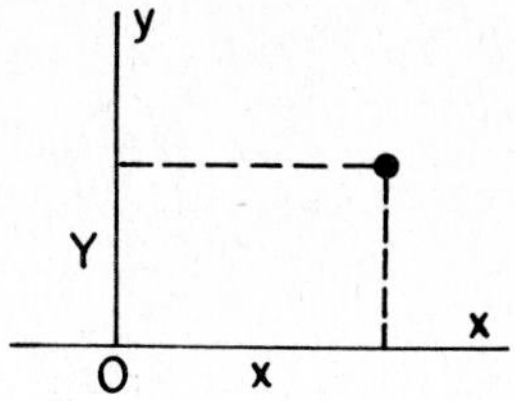

Fig. 8. Two random variables in a plane.

Geometrically, the meaning of this expression is the probability of hitting the point in the coordinate plane lower than the y line and to the left of the x line. By analogy with a single random variable, for a system of two random variables one can ask as to the probability of hitting the point in domain D (Fig. 9). We can express this probability by the distribution function and the distribution density concepts. The event which consists of the x,y point falling within the domain D, we denote

$$(X,Y) \subset D$$

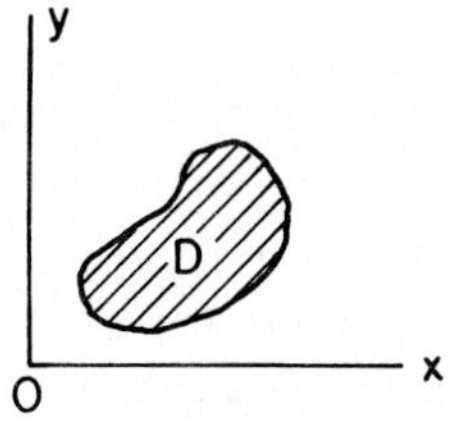

Fig. 9. A two dimensional domain.

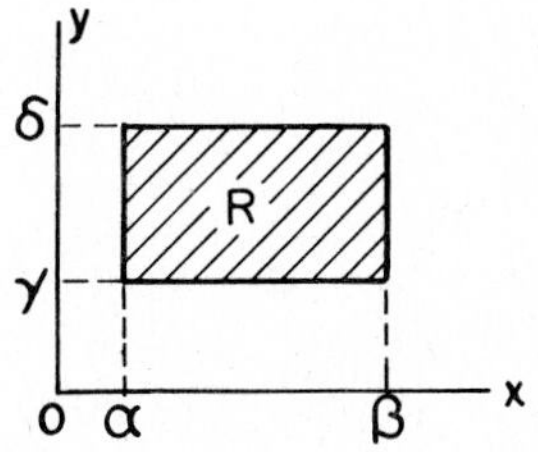

Fig. 10. A rectangular domain.

When the domain is rectangular, as in Fig. 10, we obviously obtain

$$P[(X,Y) \subset R] = F(\beta,\delta) - F(\alpha,\delta) - F(\beta,\gamma) + F(\alpha,\delta) \tag{I.20.2}$$

The distribution density for the case of two variables is defined as

$$f(x,y) = \frac{\partial^2 F(x,y)}{\partial x \partial y} = F''_{xy} \tag{I.20.3}$$

Geometrically f(x,y) can be represented by means of a curved surface which is called a <u>distribution surface</u> and is shown in Fig. 11. To find $P[(X,Y) \subset D]$,

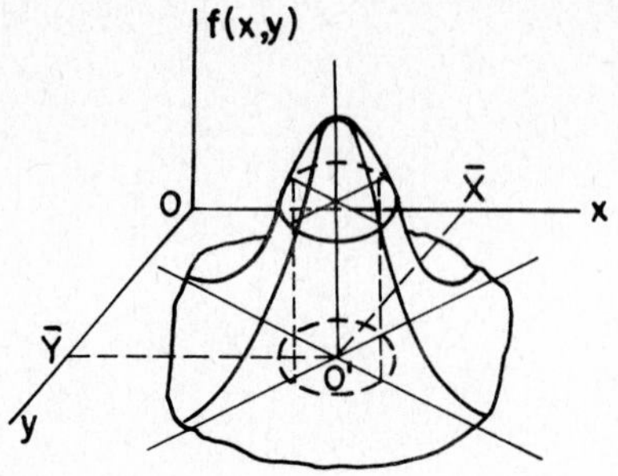

Fig. 11. A two-dimensional distribution surface.

we calculate the double integral of the distribution functions of the region D as follows

$$P[(X,Y) \subset D] = \int_D \int f(x,y)dxdy \qquad (I.20.4)$$

For a rectangular domain R, as in Fig. 10, this expression becomes:

$$P[(X,Y) \subset R] = \int_\alpha^\beta \int_\gamma^\delta f(x,y)dxdy \qquad (I.20.5)$$

The main properties of two-variable density distributions are:

$$\begin{aligned} &1.\ f(x,y) \geq 0 \\ &2.\ \int_{-\infty}^{\infty} \int f(x,y)dxdy = 1 \end{aligned} \qquad (I.20.6)$$

Here, the concept of dependent and independent random variable is of the greatest importance. Let us describe the connections between the separate distribution of the variables X and Y and the distribution of the system f(x,y). The variables X and Y are independent if:

$$f(x,y) = f_1(x) \cdot f_2(y) \qquad (I.20.7)$$

The distribution of a system of two independent random variables equals the product of the distribution of each single variable.

When dependent variables are being dealt with, the conditional distribution of one of the variables must be considered.

The conditional distribution f(x,y) of a random variable x, which belongs to a system of two variables (X,Y), can be defined as its distribution computed on condition that the other variable Y has a certain value. To denote this fact we use the following signs:

$F(x/y)$ and $f(x/y)$

The distribution $f(x,y)$ can then be expressed as

$$f(x,y) = f(x/y)f_2(y)$$

or (I.20.8)

$$f(x,y) = f_1(x)f(y/x)$$

We express the conditional distribution as follows:

$$f(x/y) = \frac{f(x,y)}{f_2(y)} \quad \text{and} \quad f(y/x) = \frac{f(x,y)}{f_1(x)} \qquad (I.20.9)$$

21. MOMENTS OF A SYSTEM OF TWO RANDOM VARIABLES

The definition of a k,s-order moment $M_{k,s}$ is:

$$M_{k,s} = E(X^k Y^s) \qquad (I.21.1)$$

The definition of a k,s-order centered moment $\overset{\circ}{M}_{k,s}$ is:

$$\overset{\circ}{M}_{k,s} = E(\overset{\circ}{X}{}^k \overset{\circ}{Y}{}^s) \qquad (I.21.2)$$

where, as before, $\overset{\circ}{X} = X - \bar{x}$ and $\overset{\circ}{Y} = Y - \bar{y}$

Thus, for the expectation we obtain

$$M_{1,0} = E(X1) = \bar{x} \qquad (I.21.3)$$

and

$$M_{0,1} = E(1Y) = \bar{y}$$

Graphically, this means that the average of the x and y coordinates defines the average position of the x,y point on the plane. Further,

$$\overset{\circ}{M}_{2,0} = E(\overset{\circ}{X}{}^2 1) = \sigma_x^2$$

and (I.21.4)

$$\overset{\circ}{M}_{0,2} = E(1\overset{\circ}{Y}{}^2) = \sigma_y^2$$

These variances and standard deviations characterize the deviations along the coordinates of the random point x,y relative to the average $\bar{x},\bar{y}$ point.

A special role in the analysis of two variable systems is played by the centered mixed moment of the second order $M_{1,1}$:

$$M_{1,1} = E(\overset{\circ}{X}\overset{\circ}{Y}) = K_{xy} \qquad (I.21.5)$$

This moment is known as the <u>correlation moment</u> (CM).

For discrete variables this can be calculated in the following way:

$$K_{xy} = \frac{\sum_{i}\sum_{j} (x_i - \bar{x})(y_i - \bar{y})}{n - 1} \qquad (I.21.6)$$

For continuous variables the calculation can be made in an integral form:

$$K_{xy} = \int_{-\infty}^{\infty} \int (x - \bar{x})(y - \bar{y}) f(x,y) dx dy \qquad (I.21.7)$$

It can be proved that for independent random variables this moment equals 0. Indeed, from equation (I.20.7) for independent variables

$$f(x,y) = f_1(x) f_2(y)$$

Thus, substituting in equation (I.21.7) we obtain

$$K_{xy} = \int_{-\infty}^{\infty} (x - \bar{x}) f(x) dx \int_{-\infty}^{\infty} (y - \bar{y}) f(y) dy = 0 \qquad (I.21.8)$$

because each integral separately equals 0 [expectation of a centered variable - see equation (I.8.10)].

The relationship

$$r_{xy} = \frac{K_{xy}}{\sigma_x \sigma_y} \qquad (I.21.9)$$

is designated the correlation coefficient. Thus, when the random values X and Y are independent, $K_{xy} = 0$. It is important to note that the opposite statement is not correct: the fact that K_{xy} equals 0 does not necessarily indicate the independence of the variables. The correlation coefficient indicates only the linear part of the dependence, and its value generally changes within the range -1 to +1:

$$-1 \leq r_{xy} \leq 1$$

Comparing the four cases (a), (b), (c) and (d) in Fig. 12, we see in

case (a) a clear positive correlation

case (b) $r_{xy} \to 1$

case (c) a weak negative correlation

case (d) $r_{xy} \to 0$

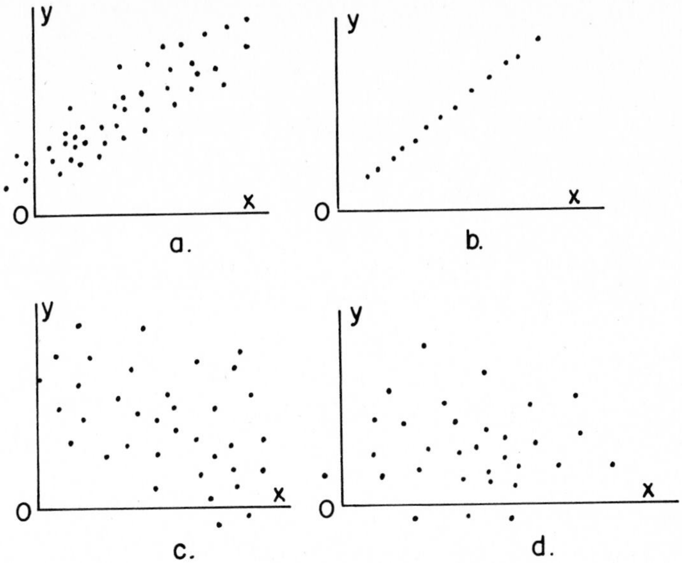

Fig. 12. (a) a positive correlation; (b) a linear dependence; (c) a weak negative correlation; (d) a lack of dependence.

22. NORMAL DISTRIBUTION FOR A TWO-VARIABLE SYSTEM

In the general case the normal distribution for two variables is given as follows:

$$f(x,y) = \frac{1}{2\pi\sigma_x\sigma_y\sqrt{1-r^2}} \exp\left\{-\frac{1}{2(1-r^2)}\left[\frac{(x-\bar{x})^2}{\sigma_x^2} - \frac{2r(x-\bar{x})(y-\bar{y})}{\sigma_x\sigma_y} + \frac{(y-\bar{y})^2}{\sigma_y^2}\right]\right\} \tag{I.22.1}$$

Here it can be proved that for this case the correlation moment equals:

$$K_{xy} = r\sigma_x\sigma_y \quad \text{or} \quad r = \frac{K_{xy}}{\sigma_x\sigma_y}$$

The surface in accordance with equation (I.22.1) is shown in Fig. 13.

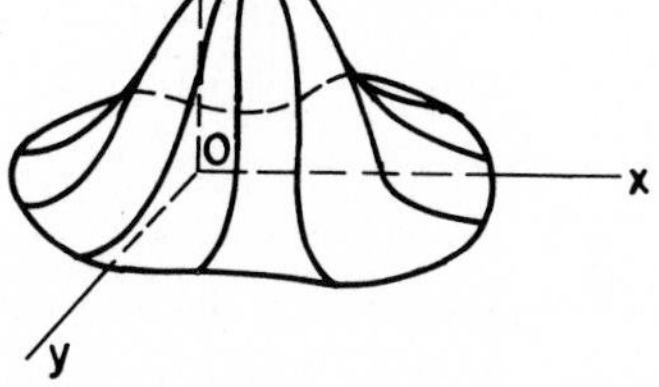

Fig. 13. A normal two-dimensional distribution.

For the case of noncorrelated variables when $r = 0$ we obtain:

$$f(x,y) = f_1(x)f_2(y) =$$

$$= \frac{1}{\sqrt{2\pi}\sigma_x} \exp\left(-\frac{(x-\bar{x})^2}{2\sigma_x^2}\right) \frac{1}{\sqrt{2\pi}\sigma_y} \exp\left(-\frac{(y-\bar{y})^2}{2\,{}_y^2}\right) \qquad (I.22.2)$$

Thus, we have shown that for noncorrelated variables the distribution of the system equals the product of two normal distributions of each variable. This means that for a normal distribution the meanings of noncorrelation and independence are equivalent.

For conditional distributions we write, corresponding to equation (I.22.1):

$$f(y/x) = \frac{1}{\sigma_y \sqrt{1-r^2}\sqrt{2\pi}} \exp -\frac{1}{2(1-r^2)} \left(\frac{y-\bar{y}}{\sigma_y} - r\,\frac{x-\bar{x}}{\sigma_x}\right)^2$$

$$f(x/y) = \frac{1}{\sigma_x \sqrt{1-r^2}\sqrt{2\pi}} \exp -\frac{1}{2(1-r^2)} \left(\frac{x-\bar{x}}{\sigma_x} - r\,\frac{y-\bar{y}}{\sigma_y}\right)^2 \qquad (I.22.3)$$

It is then obvious that the conditional expectations $E(Y/X)$ and $E(X/Y)$ equal:

$$E(Y/X) = \bar{y} + r\,\frac{\sigma_y}{\sigma_x}(X - \bar{x})$$

$$E(X/Y) = \bar{x} + r\,\frac{\sigma_x}{\sigma_y}(Y - \bar{y}) \qquad (I.22.4)$$

and conditional standard deviations

$$\sigma_{y/x} = \sigma_y \sqrt{1-r^2}$$

$$\sigma_{x/y} = \sigma_x \sqrt{1-r^2} \qquad (I.22.5)$$

The equations (I.22.5) represent straight lines in the x,y coordinate plane, and these lines are called regression lines.

23. DISTRIBUTION LAWS OF FUNCTIONS OF RANDOM VARIABLE

In sections 12-18 we discussed the computation of averages and variances of functions of random variables. Here we show the calculation of the distribution function and distribution density of a function of a random variable. For the case in which a continuous random variable X with a density of $f(x)$ is given, we wish to calculate the distribution function $G(y)$ and the density $g(y)$ of another random variable Y which is a function of X, or $Y = \phi(X)$.

Let us consider an interval $a < X < b$ (including the case when $a = -\infty$ and $b = \infty$) in which x changes. In this interval

$$P(a < X < b) = 1$$

Considering the monotonous function $y = \phi(x)$ shown in Fig. 14, we can write

$$G(y) = P(Y < y) \tag{I.23.1}$$

where y is any fixed value designated in this figure by a line parallel to the x axis. To provide the condition $Y < y$, the x point has to fall within the interval from a to x, while $y = \phi(x)$ and $x = \psi(y)$. Thus,

$$G(y) = P(Y < y) = P(a < X < x) =$$

$$= \int_a^x f(x)dx = \int_a^{\psi(y)} f(x)dx \tag{I.23.2}$$

Differentiating this expression we obtain

$$g(y) = \frac{d[G(y)]}{dy} = f[\psi(y)]\psi'(y) \tag{I.23.3}$$

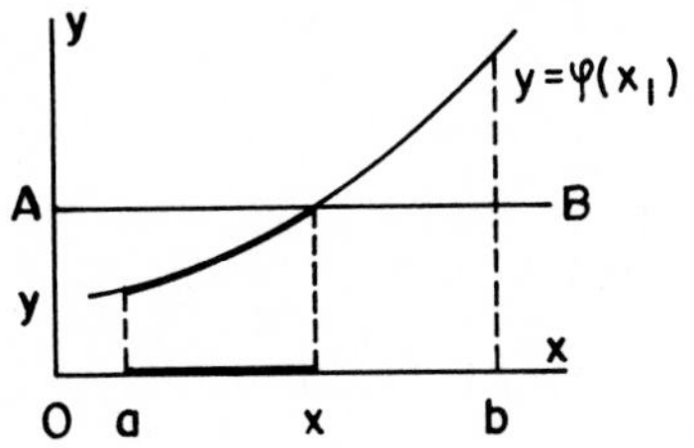

Fig. 14. An increasing function $y = \phi(x)$.

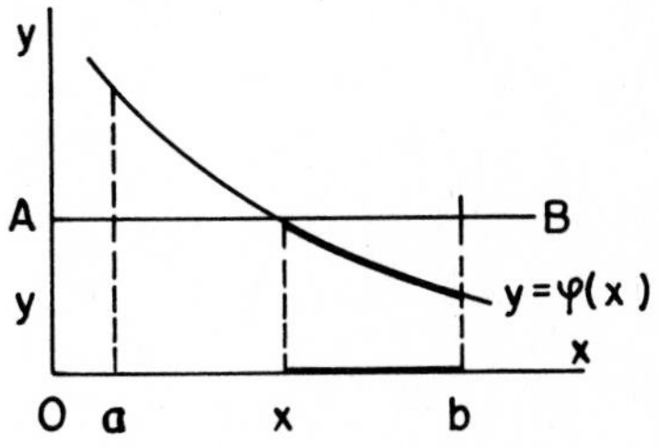

Fig. 15. A decreasing function $y = \phi(x)$.

For the case in which the function $y = \phi(x)$ decreases (Fig. 15), we obtain

$$g(y) = -f[\psi(y)]\psi'(y)$$

For the general case, we can write

$$g(y) = f[\psi(y)]\,|\psi'(y)| \tag{I.23.4}$$

An important conclusion may now be drawn with regard to the application of a normal distribution to a linear function. Thus, if $y = ax + b$, let us find g(y)

$$f(x) = \frac{1}{\sigma_x\sqrt{2\pi}} \exp\left(-\frac{(x-\bar{x})^2}{2\sigma_x^2}\right)$$

$$y = \phi(x) = ax + b$$

$$x = \psi(y) = \frac{y - b}{a}$$

$$|\psi'(y)| = \frac{1}{|a|}$$

$$g(y) = f[\psi(y)]|\psi'(y)| = \frac{1}{|a|\sigma_x\sqrt{2\pi}} \exp\left(-\frac{(\frac{y-b}{a} - \bar{x})^2}{2\sigma_x^2}\right)$$

The latter expression obtained for g(y) is nothing but a normal distribution with parameters:

$$\bar{x} = a\bar{x} + b \qquad (I.23.5)$$

and

$$\sigma_y = |a|\sigma_x$$

Thus, a linear function of a normally distributed variable is also normally distributed.

24. COMPOSITION OF DISTRIBUTION LAWS

By a composition of two distribution laws we mean the finding of the distribution law of a sum of two independent random values which are described by the two distribution laws under discussion.

Let us consider two independent random valuex X and Y with distribution laws $f_1(x)$ and $f_2(y)$, respectively. Then, we have to find the distribution law of a random value Z which has the following form:

$$Z = X + Y \qquad (I.24.1)$$

Because X and Y are independent, we have:

$$f(x,y) = f_1(x)f_2(y) \qquad (I.24.2)$$

It follows from the definition of the distribution function of a system of two random values which form a sum that

$$G(z) = \int_{-\infty}^{\infty}\int_{-\infty}^{z-x} f(x,y)dxdy = \int_{-\infty}^{\infty} \{\int_{-\infty}^{z-x} f(x,y)dy\}dx \qquad (I.24.3)$$

Differentiating equation (I.24.3) with respect to z in the upper limit of the internal integral, we obtain for the density distribution law of this two-random value system:

$$g(z) = \int_{-\infty}^{\infty} f(x,z-x)dx \qquad (I.24.4)$$

And for reasons of symmetry

$$g(z) = \int_{-\infty}^{\infty} f(y,z-y)dy \qquad (I.24.5)$$

Thus, from equations (I.24.2) and (I.24.4) or (I.24.5), we finally obtain for the composition of two distribution laws:

$$g(z) = \int_{-\infty}^{\infty} f_1(x)f_2(z-x)dx$$

or (I.24.6)

$$g(z) = \int_{-\infty}^{\infty} f_1(z-y)f_2(y)dy$$

The symbol of the composition is *. Thus:

$$g = f_1 * f_2$$

For example, to find the composition of two normally distributed random variables X and Y from equation (I.24.6), we obtain a normally distributed value Z = X + Y

$$g(z) = \frac{1}{\sqrt{\sigma_x^2 + \sigma_y^2}\sqrt{2\pi}} \exp\left(-\frac{[z - (\bar{x}+\bar{y})]^2}{2(\sigma_x^2 + \sigma_y^2)}\right) \qquad (I.24.7)$$

where

$$\bar{z} = \bar{x} + \bar{y}$$

and

$$\sigma_z^2 = \sigma_x^2 + \sigma_y^2 \qquad (I.24.8)$$

25. RANDOM FUNCTIONS

So far, our discussion has concerned random variables or values. The following sections will deal with random functions which relate to random variables, as arithmetic does to algebra.

For example, the measured size of a randomly chosen ball of a ball bearing is a random variable. For any specific ball it can become any number in a certain interval of sizes. The measured sizes along the trace on the ring of this bearing constitute a random function (the deviation of the sizes for any specific ring, when plotted vs. the length or the angle of the trace, form a randomly shaped curve, the waves of which oscillate inside a certain band).

The random functions with which we are concerned are functions of variables of different physical natures. For instance, the pressure in a centralized pressure supply network is a random function which depends on time. Such a random function is known as a random process. On the other hand, cam profile deviations are measured as a function of the profile angle, and this is known as a random function.

We define a random function as a random variable which changes during an experiment or measurement. In this chapter, we will use capital letters to designate random functions and processes. The section of probability theory which deals with such functions is called "the theory of random functions", and it is applied to the dynamics of random phenomena.

The specific shape which a random function takes as a result of an experiment is known as the realization of a random function. Fig. 16 represents a number of realizations of a random function. Strictly speaking, to depict a random function we must have an infinite number of realizations.

When a specific realization of a random function is obtained it is deterministic not random. Let us consider a random function X(t). Let us suppose that we made n independent measurements and obtained n realizations which we designate $x_1(t)$, $x_2(t),\ldots,x_n(t)$. If a specific t value is pinpointed, the random function X(t) becomes a random variable. A cross-section of x(t) at the point t gives n randomly located points, as shown in Fig. 17.

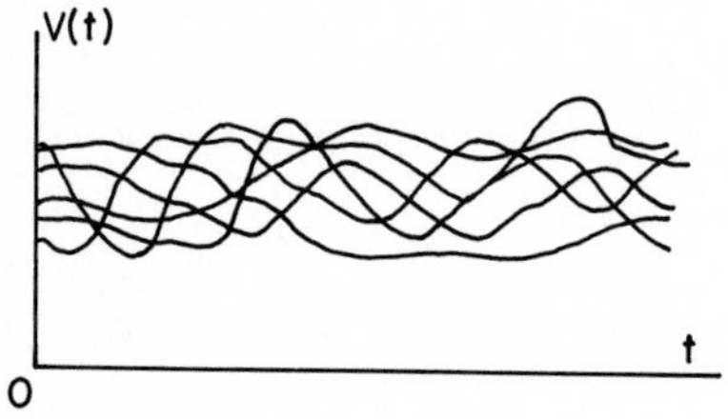

Fig. 16. Realization of a random function.

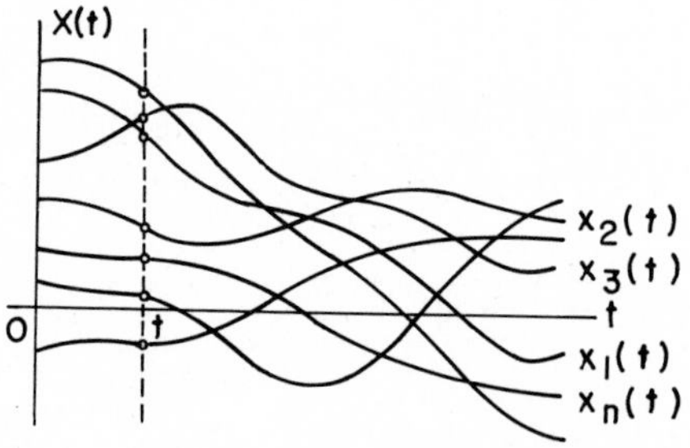

Fig. 17. Cross-section of a sample of realizations of a random function.

26. A RANDOM FUNCTION AS A SYSTEM OF RANDOM VARIABLES

Taking m cross-sections of a random function X(t), we obtain a system of m random variables. Closing the gaps between t_1 and t_2, t_2 and $t_3,\ldots,t_m$ and t_n, and increasing the number of m cross-sections infinitely, we obtain an infinite number of random variables. Thus, a random function can be thought of as a system of an infinite number of random variables. What is the distribution law of such a system? For one specific section X(t), the distribution law is a function of two variables and can be written in the form, f(x,t). For two specific sections, we obtain $f(x_1,x_2,t_1,t_2)$. Obviously, as the number of sections increases we will have to formulate a comprehensive distribution law, as follows: $f(x_1,x_2,\ldots,x_n, t_1,t_2,\ldots,t_n)$ where $n \to \infty$. This is the reason why in this discussion we will not use the concept of a distribution law of a random function.

27. CHARACTERISTICS OF RANDOM FUNCTIONS

Unlike random variables, the characteristics of random functions are not numbers but functions. We define the expectation (or mean value) of a random function as:

$$\overline{X(t)} = E[X(t)] = \frac{1}{T}\int_0^T X(t)dt$$

Thus, the expectation of a random function X(t) is a nonrandom (determined) function E[X(t)] which for every t value equals the expectation of this specific cross section. Fig. 18 illustrates this concept. In this figure the thick line represents the mean function $\overline{X(t)}$ which is the average of the multiple of realizations shown by the thin lines.

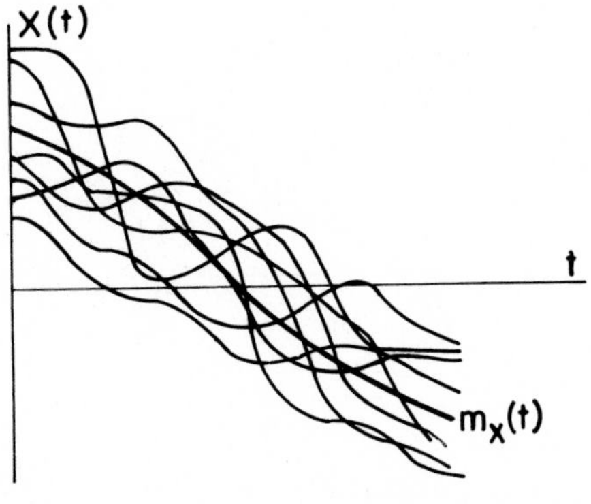

Fig. 18. The expectation of a random function.

By analogy, we define the variance of a random function. Thus, the variance of a random function X(t) is a determined function $D_x(t)$ which for every t value equals the variance of this specific cross-section. This statement can be written mathematically as follows:

$$D_x(t) = D[X(t)] = \frac{1}{T}\int_0^T \overset{\circ}{X}{}^2(t)dt$$

Obviously, $D_x(t)$ is always positive. For the standard deviation we obtain:

$$\sigma_x(t) = \sqrt{D_x(t)}$$

This characteristic is very important but it is not sufficient to describe all the properties of random functions. The additional criterion we must introduce into the discussion is the correlation or autocorrelation function K_x.

28. CORRELATION

To understand the correlation function let us turn to Fig. 19 and 20, in which the two random functions represented have the same expectations and variances. It is, however, obvious that these two functions are essentially different, the difference being expressed by the correlation function. From the figure, we can see that the correlation function describes the ties between the sections of the random function or, in other words, it reflects the frequential contents of the random function.

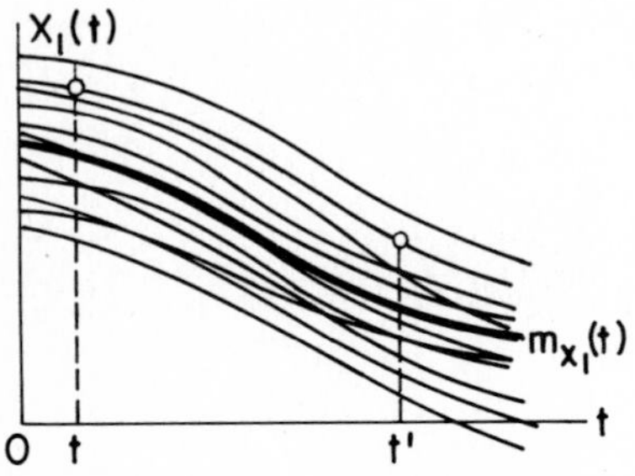

Fig. 19. An example of a low frequency random function.

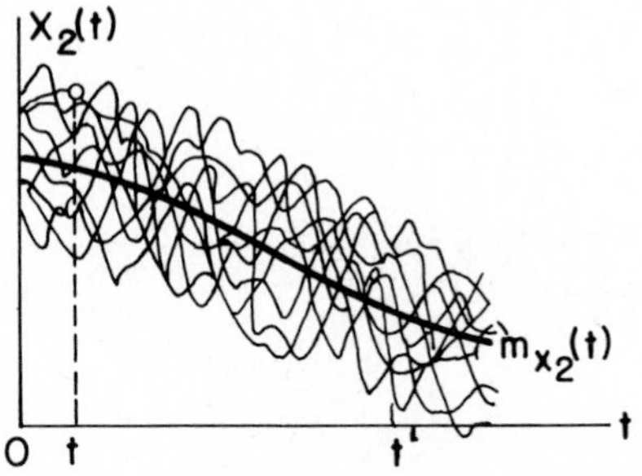

Fig. 20. An example of a high frequency random function.

Considering the random function X(t) represented in Fig. 21 by a sample of realizations, we notice for two sections in t and t' that the smaller the $|t-t'|$, the stronger the ties between the sections and the stronger the dependence of one section upon the other. The degree of this dependence can be described by means of the second mixed moment or correlation moment of the random variables X(t) and X(t').

Thus: $K_x(t,t') = E[\overset{\circ}{X}(t)\overset{\circ}{X}(t')]$

where $\overset{\circ}{X}(t) = X(t) - \overline{X(t)}$ and $\overset{\circ}{X}(t') = X(t') - \overline{X(t')}$

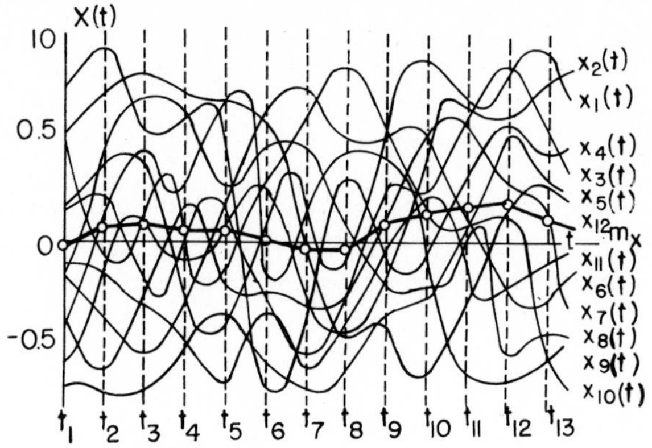

Fig. 21. A sample of realizations of a random function.

Returning to Fig. 19 and 20, we see that the correlation function must be different for each case. In the first figure (Fig. 19) will change slowly while $|t'-t|$ increases, and in the second case (Fig. 20), even for small $|t'-t|$ values, the correlation undergoes essential changes (see Fig. 28a, below).

We define the correlation function of a random function X(t) as a determined function of two variables $K_x(t,t')$ which for each pair t,t' equals the correlation moment of the corresponding sections of the random functions. When t=t', we obtain:

$$K_x(t,t) = E[\{\overset{\circ}{X}(t)\}^2] = D_x(t)$$

Thus, knowing the correlation function, we know the variance.

Another property of the correlation function is its symmetry:

$$K_x(t,t') = K_x(t',t)$$

Instead of K_x, a normalized correlation function r_x can be used:

$$r_x(t,t') = \frac{K_x(t,t')}{\sigma_x(t)\sigma_x(t')}$$

For t=t', obviously

$$r_x = 1$$

When a random function is given as a result of a certain number of experiments (as shown in Fig. 21), we can calculate the expectation, the standard deviation and the correlation function in the following way. Let us consider a series of sections of this function made at times $t_1, t_2, \ldots, t_m$. At each time we have n random variables. (It is convenient to make sections equidistant.) The results of the measurements are presented in Table I.28.1.

TABLE I.28.1.
The results of the measurements

X(t) \ t	t_1	t_2	...	t_k	...	t_ℓ	...	t_m
$x_1(t)$	$x_1(t_1)$	$x_1(t_2)$	...	$x_1(t_k)$	...	$x_1(t_\ell)$	...	$x_1(t_m)$
$x_2(t)$	$x_2(t_1)$	$x_2(t_2)$	...	$x_2(t_k)$	...	$x_2(t_\ell)$	...	$x_2(t_m)$
...	...	...	...	...	...	...	...	...
$x_i(t)$	$x_i(t_1)$	$x_i(t_2)$	...	$x_i(t_k)$	...	$x_i(t_\ell)$	...	$x_i(t_m)$
...	...	...	...	...	...	...	...	...
$x_n(t)$	$x_n(t_1)$	$x_n(t_2)$	...	$x_n(t_k)$	...	$x_n(t_\ell)$	...	$x_n(t_m)$

Each horizontal line in the table represents a specific realization of the random function under consideration, and each column, one section of it. The symbol $x_i(t_k)$ refers to the random value of the i realization at time t_k.

Therefore, for the expectation we have

$$\overline{X(t_k)} \simeq \frac{\sum_{i=1}^{n} x_i(t_k)}{n} \tag{I.28.1}$$

for the variance (and thus the standard deviation afterwards):

$$D_x(t_k) \simeq \frac{\sum_{i=1}^{n} [x_i(t_k) - \overline{X(t_k)}]^2}{n - 1} \tag{I.28.2}$$

finally, for the correlation function

$$K_x(t_k, t_\ell) \simeq \frac{\sum_{i=1}^{n} [x_i(t_k) - \overline{X(t_k)}][x_i(t_1) - \overline{X(t_1)}]}{n - 1} \tag{I.28.3}$$

29. TRANSFORMATIONS OF RANDOM FUNCTIONS

(a) Let us consider a random function $Y(t) = X(t) + \phi(t)$ where $\phi(t)$ is a deterministic function. The expectation of this new random function equals:

$$E[Y(t)] = \overline{X(t)} + \phi(t)$$

Thus, the addition to a random function of a non-random (determined) function entails the same addition to the expectation of the random function to obtain the expectation of this sum.
For the correlation function of Y(t) we have:

$$K_y(t,t') = E[\overset{\circ}{Y}(t)\overset{\circ}{Y}(t')] = E[(Y(t) - \overline{Y(t)})(Y(t') - Y(t'))] =$$

$$= E[(X(t) + \phi(t) - X(y) - \phi(t))(X(t') + \phi(t') - X(t') - \phi(t'))] =$$

$$= E[(X(t) - \bar{X}(t))(X(t') - \overline{X(t')})] = K_x(t,t')$$

The addition of a determined function to a random function does not change the correlation function.

(b) Now let us take a case in which $Y(t) = X(t)\phi(t)$ then for the expectation we obtain:

$$E[Y(t)] = E[\phi(t)X(t)] = \phi(t)\overline{X(t)}$$

Thus, the product of a random function and a determined function has an expectation which equals the product of the expectation of the random function and the determined function.
The correlation function of the function Y(t) can be expressed as follows:

$$K_y(t,t') = E[\overset{\circ}{Y}(t)\overset{\circ}{Y}(t')] = E[(Y(t) - \overline{Y(t)})(Y(t') - \overline{Y(t')})] =$$

$$= E[\phi(t)\phi(t')(X(t) - \overline{X(t)})(X(t') - \bar{X}(t'))] = \phi(t)\phi(t')K_x(t,t')$$

Multiplication of a random function by a determined function $\phi(t)$ requires multiplication of the expectation of the random function by $\phi(t)\phi(t')$ to obtain the expectation of the product.

(c) The conclusion drawn in (a) helps us to obtain an important simplification in dealing with random functions. Considering a centered random function $\overset{\circ}{X}(t) = X(t) - \overline{X(t)}$ and remembering that $\overline{X(t)}$ is a determined function, we can write that

$$K_{\overset{\circ}{x}}(t,t') = K_x(t,t')$$

(here the sign ° is used to specify that the function is centered.)

30. THE INTEGRAL OF A RANDOM FUNCTION

If a random function X(t) is given and $\overline{X(t)}$ and $K_x(t,t')$ are known, a second random function Y(t) can be tied to X(t) by the expression:

$$Y(t) = \int_0^t X(\tau)d\tau \tag{I.30.1}$$

The question is what form $\overline{Y(t)}$ and $K_y(t,t')$ take. Let us rewrite equation (I.30.1) in the following form:

$$Y(t) = \int_0^t X(\tau)d\tau = \lim_{\Delta\tau \to 0} \sum_i X(\tau_i)\Delta\tau$$

Thus

$$\overline{Y(t)} = \lim_{\Delta\tau \to 0} \sum_i E[X(\tau_i)]\Delta\tau = \lim_{\Delta\tau \to 0} \sum_i \overline{X(\tau_i)}\Delta\tau = \int_0^t \overline{X(\tau)}d\tau$$

This means that the expectation of an integral of a random function equals an integral of the expectation of the random function. This proof is arrived at on the basis of the assumption that the expectation of a limit equals the limit of an expectation. In practice we deal with functions where such assumptions are possible.

When we consider the correlation function, we are dealing with a centered random function. Thus:

$$\overset{\circ}{X}(t) = X(t) - \overline{X(t)} \quad \text{and} \quad \overset{\circ}{Y}(t) = Y(t) - \overline{Y(t)} \tag{I.30.2}$$

Obviously,

$$\overset{\circ}{Y}(t) = \int_0^t \overset{\circ}{X}(\tau)d\tau \tag{I.30.3}$$

in accordance with the definition and equation (I.30.2).

Then

$$K_y(t,t') = E[\overset{\circ}{Y}(t)\overset{\circ}{Y}(t')] \tag{I.30.4}$$

where

$$\overset{\circ}{Y}(t) = \int_0^t \overset{\circ}{X}(\tau)d\tau \quad \text{and} \quad \overset{\circ}{Y}(t') = \int_0^{t'} \overset{\circ}{X}(\tau')d\tau'$$

Then

$$\overset{\circ}{Y}(t)\overset{\circ}{Y}(t') = \int_0^t \overset{\circ}{X}(\tau)d\tau \int_0^{t'} \overset{\circ}{X}(\tau')d\tau' = \int_0^t \int_0^{t'} \overset{\circ}{X}(\tau)\overset{\circ}{X}(\tau')d\tau d\tau'$$

Thus

$$K_y(t,t') = E[\overset{\circ}{Y}(t)\overset{\circ}{Y}(t')] = \int_0^t \int_0^{t'} E[\overset{\circ}{X}(\tau)\overset{\circ}{X}(\tau')d\tau d\tau']$$

and finally $K_y(t,t') = \int_0^t \int_0^{t'} K_x(\tau,\tau')d\tau d\tau'$ (I.30.5)

31. THE DERIVATIVE OF A RANDOM FUNCTION

Let us consider a random function $X(t)$ with an expectation $\overline{X(t)}$ and correlation function $K_x(t,t')$, which is connected to another random function $Y(t)$ having the form

$$Y(t) = \frac{dX(t)}{dt} \tag{I.31.1}$$

Now we have to find $\overline{Y(t)}$ and $K_y(t,t')$.

Let us rewrite equation (I.31.1) in the following form

$$Y(t) = \lim_{\Delta t \to 0} \frac{X(t + \Delta t) - X(t)}{\Delta t}$$

and

$$\overline{Y(t)} = E[Y(t)] = \lim_{\Delta t \to 0} \frac{\overline{X(t + \Delta t)} - \overline{X(t)}}{\Delta t} = \frac{d\overline{X(t)}}{dt}$$

Thus

$$\overline{Y(t)} = \frac{d\overline{X(t)}}{dt} \tag{I.31.2}$$

The expectation of a derivative of a random function equals the derivative of the expectation of the random function.

To find the correlation function $K_y(t,t')$ we use the concept of centered random functions and write

$$\mathring{Y}(t) = \frac{d\mathring{X}(t)}{dt} \tag{I.31.3}$$

Corresponding to the definition

$$K_y(t,t') = E[\mathring{Y}(t)\mathring{Y}(t')] \tag{I.31.4}$$

or substituting equation (I.31.4) from equation (I.31.3), we obtain

$$K_y(t,t') = E\left(\frac{d\mathring{X}(t)}{dt}\,\frac{d\mathring{X}(t')}{dt}\right) = E\left(\frac{\partial^2 \mathring{X}(t)\mathring{X}(t')}{\partial t \partial t'}\right) = \frac{\partial^2 E[\mathring{X}(t)\mathring{X}(t')]}{\partial t \partial t'}$$

Thus,

$$K_y(t,t') = \frac{\partial^2}{\partial t \partial t'} K_x(t,t') \tag{I.31.5}$$

The correlation function of a derivative of a random function equals the double derivative of the correlation function of the initial random function. It can also be shown that a random function and its derivative are not correlated. The variance and standard deviation are given as

$$\sigma_y^2(t) = D_y(t) = K_y(t,t) \quad \text{and} \quad \sigma_y(t) = \sqrt{K_y(t,t)}$$

32. COMPOSITION OF RANDOM FUNCTIONS

For independent functions the composition of random functions is simple. We will, however, discuss this problem in brief for the general case of dependent random functions. To describe the extent of the dependence between two random functions $X(t)$ and $Y(t)$ we will use the concept of a mutual correlation function $R_{xy}(t,t')$

$$R_{xy}(t,t') = E[\overset{\circ}{X}(t)\overset{\circ}{Y}(t')]$$

which can sometimes be replaced by a normalized mutual correlation function $r_{xy}(t,t')$

$$r_{xy}(t,t') = \frac{R_{xy}(t,t')}{\sigma_x(t)\sigma_y(t')}$$

For independent functions

$$R_{xy} = 0$$

Let us consider a function $Z(t)$ which equals

$$Z(t) = X(t) + Y(t)$$

then

$$\bar{Z}(t) = \bar{X}(t) + \bar{Y}(t) \tag{I.32.1}$$

or, the expectation of a composition equals the sum of expectations of the separate items. This is true for dependent and independent items.

In this case the correlation function $K_z(t,t')$ will be expressed as:

$$K_z(t,t') = E[\overset{\circ}{Z}(t)\overset{\circ}{Z}(t')] = E[(\overset{\circ}{X}(t) + \overset{\circ}{Y}(t))(\overset{\circ}{X}(t') + \overset{\circ}{Y}(t'))] =$$

$$= E[\overset{\circ}{X}(t)\overset{\circ}{X}(t')] + E[\overset{\circ}{Y}(t)\overset{\circ}{Y}(t')] + E[\overset{\circ}{X}(t)\overset{\circ}{Y}(t)] + E[\overset{\circ}{X}(t')\overset{\circ}{Y}(t)] =$$

$$= K_x(t,t') + K_y(t,t') + R_{xy}(t,t') + R_{xy}(t',t)$$

For independent $X(t)$ and $Y(t)$ we obtain

$$K_x(t,t') = K_x(t,t') + K_y(t,t') \tag{I.32.2}$$

The sum of n items, as shown below:

$$X(t) = \sum_{i=1}^{n} X_i(t)$$

has an expectation

$$\overline{X(t)} = \sum_{i=1}^{n} \overline{X_i(t)}$$

and a correlation function

$$K_x(t,t') = \sum_{i=1}^{n} K_{x_i}(t,t') + \sum_{i \neq j}^{n} R_{x_y x_j}(t,t') \tag{I.32.3}$$

Let us now consider a composition Z(t) of random function X(t) and a random variable Y:

$$\overline{Z(t)} = \overline{X(t)} + \overline{Y} \tag{I.32.4}$$

Assuming independence of these values, or $E[\overset{\circ}{X}(t)Y]$ we obtain for the expectation

$$\overline{Z(t)} = \overline{X(t)} + \overline{Y} \tag{I.32.5}$$

and the correlation function $K_z(t,t')$

$$K_z(t,t') = K_x(t,t') + E[\overset{\circ}{Y}(t)\overset{\circ}{Y}(t')] =$$

$$= K_x(t,t') + E[\{\overset{\circ}{Y}(t)\}^2] =$$

$$= K_x(t,t') + D_y$$

33. STATIONARY RANDOM FUNCTIONS

Comparing the random functions represented in Fig. 22 and 23, we come to the concept of stationariness. The process of function in Fig. 22 shows random oscillations around a constant average value with approximately equal deviations. In contrast, the random function in Fig. 23 consists of realizations which oscillate around a variable average and the deviations are not even approximately equal along the variable X. The former case is an illustration of a stationary random process. Physically, such functions occur when the transient processes are over.

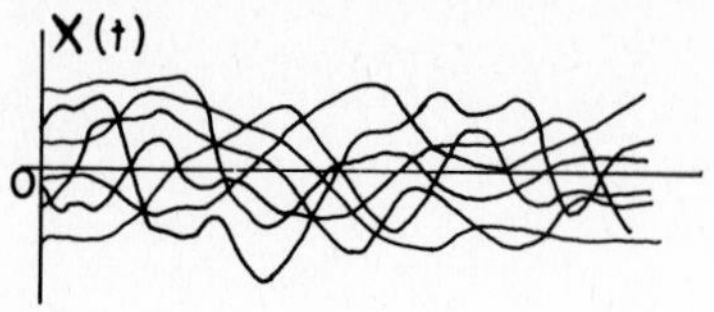

Fig. 22. An example of an approximately stationary random function.

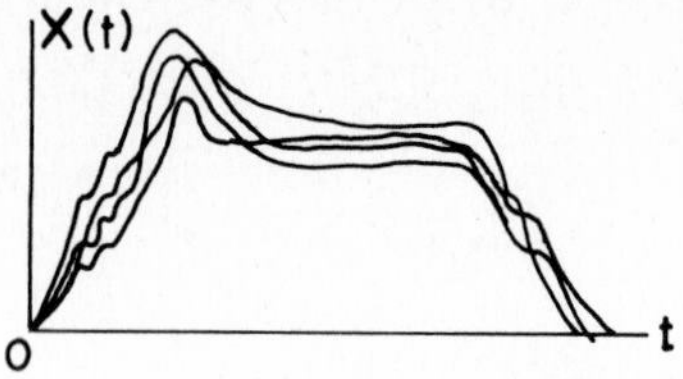

Fig. 23. An example of a non-stationary random function.

A random function X(t) is stationary if its characteristics do not depend on it. In this book, we will comply a limited definition of stationariness. A random function which has a constant expectation, a constant standard deviation, and a correlation function depending only on t-t' will be taken as stationary. This statement can be expressed mathematically in the following manner:

$$E[X(t)] = E[X] = \text{const}$$

$$D_x[t] = D_x = \text{const}$$

and

$$K_x(t,t') = K_x(t,t+\tau) = K_x(\tau) \qquad (I.33.1)$$

From $K_x(t,t') = K_x(t',t)$, it follows that $K_x(\tau) = K_y(-\tau)$ for stationary random functions. This is the reason why we use only the positive part of this function as in Fig. 24.

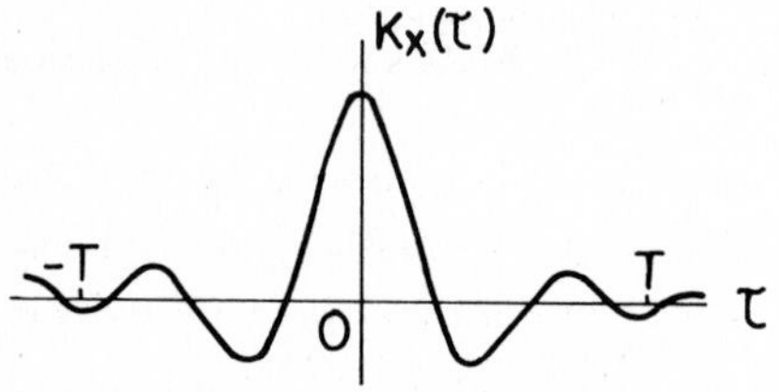

Fig. 24. An example of a correlation function.

A normalized correlation function in this case will take the following form:

$$\rho_x(\tau) = \frac{K_x(\tau)}{D_x} \qquad (I.33.2)$$

When $\tau = 0$ correlation function equals the dispersion

$$K_x(0) = D_x \quad \text{or} \quad \rho_x(0) = 1 \qquad (I.33.3)$$

If the random function is nonstationary only for reasons of a variable expectation, it can be treated like a stationary random function when it is centralized.

It is obvious from $X(t) - \overline{X(t)} = \overset{\circ}{X}(t)$ that the expectation equals 0.

Because of the importance of this kind of correlation function we illustrate the method of its calculation by means of an example:
A random function is given 12 realizations, as shown in Fig. 25.

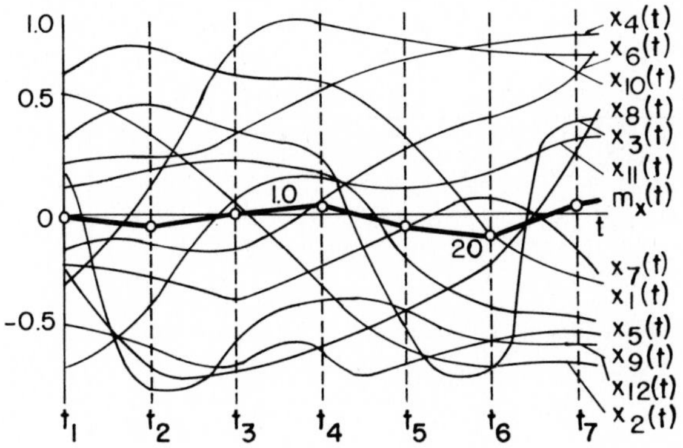

Fig. 25. A sample of measured realizations.

Let us calculate:

a) $\overline{X}(t)$, $D_x(t)$, $K_x(t)$ and $\rho_x(t,t')$

b) assuming this function is stationary, we can define $\bar{X}$, D_x, $K_x(\tau)$ and $\rho_x(\tau)$.

<u>Solution</u>. This function changes relatively smoothly, and thus the sections of the function need not be chosen very close to one another; for instance, every 4 seconds (see the figure, the measurements continued for about 24 seconds). Thus, instead of the random function we obtain 7 sets of random variables corresponding to sections made at 0, 4, 8, 12, 16, 20 and 24 seconds.

These sets are presented in Table I.33.I.

TABLE I.33.I

An example of measurements

Realization number \ t	0	4	8	12	16	20	24
1	6.4	7.4	6.2	5.9	3.5	-0.9	-3.9
2	5.4	3.7	0.6	-3.2	-6.0	-6.9	-6.7
3	3.4	5.0	3.7	2.6	-5.2	-7.2	4.2
4	2.3	2.6	3.5	5.5	6.0	7.5	8.0
5	1.2	2.0	2.4	1.8	-2.9	-4.2	-4.6
6	-1.6	-1.2	-1.5	0.5	2.9	4.3	6.3
7	-2.2	-2.9	-3.8	-2.4	-0.6	0.7	-1.6
8	-2.6	-6.9	-7.0	-6.1	-4.3	-2.2	2.9
9	-5.0	-6.0	-6.8	-6.2	-6.8	-5.6	-5.1
10	-3.0	1.3	-7.5	8.4	7.8	7.3	7.1
11	-6.9	-4.0	0.8	1.6	1.2	1.8	3.3
12	1.8	-7.9	-5.6	-3.9	-4.2	-5.8	-5.3

Further, we calculate the estimation of the characteristics of random variables x(0), x(4),...,x(24). Summing the values in the columns and dividing them by the number of realizations n=12 we obtain the expectation $\overline{x(t)}$.

[For t=8, $\overline{x(8)} = \dfrac{6.2+0.6+3.7+3.5+2.4-1.5-3.8-7-6.8+7.5+0.8-5.6}{12} = 0$]

t	0	4	8	12	16	20	24
$\bar{x}(t)$	-0.07	-0.57	0.000	0.37	-0.57	-0.93	0.36

To calculate the second mixed moment $K_x(t,t')$, we multiply numbers corresponding to t and t' in the corresponding columns; the 12 products in each pair of columns are divided by 12. We then substract the product of the corresponding expectations and multiply by n/n-1 = 12/11. The results are given in Table I.33.II.

TABLE I.33.II

The values of the second mixed moment

$K_x(t,t')$ \ t	0	4	8	12	16	20	24
0	16.32	13.79	7.95	4.57	-1.06	-6.42	-6.48
4		23.85	20.29	16.21	8.27	2.29	2.51
8			23.56	21.52	15.27	9.82	8.96
12				22.07	19.10	14.91	13.22
16					24.67	23.48	17.11
20						26.91	21.14
24							28.78

For instance:

$$K(4,12) = \frac{12}{11}\left[\frac{7.4\cdot5.9-3.7\cdot3.2+5\cdot2.6+2.6\cdot5.5+2\cdot1.8-1.2\cdot5+2.9\cdot2.4+6.9\cdot6.1}{12}+\right.$$

$$\left.+\ 6\cdot6.2+1.3\cdot8.4-4\cdot1.6+7.9\cdot3.9+0.57\cdot0.37\right] = 16.21$$

The variance is located on the diagonal of the table.

t	0	4	8	12	16	20	24
$D_x(t)$	16.32	23.85	23.56	22.07	24.07	26.91	28.78

Extracting the square root of $D_x(t)$ we obtain the standard deviation

t	0	4	8	12	16	20	24
$\sigma_x(t)$	4.04	4.88	4.85	4.70	4.91	5.19	5.36

Dividing the values in Table I.33.II by the corresponding products of $\sigma_x(t)$, we obtain normalized mixed moments $\rho_x(t,t')$ which are shown in Table I.33.III.

TABLE I.33.III

The normalized values of the mixed moment.

ρ \ t	0	4	8	12	16	20	24
0	1	0.700	0.405	0.241	-0.053	-0.306	-0.299
4		1	0.856	0.707	0.345	0.090	0.095
8			1	0.943	0.643	0.390	0.344
12				1	0.829	0.612	0.524
16					1	0.923	0.650
20						1	0.760
24							1

Let us analyze these results we have obtained so far. As can be clearly seen from Fig. 25, the expectation scarcely deviates relative to zero. Thus, it is expedient to simplify the consideration by assuming this function to be stationary. The existing deviation can be explained by the relatively small number of measured realizations.

To bring these calculated results to stationariness, we find the average constant value of the expectation of the function:

$$\bar{X} \simeq \frac{\overline{X(0)} + \overline{X(4)} + \overline{X(8)} + \overline{X(12)} + \overline{X(16)} + \overline{X(20)} + \overline{X(24)}}{7} \simeq -0.2$$

By analogy

$$D_x \simeq \frac{D_x(0) + D_x(4) + D_x(8) + D_x(12) + D_x(16) + D_x(20) + D_x(24)}{7} \simeq 23$$

Then

$\sigma_x \simeq 4.86$

The normalized correlation function depends only upon $t'-t = \tau$. Thus, for τ=const. the correlation function becomes constant. The results are shown in Table I.33.IV.

TABLE I.33.IV
The normalized correlation function

t	0	4	8	12	16	20	24
$\rho_x(\tau)$	1.00	0.84	0.60	0.38	0.13	-0.10	-0.30

34. SPECTRAL DENSITY OF A STATIONARY RANDOM FUNCTION

Our discussion in the previous paragraphs has led us to the conclusion that the correlation function indicates the internal structure of the random function. The higher the frequencies making up this function, the sharper the slope of the correlation function. In other words, the shape of the correlation function reflects the content of the random process or function. Here we come close to the concept of a frequential spectrum of such a function. We will consider only the spectra of stationary random functions. Physically this concept describes the distribution of the variance.

Let us now consider the following two statements which form the basis of the spectral theory of stationary random processes or functions:

(1) The correlation function $K_x(\tau)$ is an even function, i.e. $K_x(\tau) = K_x(-\tau)$ and its graphic image (see Fig. 24) is a symmetrical curve. The correlation function can thus be expressed as a Fourier expansion in the following form:

$$K_x(\tau) = \sum_{k=0}^{\infty} D_k \cos k\omega\tau$$

where $\omega_1 = \pi/T$ and $-T_1 + T$ is the consideration interval. The D_k coefficients are found from:

$$D_0 = \frac{1}{T}\int_0^T K_x(\tau)d\tau \qquad \text{(I.34.1)}$$

and

$$D_k = \frac{2}{T}\int_0^T K_x(\tau)\cos k\omega\tau d\tau \qquad k \neq 0$$

(2) It can be proved that a centralized random function can represent the following expansion:

$$\overset{\circ}{X}(t) = \sum_{k=0}^{\infty} (U_k \cos k\omega t + V_k \sin k\omega t) \qquad (I.34.2)$$

where U_k, V_k are random values with expectations which equal 0 and $D[U_k] = D[V_k] = D_k$

From equation (I.34.2) we can find the variance of the $\overset{\circ}{X}(t)$ function

$$D_x = D[\overset{\circ}{X}(t)] = \sum_{k=0}^{\infty} (\cos^2 k\omega t + \sin^2 k\omega t) D_k = \sum_{k=0}^{\infty} D_k$$

Thus, the variance of the stationary random function equals the sum of the variances of all harmonics of its spectral expansion. The distribution of these variances in accordance with the frequencies is shown graphically in Fig. 26.

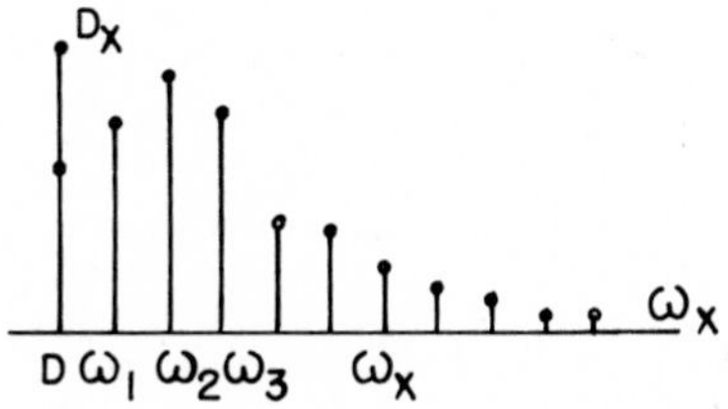

Fig. 26. Variance - frequency diagram.

So far, we have discussed the spectral expansion when the consideration interval is limited to -T, +T. It is natural to extend the borders of the interval to infinite limits. Thus for $T \to \infty$, $\omega_1 = \pi/T \to 0$; the distance $k\omega - (k-1)\omega = \Delta\omega$ tends to zero; and instead of a discrete spectrum (Fig. 27a) we will obtain a continuous smooth curve (Fig. 27b). But (by analogy with the

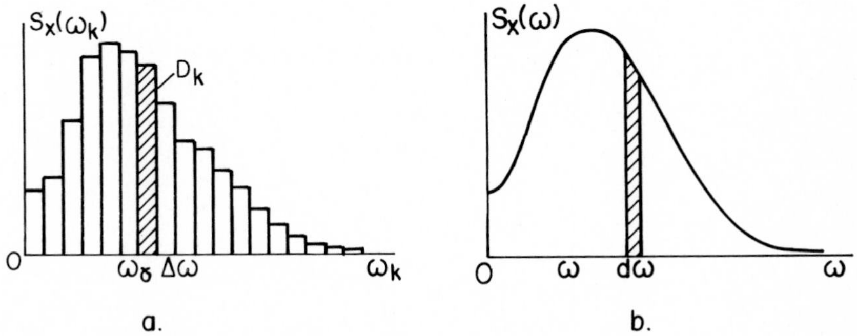

Fig. 27. (a) discrete spectrum; (b) continuous spectrum.

distribution function and the distribution density) the D_k values corresponding to each ω will be infinitesimal. This brings us to the concept of the spectral density S:

$$S_x(\omega_k) = \frac{D_k}{\Delta\omega} \quad \text{and} \quad D_x = \sum_{k=0}^{\infty} S_x(\omega_k)\Delta\omega$$

Or in an integral form:

$$D_x = \int_0^{\infty} S_x(\omega)d\omega \tag{I.34.3}$$

The area below the $S_x(\omega)$ curve equals D_x as is shown in Fig. 27b.

There is an unequivocal between correlation function and spectral density of a stationary random function

$$K_x(\tau) = \int_0^{\infty} S_x(\omega)\cos\omega\tau d\omega \tag{I.34.4}$$

and

$$S_x(\omega) = \frac{2}{\pi}\int_0^{\infty} K_x(\tau)\cos\omega\tau d\tau \tag{I.34.5}$$

Below we show some well-known analytical forms describing correlation functions of random processes and the corresponding analytical expressions for their spectral density.

(1)

$$K(\tau) = \sigma^2 e^{-\alpha|\tau|} \qquad , \alpha > 0$$

$$S(\omega) = \frac{\sigma^2}{\pi}\frac{\alpha}{\omega^2 + \alpha^2}$$

(For random processes we do not search for derivatives.)

These characteristics are shown in Fig. 28, from which an important conclusion can be drawn: the higher the α value, the nearer the spectral density to a constant. This conclusion brings us to the concept of "white noise," wherein every frequency is almost equally represented. In the limiting case

$$S(\omega) = c = \text{const}$$

$$c = \frac{\sigma^2}{\pi\alpha}$$

$$K(\tau) = 2\pi c\delta(\tau)$$

where $\delta(\tau)$ - δ - function.

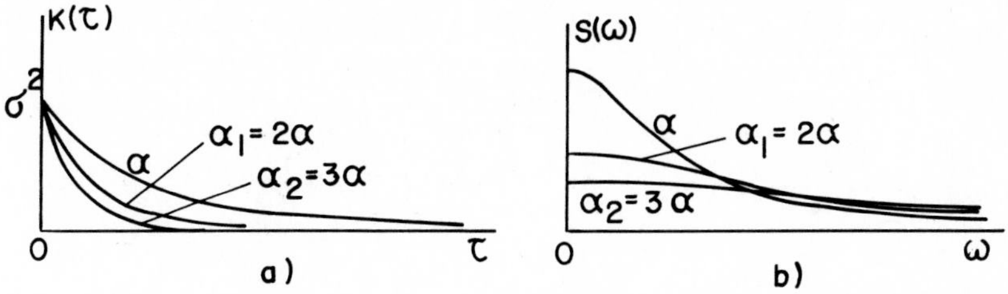

Fig. 28. (a) Correlation function for different time constants α; (b) spectra for different time constants α.

(2)

$$K(\tau) = \sigma^2 e^{-\alpha|\tau|}\cos\beta\tau, \qquad \alpha > 0$$

$$S(\omega) = \frac{\alpha\sigma^2}{\pi}\,\frac{\omega^2 + \alpha^2 + \beta^2}{(\omega^2-\beta^2-\alpha^2)^2 + 4\alpha^2\omega^2}$$

(For random processes we do not search for derivatives.)

(3)

$$K(\tau) = \sigma^2 e^{-\alpha|\tau|}\left(\cos\beta\tau + \frac{\alpha}{\beta}\sin\beta|\tau|\right), \qquad \alpha > 0$$

$$S(\omega) = \frac{2\alpha\sigma^2}{\pi}\,\frac{\alpha^2 + \beta^2}{(\omega^2-\beta^2-\alpha^2)^2 + 4\alpha^2\omega^2}$$

(For random processes we do not search for derivatives.)

(4)

$$K(\tau) = \sigma^2 e^{-\alpha^2\tau^2}\cos\beta\tau$$

$$S(\omega) = \frac{\sigma^2}{4\alpha\sqrt{\pi}}\left[\exp\left[-\frac{(\omega+\beta)^2}{4\alpha^2}\right] + \exp\left[-\frac{(\omega-\beta)^2}{4\alpha^2}\right]\right]$$

(5)

$$\rho_x = \begin{cases} 1 - \dfrac{\tau}{\tau_0} & \text{for} \quad 0 < \tau < \tau_0 \\ 0 & \text{for} \quad \tau > \tau_0 \end{cases}$$

(see Fig. 29)

$$S(\omega) = \frac{S(\omega)}{\sigma_x^2} = \frac{2}{\pi\tau_0\omega^2}(1 - \cos\omega\tau_0)$$

(see Fig. 30).

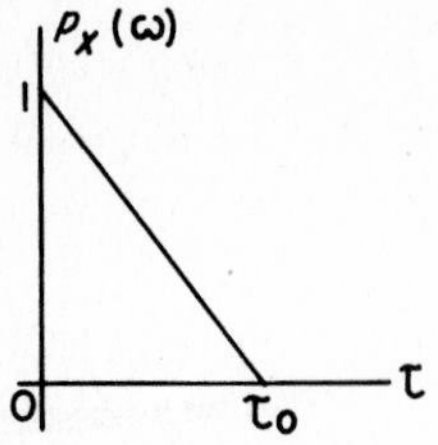

Fig. 29. Normalized correlation function.

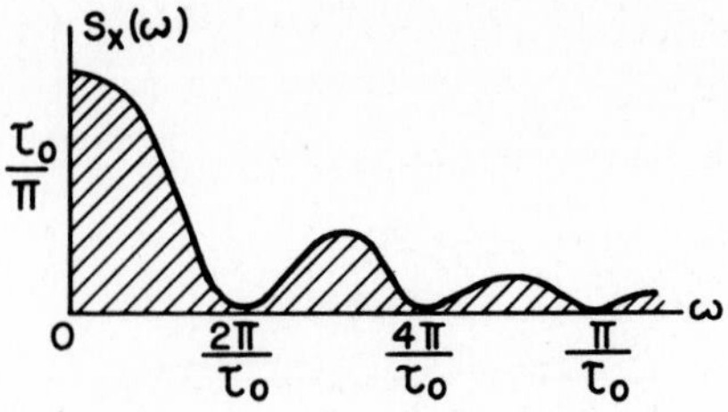

Fig. 30. Normalized spectrum.

(6)

$$\rho_x = \frac{2}{\tau(\omega_2-\omega_1)} \cos\left(\frac{\omega_2+\omega_1}{2}\tau\right)\sin\left(\frac{\omega_2-\omega_1}{2}\tau\right)$$

(see Fig. 31)

$$S(\omega) = \frac{1}{\omega_2 - \omega_1}$$

(see Fig. 32)

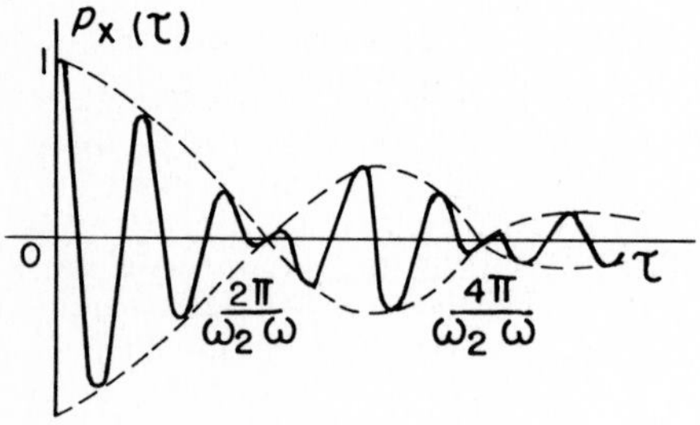

Fig. 31. Normalized correlation function.

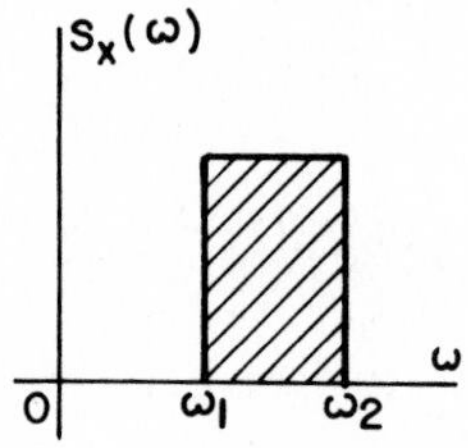

Fig. 32. Normalized spectrum

The spectral density of a derivative of a random function X(t) is calculated by multiplying the spectral density $S_x(\omega)$ by ω^2. Thus, if

$$Y(t) = \frac{d[X(t)]}{dt}$$

and $S_x(\omega)$ is the spectral density of X(t), then the spectral density of the Y(t) function $S_y(\omega)$ equals:

$$S_y(\omega) = S_x(\omega) \cdot \omega^2 \qquad (I.34.6)$$

35. TRANSFORMATION OF A STATIONARY RANDOM FUNCTION BY A LINEAR SYSTEM

Let us consider the case of a random process X(t) exciting a linear dynamic system with a transfer function $\phi(j\omega)$, and as a result at the output of the system we obtain a random process Y(t), as shown in Fig. 33 (where $j = \sqrt{-1}$).

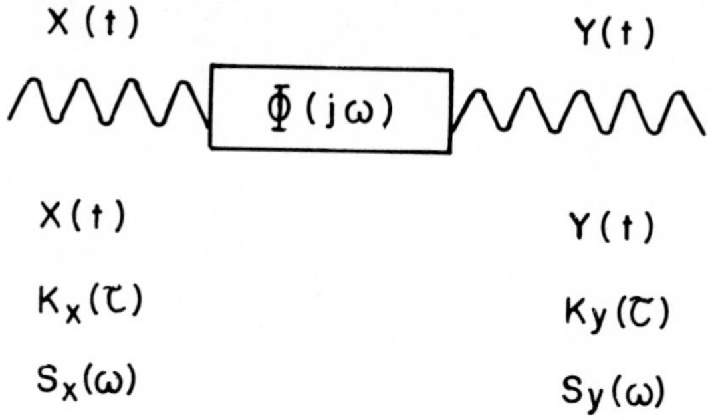

Fig. 33. The layout of a dynamic transformation.

Now, let us consider a linear dynamic system with constant parameters as if it were stationary random function transformer. Because of the linearity of the system the superposition principle can be applied. Thus, the expectation of the transformed function $\overline{Y(t)}$ can be found in the conventional manner when the exciter at the input of the system is the expectation $\overline{X(t)}$. To find the other characteristics we will use the relationship:

$$S_y(\omega) = |\Phi(j\omega)|^2 S_x(\omega) \qquad (I.35.1)$$

Using equation (I.34.4), we find $K_y(t)$, and from equation (I.34.3) we obtain:

$$D_y = \int_0^\infty |\Phi(j\omega)|^2 S_x(\omega)\,d\omega \qquad (I.35.2)$$

We will clarify this calculation by means of an example. The system represented in Fig. 34 consists of a spring with stiffness c and an oscillating mass m. The equation describing the movement of the mass m has the following form:

$$m\ddot{y} + cy = X(t)$$

or

$$\ddot{y} + k^2 y = \frac{1}{m} X(t)$$

where $k^2 = \frac{c}{m}$, and X(t) is described by a spectral density $S_x(\omega)$

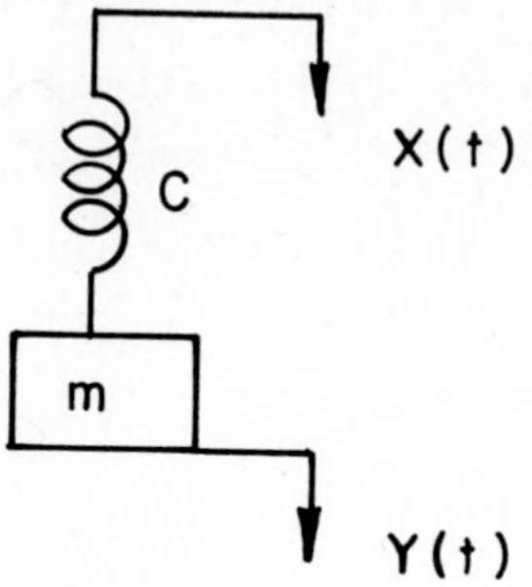

Fig. 34. A dynamic model.

$$S_x(\omega) = \frac{1}{\omega_2 - \omega_1}$$

In terms of operators, the equation can be rewritten as

$$y(p)(p^2 + k^2) = \frac{1}{m} X(p)$$

Thus, $\Phi(j\omega) = \dfrac{1}{m(p^2-\omega^2)}$.

Now the spectral density of the output process $S_y(\omega)$ equals:

$$S_y(\omega) = \frac{S_x(\omega)}{m(k^2-\omega^2)} = \frac{1}{m(\omega_2-\omega_1)(k^2-\omega^2)}$$

36. ERGODICAL RANDOM FUNCTIONS

A random function X(t) is ergodical if its average value during a sufficiently long time interval equals the average calculated from a sufficient number of realizations.

An ergodical function can be handled when only one sufficiently long realization is measured. It is as we were considering separate sections of this long realization as different realizations. Fig. 35 shows an example of an ergodic process, in contrast to Fig. 36, which illustrates a nonergodic process. A striking indication of an ergodical process is that its correlation function tends to zero when $\tau \to \infty$.

For a nonergodic process the correlation function aspires to a constant value.

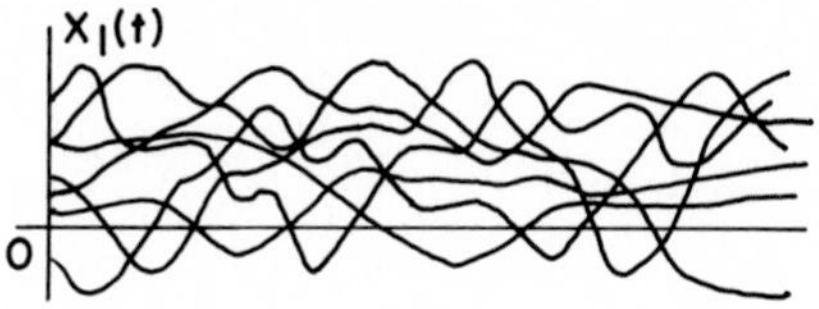

Fig. 35. An ergodic process.

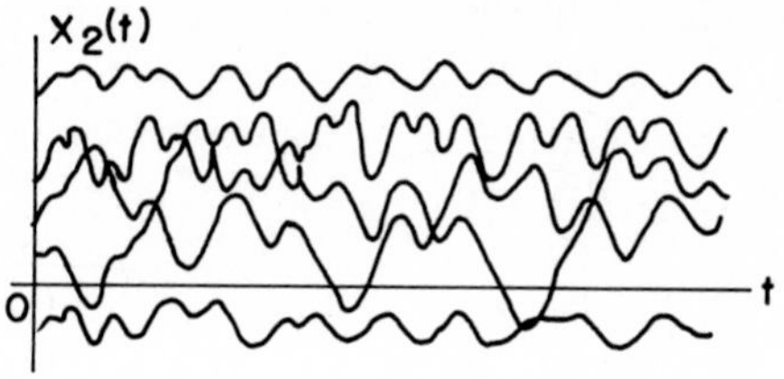

Fig. 36. A nonergodic process.

37. THE LEVEL CROSSING PROBLEM

Dealing with a random function X(t), the realization of which is presented in Fig. 37, we can state that the value of the function sometimes crosses the previously fixed level a. The questions then arise as to:

1) The average number $\bar{\nu}$ of times the function exceeds the "a" value during a time unit;
2) The average duration $\bar{\tau}$ of the function above the "a" value.

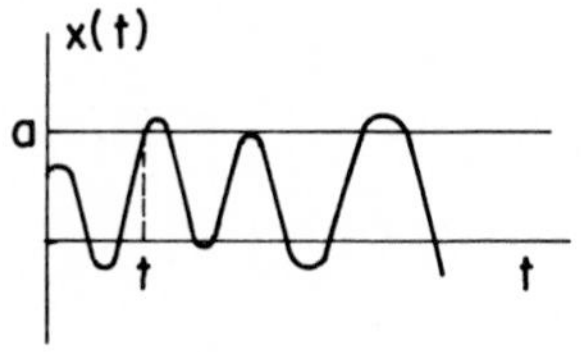

Fig. 37. An example of the level crossing problem.

There are, of course, other problems; for instance, the definition of the distribution of the function's durations above the fixed value "a" etc. But we have mentioned only those which are relatively easily answered, and we will use these answers in our further discussions.

The general formulas defining $\bar{\nu}$ and $\bar{\tau}$ were obtained in 1944-1945 by Rice and applied to differentiable random processes, although a simple numerical result can be reached only for normally distributed processes.

Let us first define the probability that during an infinitesimal period of time dt which follows immediately after the moment t, the crossing of level "a" will occur. This situation can be described analytically:

$$X(t) < a, \tag{I.37.1}$$

$$X(t + dt) > a \tag{I.37.2}$$

and the probability will be

$$P[X(t) < a < X(t + dt)] \tag{I.37.3}$$

The condition of differentiability of the random function X(t) permits us to rewrite equation (I.37.2) in the following form:

$$X(t + dt) = X(t) + V(t)dt \quad \text{where} \quad V(t) \equiv \dot{X}(t)$$

then, instead of inequality X(t + dt) > a, we have: X(t) > a - V(t)dt.

Now the probability (I.37.3) can be rewritten in the following way:

$$P[a - V(t)dt < X(t) < a] = \int_{o}^{\infty} \int_{a-Vdt}^{a} f(x,v|t)dxdv \tag{I.37.4}$$

The internal integral can be calculated simply (because its limits differ by a infinitesimal value Vdt) as:

$$\int_{a-Vdt}^{a} f(x,v|t)dx = dtVf(a,v|t) \tag{I.37.5}$$

Substituting equation (I.37.5) into equation (I.37.4) we obtain

$$P[a - V(t)dt < X(t) < a] = dt \int_{o}^{\infty} f(a,v|t)vdv \tag{I.37.6}$$

This expression allows us to introduce a concept of time density for the probability and to write

$$P[a - V(t)dt < X(t) < a] = P(a|t)dt \tag{I.37.7}$$

Thus, comparing equation (I.37.6) with equation (I.37.7) we obtain:

$$P(a|t) = \int_{o}^{\infty} f(a,v|t)vdv \tag{I.37.8}$$

By analogy, for the time density for the probability that the crossing of level "a" occurs in the opposite direction:

$$P'(a|t) = - \int_{-\infty}^{o} f(a,v|t)vdv \tag{I.37.9}$$

Thus the total density:

$$P(a|t) + P'(a|t) = \int_{-\infty}^{\infty} f(a,v|t)|v|dv \tag{I.37.10}$$

Omitting the intermediate calculations, we obtain:

(1) for the average time $\bar{t}$ the random function is bigger than "a" during the period T:

$$\bar{t} = \int_{o}^{T}\int_{a}^{\infty} f(x|t)dxdt \qquad (I.37.11)$$

(2) for the average number $\bar{n}$ of crossings of the level "a" during the same period T:

$$\bar{n} = \int_{o}^{T}\int_{o}^{\infty} vf(a,v|t)dvdt \qquad (I.37.12)$$

(3) for the average duration $\bar{\tau}$ of the crossings:

$$\bar{\tau} = \frac{\bar{t}}{\bar{n}} = \frac{\int_{o}^{T}\int_{a}^{\infty} f(x|t)dxdt}{\int_{o}^{T}\int_{o}^{\infty} vf(a,v|t)dvdt} \qquad (I.37.13)$$

For stationary processes these formulas can be simplified and become, respectively:

$$\bar{t} = T\int_{a}^{\infty} f(x)dx \qquad (I.37.14)$$

$$\bar{n} = T\int_{o}^{\infty} vf(a,v)dv \qquad (I.37.15)$$

$$\bar{\tau} = \frac{\int_{o}^{\infty} f(x)dx}{\int_{o}^{\infty} vf(a,v)dv} \qquad (I.37.16)$$

In this case, we can introduce the concept of an average number of crossings per time unit:

$$\bar{\nu} = \frac{\bar{n}}{T} = \int_{o}^{\infty} vf(a,v)dv \qquad (I.37.17)$$

To obtain the final result from formulas (I.37.14), (I.37.15), (I.37.16) and (I.37.17), we have to know the distribution law of the random function under consideration. Assuming a normal distribution and stationariness of the process we have:

$$f(x,v) = \frac{1}{\sigma_x\sqrt{2\pi}} \exp[-\frac{(x-\bar{x})^2}{2\sigma_x^2}] \cdot \frac{1}{\sigma_v\sqrt{2\pi}} \exp(-v^2/2\sigma_v^2) \qquad (I.37.18)$$

(This equation is obtained on the basis of the noncorrelation between a random function and its derivative.)

where

$$\sigma_v^2 = \frac{d^2 K_x(\tau)}{dt^2} \qquad \text{for } \tau = 0$$

Thus:

$$\bar{\nu} = \frac{\sigma_v}{2\pi\sigma_x} \exp[-\frac{(a-\bar{x})^2}{2\sigma_x^2}] \tag{I.37.19}$$

$$\bar{\tau} = \pi \frac{\sigma_x}{\sigma_v} \exp[\frac{(a-\bar{x})^2}{2\sigma_x^2}][1 - \phi(\frac{a-\bar{x}}{\sigma_x})] \tag{I.37.20}$$

For the particular case $a=\bar{x}$ we obtain:

$$\bar{\tau} = \pi \frac{\sigma_x}{\sigma_v} = \pi \sqrt{- \frac{K_x(\tau)}{\ddot{K}_x(\tau)}}\Bigg|_{\tau=0} \tag{I.37.21}$$

SELECTED BIBLIOGRAPHY

1. Dwass, M. Probability Theory and Applications, New York, W.A. Benjamin, Inc. 1970.
2. Mood, A.M., Graybill, F.A. and Boes, D.C. Introduction to the Theory of Statistics, 3rd edn. McGraw Hill, Kogakusha Ltd., 1974. International Student Edition.
3. Bendat, J.S. and Piersol, A.G. Randon Data: Analysis and Measurement Procedures, New York, Wiley-Interscience, 1967.
4. Cramer, H. and Leadbetter, R.M. Stationary and Related Stochastic Processes, New York, John Wiley, 1967.
5. Crandall, S.H. Random Vibration. Cambridge, Massachusetts, M.I.T. Press, 1963.

CHAPTER II

KINEMATICS AND DYNAMICS OF MECHANISMS

1. MOTION FUNCTION OF MECHANISM

Before we examine the probabilistic approach to the analysis of mechanisms, let us consider mechanisms in general. Every mechanism has a driving link and a driven link. The first question in kinematics is that of the relationship between the input-driving motion and the output-driven motion. Let us denote:
x - the input motion, which can be linear or angular
s - the output motion which, in turn, can be linear or angular.
Thus, we can write the relationship between these two values as:

$$s = \Pi(x) \tag{II.1.1}$$

From equation (II.1.1), it follows that:

$$\dot{s} = \Pi'(x)\cdot\dot{x} \tag{II.1.2}$$

and

$$\ddot{s} = \Pi''(x)\cdot\dot{x}^2 + \ddot{x}\cdot\Pi'(x) \tag{II.1.3}$$

The importance of equation (II.1.2) lies in its applicability to see the analysis of forces: by multiplying both sides of equation (II.1.2) by the force (or torque when the motion is angular) we obtain an equality for the power on the driving and driven sides of the mechanism (at this stage frictional losses of power are neglected). Hence,

$$\dot{s}F_{output} = \dot{x}F_{input}$$

From equation (II.1.2)

$$\dot{s}/\dot{x} = \Pi'(x)$$

then

$$F_{input}/F_{output} = \Pi'(x) \tag{II.1.4}$$

In the particular case where the input motion can be considered uniform (i.e. $\dot{x}$ = const and $\ddot{x} = 0$), it follows from expression (II.1.3) that

$$\ddot{s} = \Pi''(x)\cdot\dot{x}^2 \tag{II.1.5}$$

The designer often has to deal with a chain of mechanisms, for which

$$s_n = \Pi_n\{\Pi_{n-1}[\Pi_{n-2}(\ldots\Pi_1[x_1])]\} \tag{II.1.6}$$

Then

$$\dot{s}_n = \dot{x}_1 \prod_{j=1}^{n} \Pi'_j(x_j) \qquad \text{(II.1.7)}$$

where

$$x_j = s_{j-1} \quad \text{and} \quad s_j = \Pi_j(x_j)$$

Further

$$\ddot{s}_n = \ddot{x}_1 \prod_{j=1}^{n} \Pi'_j(x_j) + x_1 \frac{d\{\prod_{j=1}^{n} \Pi'_j(x_j)\}}{dt} \qquad \text{(II.1.8)}$$

For the simplified case in which $\dot{x}_1$ = const and $\ddot{x} = 0$, from equation (II.1.8) we obtain:

$$\ddot{s}_n = \dot{x}_1 \frac{d\{\prod_{j=1}^{n} \Pi'_j(x_j)\}}{dt} \qquad \text{(II.1.9)}$$

Let us take the Geneva mechanism as an example of the calculation of a Π function. The layout shown in Fig. 38 will aid us in this task. It is obvious

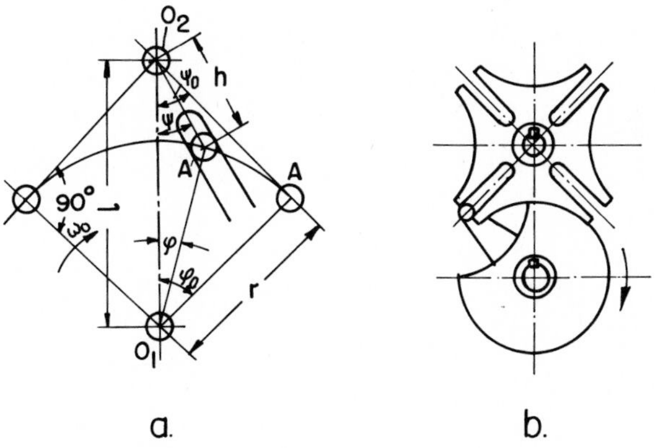

Fig. 38. a) The layout of Geneva mechanism; b) four-slot Geneva mechanism.

that this mechanism can be analyzed only during its motion, when the driving link is engaged with the driven one. For the four-slot Geneva cross shown on the right-hand side of the figure such engagement exists only for the 90° rotation angle of the driving link, while the rest of the rotation angle (270°) is idle.

To avoid impact between the links at the moment of engagement the mechanism is usually designed so as to provide at that very moment, a right angle between 0_1A and 0_2A.

A schematic representation of this mechanism is given on the left-hand side of the figure. Here $0_1A = r$ is the driving link at the very moment of engagement and $0_1A' = r$ is constant at any intermediate time.

The number of slots n on the cross determines the angle ψ_o i.e.:

$$\psi_o = \frac{180°}{n} \tag{II.1.10}$$

and obviously,

$$\phi_o = 90° - \frac{180°}{n}$$

From the triangle $0_1 0_2 A$ we obtain

$$\ell = \frac{r}{\cos\phi_o} \tag{II.1.11}$$

Applying equation (II.1.11) to the triangle $0_1 0_2 A'$ we can express

$$\overline{0_1 0_2} = \ell = r\cos\phi + h\cos\psi \tag{II.1.12}$$

Where the values of ψ are unknown, and the length of $0_1A' = h$.

From the sin theorem, we obtain

$$\frac{h}{\sin\phi} = \frac{r}{\sin\psi} \tag{II.1:13}$$

And thus from equations (II.1.11) and (II.1.12):

$$\frac{r}{\cos\phi_o} = r\cos\phi + r\,\frac{\cos\psi\sin\phi}{\sin\psi} \tag{II.1.14}$$

Denoting $\lambda = r/\ell$ and simplifying equation (II.1.14) we obtain

$$\tan\psi = \frac{\lambda\sin\phi}{1 - \lambda\cos\phi} \tag{II.1.15}$$

or

$$\psi = \Pi(\phi) = \arctan\frac{\lambda\sin\phi}{1 - \lambda\cos\phi} \tag{II.1.16}$$

i.e. for this particular case $\psi = \Pi(\phi)$.

From equation (II.1.15) we obtain for the velocity of the driven link $\dot{\psi}$ the following expression:

$$\dot{\psi} = \frac{\lambda(\cos\phi - \lambda)}{1 - 2\lambda\cos\phi + \lambda^2}\;\frac{d\phi}{dt} \tag{II.1.17}$$

or

$$\Pi'(\phi) = \frac{\lambda(\cos\phi - \lambda)}{1 - 2\lambda\cos\phi + \lambda^2}$$

when $\omega_o = \frac{d\phi}{dt} = \text{const}$, we get

$$\dot{\psi} = \frac{\lambda(\cos\phi - \lambda)\omega_o}{1 - 2\lambda\cos\phi + \lambda^2} \tag{II.1.18}$$

For acceleration of the driven link we obtain:

$$\varepsilon = \ddot{\psi} = \frac{-\lambda(1-\lambda^2)\sin\phi}{(1 - 2\lambda\cos\phi + \lambda^2)^2}(d\phi/dt)^2 + \frac{\lambda(\cos\phi - \lambda)}{1 - 2\lambda\cos\phi + \lambda^2}\frac{d^2\phi}{dt^2} \tag{II.1.19}$$

or when $\frac{d\phi}{dt} = \omega_o$ we can simplify the expression to the form:

$$\varepsilon = \frac{-\lambda(1-\lambda^2)\sin\phi}{(1 - 2\lambda\cos\phi + \lambda^2)^2}\omega_o^2 \quad \text{or} \quad \Pi''(\phi) = \frac{-\lambda(1-\lambda^2)\sin\phi}{(1 - 2\lambda\cos\phi + \lambda^2)^2} \tag{II.1.20}$$

2. KINEMATIC ACCURACY OF MECHANISMS

Random factors, such as limited manufacturing accuracy, assembling errors, speed deviations, backlashes, deformations, variable forces, and wear, cause the motions of the links in mechanisms and machines to differ from the calculated or ideal values. Thus, we can write:

$$\begin{aligned} x &= x^* + \Delta x \\ s &= s^* + \Delta s \\ \Pi &= \Pi^* + \Delta\Pi \end{aligned} \tag{II.2.1}$$

where the asterisk denotes the calculated or ideal value, and Δ represents the deviation. The deviations Δx, Δs and $\Delta\Pi$ and their derivatives are random in nature and can be represented in the following form:

$$\begin{aligned} \Delta x &= \bar{x} + \mathring{x} \\ \Delta s &= \bar{s} + \mathring{s} \\ \Delta\Pi &= \bar{\Pi} + \mathring{\Pi} \end{aligned} \tag{II.2.2}$$

where "-" symbolizes the average value or expectation and "°", the centralized values. Naturally, the derivatives of these values can be represented analogically:

$$\Delta\dot{x} = \dot{\bar{x}} + \mathring{\dot{x}} \qquad \Delta\ddot{x} = \ddot{\bar{x}} + \mathring{\ddot{x}}$$

$$\Delta\dot{s} = \dot{\bar{s}} + \mathring{\dot{s}} \qquad \Delta s = \ddot{\bar{s}} + \mathring{\ddot{s}} \qquad \text{(II.2.3)}$$

$$\Delta\Pi' = \bar{\Pi}' + \mathring{\Pi}' \qquad \Delta\Pi'' = \bar{\Pi}'' + \mathring{\Pi}''$$

In Fig. 39 we show the movements $s_1(t)$ and $s_2(t)$ of two of the links in a cyclic mechanism and how a relative error $\Delta s = |\Delta s_1 - \Delta s_2|$ arises between these two links at any moment t. Let us fix several planes at moments $t_1, t_2, \ldots, t_i, \ldots, t_n$ each t being separated from its nearest neighbor by T, the period of one cycle. (In the figure only two planes are shown.) The curves pass through the planes t_i at the points s_{1i} and s_{2i} described by coordinates u_{1i} v_{1i} and u_{2i} v_{2i} respectively. The calculated or ideal points s^*_{1i} and s^*_{2i} where the links should be located at times t_{1i} are described by the coordinates u^*_{1i} v^*_{1i} and u^*_{2i} v^*_{2i}, respectively. This means that in each cycle the crossing points hit the planes in the domains d_{1i} and d_{2i} in the close neighborhood of the points points s^*_{1i} and s^*_{2i}.

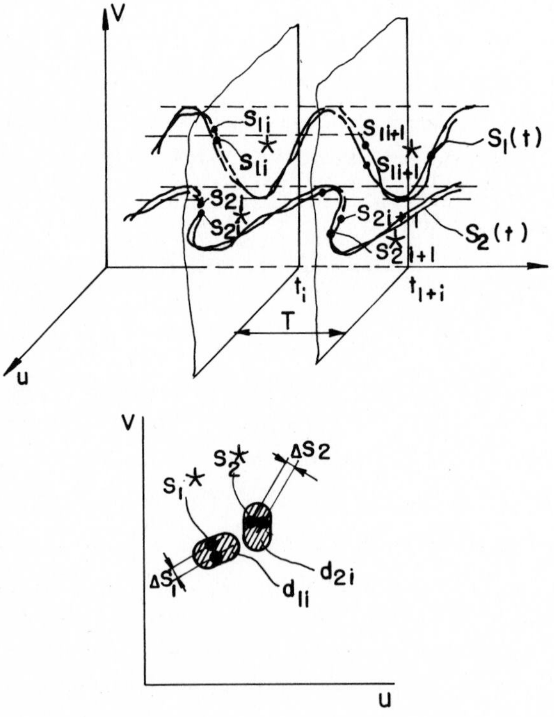

Fig. 39. The layout of the birth of the motion error.

From this graphical interpretation it becomes obvious that:

$$\Delta s_i^2 = (\Delta s_{1i} - \Delta s_{2i})^2 = (\Delta v_{1i} - \Delta v_{2i})^2 + (\Delta u_{1i} - \Delta u_{2i})^2 \qquad (II.2.4)$$

where

$$\Delta v_{1i} = v_{1i} - v_{1i}^* \qquad \Delta u_{1i} = u_{1i} - u_{1i}^*$$

$$\Delta v_{2i} = v_{2i} - v_{2i}^* \qquad \Delta u_{2i} = u_{2i} - u_{2i}^*$$

i.e. instead of an ideal calculated distance between the links $\vec{s}^* = \vec{s}_1^* - \vec{s}_2^*$, there is an additional deviation Δs. Obviously,

$$s^{*2} = (v_2^* - v_1^*)^2 + (u_2 - u_1^*)^2 \qquad (II.2.5)$$

Spatial problems can be described in the same manner.

Considering a one-dimensional situation we can obtain from equations (II.1.1) and (II.2.1)

$$s = s^* + \Delta s = \Pi^*(x^*) + \Pi^{*\prime}\cdot\Delta x + \Delta\Pi(x^*) + \Delta\Pi'\cdot\Delta x \qquad (II.2.6)$$

where it is obvious that $s^* = \Pi^*(x^*)$, and then,

$$\Delta s \simeq \Pi^{*\prime}\cdot\Delta x + \Delta\Pi + \Delta\Pi'\cdot\Delta x \qquad (II.2.7)$$

These expressions are obtained on the assumption that

$$\Pi^{*\prime}(x) \simeq \Pi^{*\prime}(x^*) \quad \text{and} \quad \Delta\Pi'(x) \simeq \Delta\Pi'(x^*) \qquad (II.2.8)$$

Differentiating equation (II.2.7) with respect to t we obtain for the speed deviation $\Delta\dot{s}$ the following expression:

$$\Delta\dot{s} \simeq \Pi^{*\prime\prime}\cdot\Delta x\cdot\dot{x}^* + \Pi^{*\prime}\cdot\Delta\dot{x} + \Delta\Pi'\cdot\dot{x}^* + \Delta\Pi''\cdot\Delta x\cdot\dot{x}^* + \Delta\Pi'\cdot\Delta\dot{x} \qquad (II.2.9)$$

Differentiating once more, we get the deviation of the acceleration in the following form:

$$\Delta\ddot{s} \simeq \Pi^{*\prime\prime\prime}\cdot\Delta x\cdot\dot{x}^{*2} + 2\Pi^{*\prime\prime}\cdot\Delta\dot{x}\cdot\dot{x}^* + \Pi^{*\prime\prime}\cdot\Delta x\cdot\ddot{x}^* + \Pi^{*\prime}\cdot\Delta\ddot{x} + \Delta\Pi''\cdot\dot{x}^{*2} + \Delta\Pi'\cdot\ddot{x}^* + \Delta\Pi'''\cdot\Delta x\cdot\dot{x}^{*2} + 2\Pi''\cdot\Delta\dot{x}\cdot\dot{x}^* + \Delta\Pi''\cdot\Delta x\cdot\ddot{x}^* + \Delta\Pi'\cdot\Delta\ddot{x} \qquad (II.2.10)$$

The only assumption we have made so far is that used in equation (II.2.8). In practical problems these cumbersome expressions can be simplified by introducing an additional assumption. For instance, when $\dot{x}^* = \text{const}$ then $\ddot{x}^* = 0$ and the third, sixth and ninth terms of equation (II.2.10) equal 0. In many cases the second order of infinitesimality is negligible, and then instead of equations (II.2.7), (II.2.9) and (II.2.10) we can write:

$$\Delta s \simeq \Pi^{*\prime}\cdot\Delta x + \Delta\Pi \qquad (II.2.11)$$

$$\Delta\dot{s} \simeq \Pi^{*''}\cdot\Delta x\cdot\dot{x}^{*} + \Pi^{*'}\cdot\Delta\dot{x} + \Delta\Pi'\cdot\dot{x}^{*} \qquad \text{(II.2.12)}$$

and

$$\Delta\ddot{s} \simeq \Pi^{*'''}\cdot\Delta x\cdot\dot{x}^{*2} + 2\Pi^{*''}\cdot\Delta x\cdot\dot{x}^{*} + \Pi^{*''}\cdot\Delta\ddot{x} + \Delta\Pi''\cdot\dot{x}^{*2} \qquad \text{(II.2.13)}$$

This latter assumption must be used very carefully. When the error is small relative to the basic value, the assumption is justified. But a derivative of this small error can be considerable and multiplying by it or squaring it does not bring us to the second order of infinitesimality.

3. GENERAL STATISTICAL APPROACH

The simplest probabilistic criterion which can be used as an estimator of kinematic error is the deviation tolerance width. Let us designate

$$T_s = \pm 3\sigma_s \quad T_{\dot{s}} = \pm 3\sigma_{\dot{s}} \quad T_{\ddot{s}} = \pm 3\sigma_{\ddot{s}} \qquad \text{(II.3.1)}$$

where σ_s, $\sigma_{\dot{s}}$ and $\sigma_{\ddot{s}}$ - standard deviation of motion, speed and acceleration, respectively.

We will now show how the values of σ_s, $\sigma_{\dot{s}}$ and $\sigma_{\ddot{s}}$ can be obtained. Let us formulate two problems. The first one (used more frequently in practice) relates to a definite moment in time so that x(t) becomes a number (rather than a function). As a result of the above-mentioned factors this number includes a random component [see equations (II.2.1) and (II.2.2)], and therefore the values s, $\dot{s}$ and $\ddot{s}$ we are seeking also become random variables, i.e. s, $\dot{s}$ and $\ddot{s}$ are functions of the random variable x.

The second problem deals with the more general case in which x(t) is considered as a function which consists of two components, one determined $x^*(t)$ and one random x(t). Thus, the values sought must also be functions, and therefore s(t), $\dot{s}(t)$ and $\ddot{s}(t)$ consist of determined parts $s^*(t)$, $\dot{s}^*(t)$ and $\ddot{s}^*(t)$, respectively, and random components $\Delta s(t)$, $\Delta\dot{s}(t)$ and $\Delta\ddot{s}(t)$, respectively. In this chapter we will deal with the first problem. For particular cases the second approach will be discussed.

Now let us turn our attention to expression (II.2.7). Taking equations (II.2.2) and (II.2.3) into account, we can write:

$$\Delta s \simeq \Pi^{*'}\cdot(\bar{x} + \mathring{x}) + \bar{\Pi} + \mathring{\Pi} + (\bar{\Pi}' + \mathring{\Pi}')\cdot(\bar{x} + \mathring{x}) \qquad \text{(II.3.2)}$$

or

$$\Delta s \simeq \Pi^{*'}\cdot\bar{x} + \Pi^{*'}\cdot\mathring{x} + \bar{\Pi} + \mathring{\Pi} + \bar{\Pi}'\cdot\bar{x} + \mathring{\Pi}'\cdot\bar{x} + \bar{\Pi}'\cdot\mathring{x} + \mathring{\Pi}'\cdot\mathring{x} \qquad \text{(II.3.3)}$$

Remembering that Π, x and Π' are not correlated because:

1) Π and x are independent;
2) Π and Π' (see Chapter I, section 31).

Thus,

$$E[\Delta s] = \bar{s} = \Pi^{*\prime}\cdot\bar{x} + \bar{\Pi} + \bar{\Pi}'\cdot\bar{x} \qquad \text{(II.3.4)}$$

then

$$\mathring{s} = \Pi^{*\prime}\cdot\mathring{x} + \mathring{\Pi} + \mathring{\Pi}'\cdot\bar{x} + \bar{\Pi}'\cdot\mathring{x} + \mathring{\Pi}'\cdot\mathring{x} \qquad \text{(II.3.5)}$$

and

$$\sigma_s^2 = D_s \simeq [(\Pi^{*\prime})^2 + (\bar{\Pi}')^2 + \sigma^2_{\mathring{\Pi}'}]\cdot\sigma_x^2 + \sigma^2_{\mathring{\Pi}} + \bar{x}^2\cdot\sigma^2_{\mathring{\Pi}'} \qquad \text{(II.3.6)}$$

We handle the deviations of speed and acceleration in the same manner. Thus, for speed it is obvious that the expectation of speed and acceleration deviations equals 0 (derivative of a constant value):

$$E[\Delta\dot{s}] = \bar{\dot{s}} = 0 \quad \text{and} \quad E[\Delta\ddot{s}] = \bar{\ddot{s}} = 0 \qquad \text{(II.3.7)}$$

For the variance we obtain [from equation (II.2.9)]:

$$\sigma^2_{\dot{s}} = (\Pi^{*\prime\prime}\cdot x^*)^2\cdot\sigma_x^2 + (\Pi^{*\prime})^2\cdot\sigma^2_{\dot{x}} + (x^*)^2\cdot\sigma^2_{\Pi'} + (\dot{x}^*)^2\cdot\sigma^2_{\Pi''}\cdot\sigma^2_x + \sigma^2_{\Pi'}\cdot\sigma^2_x \qquad \text{(II.3.8)}$$

For the acceleration [from equation (II.2.10)]:

$$\sigma^2_{\ddot{s}} = [(\Pi^{*\prime\prime\prime}\cdot\dot{x}^{*2})^2 + (\Pi^{*\prime\prime}\cdot\ddot{x}^*)^2]\cdot\sigma^2_x + 2(\Pi^{*\prime\prime}\cdot\dot{x}^*)^2\cdot\sigma^2_{\dot{x}} + (\Pi^{*\prime})^2\cdot\sigma^2_{\ddot{x}} + (\sigma^2_{\Pi''} + \sigma^2_{\Pi'''}\cdot\sigma^2_x)\cdot\dot{x}^{*4} + (\sigma^2_{\Pi'} + \sigma^2_{\Pi''}\cdot\sigma^2_x)\cdot\ddot{x}^{*2} + 2x^{*2}\cdot\sigma^2_{\Pi''}\cdot\sigma^2_{\dot{x}} + \sigma^2_{\Pi'}\cdot\sigma^2_{\ddot{x}} \qquad \text{(II.3.9)}$$

Let us now look at some cases for which these expressions can be considerably simplified. For instance, for a gear transmission

$$\Pi^* = \text{const} \qquad \text{(II.3.10)}$$

then, instead of equations (II.3.8) and (II.3.9)

$$\sigma^2_{\dot{s}} = (\sigma^2_{\Pi'} + \sigma^2_{\Pi''}\cdot\sigma^2_x)\cdot\dot{x}^{*2} + \sigma^2_{\Pi'}\cdot\sigma^2_x \qquad \text{(II.3.11)}$$

and

$$\sigma^2_{\ddot{s}} = (\sigma^2_{\Pi''} + \sigma^2_{\Pi'''}\cdot\sigma^2_x)\cdot\dot{x}^{*4} + (\sigma^2_{\Pi'} + \sigma^2_{\Pi''}\cdot\sigma^2_x)\cdot\ddot{x}^{*2} + 2\dot{x}^{*2}\cdot\sigma^2_{\Pi''}\cdot\sigma^2_{\dot{x}} + \sigma^2_{\Pi'}\cdot\sigma^2_{\ddot{x}} \qquad \text{(II.3.12)}$$

4. KINEMATIC ACCURACY

At this stage, we must discuss the methods of obtaining the initial statistical information we use in the formulas derived in section 3. From an analysis of expressions (II.3.6), (II.3.11) and (II.3.12), we are able to draw the conclusion that, formally speaking, only two random variables define the values for which we seek. Thus, if we know the statistical characteristics of $\Pi(x^*)$ and $x(t)$, we are able to calculate the statistical characteristics of the kinematic errors in the motion, speed and acceleration of the driven link.

From equations (II.2.1) and (II.2.2)

$$\Pi \simeq \Pi^* + \bar{\Pi} + \mathring{\Pi} \quad \text{and} \quad x \simeq x^* + \bar{x} + \mathring{x} \tag{II.4.1}$$

[The approximation sign in the first formula appears because of the aforementioned assumption that $\Pi(x) \simeq \Pi(x^*)$.]

Once the expectations $\bar{\Pi}$ and $\bar{x}$ have been determined they become nonrandom. Thus, the statistical characteristics we are seeking relate only to the centered variables $\mathring{\Pi}$ and $\mathring{x}$. It is important to note that $\bar{\Pi}$ and $\bar{x}$ constitute the so-called systematic errors of the mechanism and drive.

Let us consider how the derivatives [which are members of expressions (II.3.6), (II.3.8) and (II.3.9)] of the variances of $\Delta\Pi$ and Δx can be determined. To do this we must know the correlation functions of the random functions $\mathring{\Pi}$ and $\mathring{x}$:

$K_\Pi(x_1,x_2)$ - correlation function of the $\Pi(x)$ function

and

$K_x(t_1,t_2)$ - correlation function of the $x(t)$ function

Then on the basis of equation (I.31.5) we can calculate the correlation functions of the derivatives of $x(t)$ and $\Pi(x)$:

$$K_{\Pi'}(x_1,x_2) = -\frac{\partial^2 K_\Pi(x_1,x_2)}{\partial x_1 \partial x_2} \quad \text{for a stationary case} \quad K_{\Pi'}(x) = -\frac{d^2 K_\Pi(x)}{dx^2}$$

$$K_{\Pi''}(x_1,x_2) = -\frac{\partial^2 K_{\Pi'}(x_1,x_2)}{\partial x_1 \partial x_2} \quad \text{for a stationary case} \quad K_{\Pi''}(x) = -\frac{d^2 K_{\Pi'}(x)}{dx^2}$$

$$K_{\Pi'''}(x_1,x_2) = -\frac{\partial^2 K_{\Pi''}(x_1,x_2)}{\partial x_1 \partial x_2} \quad \text{for a stationary case} \quad K_{\Pi'''}(x) = -\frac{d^2 K_{\Pi''}(x)}{dx^2}$$

$$K_{\dot{x}}(t_1,t_2) = -\frac{\partial^2 K_x(t_1,t_2)}{\partial t_1 \partial t_2} \quad \text{for a stationary case} \quad K_x(\tau) = -\frac{d^2 K_x(\tau)}{d\tau^2}$$

$$K_{\ddot{x}}(t_1,t_2) = -\frac{\partial^2 K_{\dot{x}}(t_1,t_2)}{\partial t_1 \partial t_2} \quad \text{for a stationary case} \quad K_{\ddot{x}}(\tau) = -\frac{d^2 K_{\dot{x}}(\tau)}{d\tau^2}$$

Further, using equations (I.31.6) and (I.33.3) we obtain the variance:

$$\sigma^2_{\Pi'}(x) = K_{\Pi'}(x_1,x_2) \quad \text{when } x_1 = x_2 = x \quad \text{for a stationary case} \quad \sigma^2_{\Pi'} = K_{\Pi'}(0)$$

$$\sigma^2_{\Pi''}(x) = K_{\Pi''}(x_1,x_2) \quad \text{when } x_1 = x_2 = x \quad \text{for a stationary case} \quad \sigma^2_{\Pi''} = K_{\Pi''}(0)$$

$$\sigma^2_{\Pi'''}(x) = K_{\Pi'''}(x_1,x_2) \quad \text{when } x_1 = x_2 = x \quad \text{for a stationary case} \quad \sigma^2_{\Pi'''} = K_{\Pi'''}(0)$$

$$\sigma^2_{\dot{x}}(t) = K_{\dot{x}}(t_1,t_2) \quad \text{when } t_1 = t_2 = t \quad \text{for a stationary case} \quad \sigma^2_{\dot{x}} = K_{\dot{x}}(0)$$

$$\sigma^2_{\ddot{x}}(t) = K_{\ddot{x}}(t_1,t_2) \quad \text{when } t_1 = t_2 = t \quad \text{for a stationary case} \quad \sigma^2_{\ddot{x}} = K_{\ddot{x}}(0)$$

(II.4.3)

The more accurate the approximation of the initial correlation function, the higher the reliability of the results obtained. In practice, $\Pi(x)$ can be determined by measurements of the action of the mechanism at low speeds to avoid the dynamic effects. For the $x(t)$ function, practice sometimes dictates that its derivatives - either $\dot{x}(t)$ or $\ddot{x}(t)$ - be measured. Obviously then, to obtain the correlation function we must use equation (I.30.5).

Thus, for a stationary case:

$$K_{\dot{x}}(\tau) = \int_0^\tau \int K_{\ddot{x}}(\tau)d\tau d\tau \qquad \text{(II.4.4)}$$

and

$$K_{x}(\tau) = \int_0^\tau \int K_{\dot{x}}(\tau)d\tau d\tau \qquad \text{(II.4.5)}$$

In this case the errors introduced due to calculations decrease. It is important to note that even when Δs is small, $\Delta\dot{s}$ and especially $\Delta\ddot{s}$ can be considerably large and cause serious difficulties in exploiting the mechanism. Undesired errors in acceleration can restrict the productivity of the machines.

5. DYNAMIC ACCURACY

Up to now, we have discussed the problem of motion errors at the level of kinematics without taking into account the elastic deformation of the links in the mechanism. This section deals with the problem of the appearance of motion errors caused by dynamics. To clarify the discussion we use as an example the mechanism shown in Fig. 40. This mechanism consists of a flywheel with a

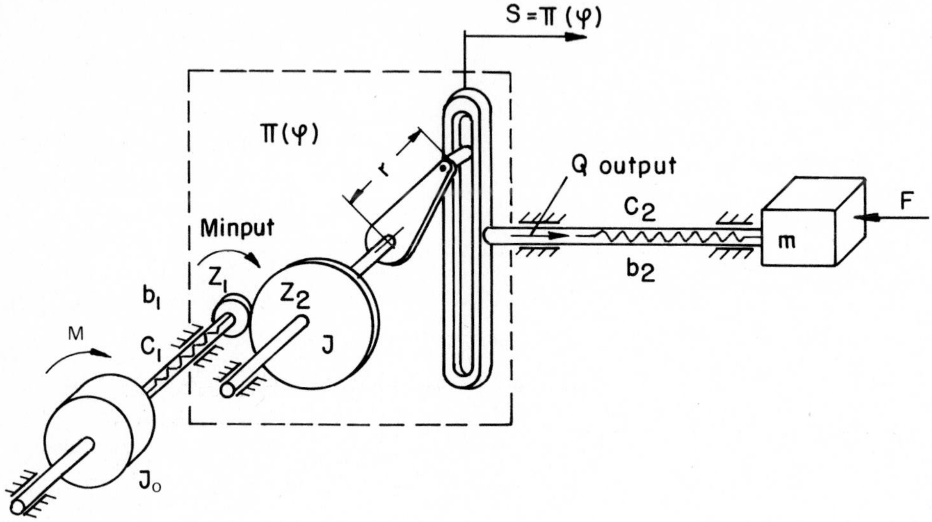

Fig. 40. A sin mechanism.

moment of inertia J_o, which drives a gear wheel z_1 through a shaft with a stiffness of c_1. The gear wheel z_1 is engaged with another wheel z_2 which drives a lever (the length of which is r) and the latter, in turn, drives a sliding link. The motion s(t) of the link is described by the motion function and equals $\Pi(\phi)$. By means of a connecting rod the sliding link drives a mass m and overcomes an external force F. The rod connecting the link to the mass has a stiffness c_2. The damping effects in the system are described by damping coefficients b_1 and b_2. These coefficients will help us to take into consideration the energy losses due to internal and external friction in and between the links of the mechanism. To simplify the calculations we use the following for the damping forces and torques, respectively:

$$F_d \approx b\dot{s} \tag{II.5.1}$$

and

$$M_d \approx b\dot{\phi}$$

The dissipate forces and torques are proportional to the linear or angular speed, respectively.

For the mechanism described the motion function relating the rotation ϕ of the drive shaft to the motion s of the sliding link obviously has the following form:

$$s = \Pi(\phi) = r\cos\phi \frac{z_1}{z_2} \tag{II.5.2}$$

The simplest approach to analyzing this mechanism is, of course, the kinematic one. (The development of the differential equations used in this section can be found in section 7, the appendix to this chapter.) In this case, the mechanism can be represented by the model shown in Fig. 41a, and described analytically as follows:

$$M_{input} = -\Pi'(\phi^*)Q_{output} = r \frac{z_1}{z_2} (\sin \frac{z_1}{z_2} \phi^*) \cdot Q_{output}$$

$$Q_{output} = F + m\ddot{s}^* \tag{II.5.3}$$

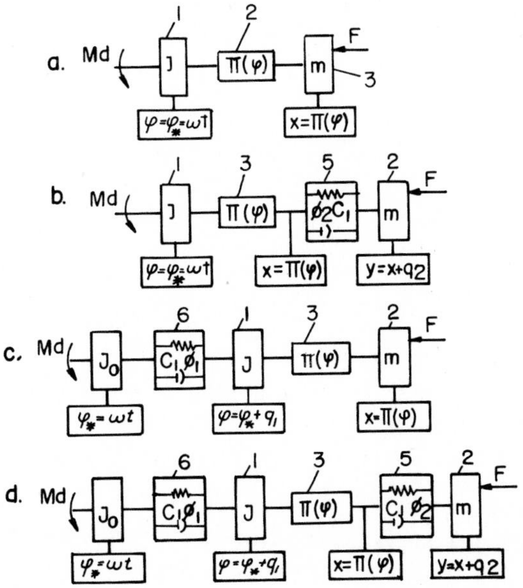

Fig. 41. Different levels of computation models for the mechanism represented in Fig. 40 and Fig. 42.

Here all the designations are clear from Fig. 40, and Q is the force at the output of the kinematic layout. In the next step we take the definite stiffness c_2 of the connecting rod into account. The model is represented in Fig.41b and described in the following way:

$$\begin{cases} M_{input} = -\Pi'(\phi^*)\cdot(b_2\dot{q}_2 + c_2q_2) = r\,\frac{z_1}{z_2}\,(\sin\frac{z_1}{z_2}\,\phi^*)\cdot(b_2\dot{q}_2 + c_2q_2) \\ m\ddot{q}_2 + b_2\dot{q}_2 + c_2q_2 = -F - m\ddot{s}^* \end{cases} \qquad (II.5.4)$$

where q_2 is the additional motion caused by the dynamic effect. Thus, the real motion of the mass m is:

$$y = s^* + q_2$$

s^* is the ideal motion at the output of the mechanism on the assumption that

$$\phi = \phi^* = \omega t$$

where ω = const.

Let us consider a different approach by taking the limited stiffness of the drive shaft into account and assuming the connecting rod to be absolutely stiff. This model is shown in Fig. 41c and is described analytically below:

$$\begin{cases} J\ddot{q}_1 + b_1\dot{q}_1 + c_1q_1 = -\Pi'(\phi^* + q_1)\cdot Q_{output} = r\,\frac{z_1}{z_2}\,[\sin\frac{z_1}{z_2}\,(\phi^* + q_1)]\cdot Q_{output} \\ Q_{output} = F + m\ddot{s} \end{cases} \qquad (II.5.5)$$

where q_1 is the additional output rotating angle of the shaft so that

$$\phi = \phi^* + q_1$$

Lastly, the model Fig. 41d takes into consideration the stiffness of both the driving shaft and the connecting rod. Then the equations are:

$$\begin{cases} J\ddot{q}_1 + b_1\dot{q}_1 + c_1q_1 = [\Pi'(\phi^* + q_1)]\cdot(b_2\dot{q}_2 + c_2q_2) \\ m\ddot{q}_2 + b_2\dot{q}_2 + c_2q_2 = -F - m\ddot{s} \end{cases} \qquad (II.5.6)$$

or

$$\begin{cases} J\ddot{q}_1 + b_1\dot{q}_1 + c_1q_1 = r\,\frac{z_1}{z_2}\,[\sin\frac{z_1}{z_2}\,(\phi^* + q_1)]\cdot(b_2\dot{q}_2 + c_2q_2) \\ m\ddot{q}_2 + b_2\dot{q}_2 + c_2q_2 = -F - m\ddot{s} \end{cases}$$

For cases c and d, s does not equal s^* because at the input of the mechanism the rotation of the driving shaft equals $\phi = \phi^* + q_1$ and the driven mass moves in accordance with $y = s + q_2$ where $s = \Pi(\phi^* + q_1)$.

From equation (II.1.3) we have

$$\ddot{s}^* = \Pi^{*''}(\phi^*)\cdot\dot{\phi}^{*2} \qquad \text{(II.5.7)}$$

and

$$\ddot{s} = [\Pi''(\phi^* + q_1)]\cdot(\dot{\phi}^* + \dot{q}_1)^2 + [\Pi'(\phi^* + q_1)]\cdot\ddot{q}_1$$

By substituting equation (II.5.7) in expressions (II.5.6), (II.5.5) and (II.5.4), we obtain a system of equations which can be solved with respect to q_1 and q_2. These additional motions q_1 and q_2 create the determined dynamic errors or deviations. Obviously, these deviations are not of a random nature: they appear as a result of the dynamic parameters of the mechanism. Equations (II.5.3), (II.5.4), (II.5.5) and (II.5.6) become linear when $\Pi'(\phi)$ = const, otherwise we must deal with nonlinear equations. An example of such a linear situation is given in Fig. 42, in which the driven mass m is actuated by a gear

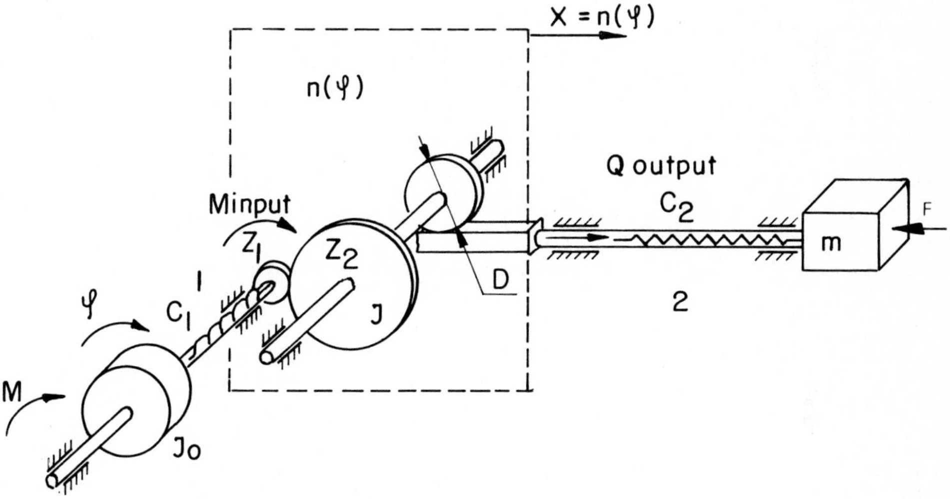

Fig. 42. A gear mechanism.

transmission engaged with a tooth rack. Thus, is the diameter of the wheel z_3 equals D, we have:

$$s = \Pi^*(\phi) = \frac{z_1 D}{2z_2} \qquad \text{(II.5.8)}$$

and

$$\Pi^{*'}(\phi) = \frac{z_1 D}{2z_2} = \text{const} \qquad \text{(II.5.9)}$$

The discussion in this paragraph is based on Vulfson's book [1] where the reader can find additional explanations, as well as some idea of the means for solving these generally nonlinear equations.

6. STATISTICAL APPROACH TO DYNAMIC ANALYSIS OF MECHANISMS

As was said earlier, in a real mechanism random factors cause random errors. We will now consider random errors of the input motion, force and motion function. Thus:

$$\phi = \phi^* + q_1 + \bar{\phi} + \mathring{\phi} = \phi^* + q_1 + \Delta\phi = \phi_1^* + \Delta\phi$$

$$\Pi = \Pi^* + \bar{\Pi} + \mathring{\Pi} = \Pi^* + \Delta\Pi$$

$$F = F^* + \bar{F} + \mathring{F} = F^* + \Delta F$$

$$M = M^* + \bar{M} + \mathring{M} = M^* + \Delta M \qquad \text{(II.6.1)}$$

ϕ_1^* includes the determined displacement q_1. And then in the general case the output motion equals:

$$y = s^* + q_2 + \bar{y} + \mathring{y} \qquad \text{or} \qquad y = y^* + \bar{y} + \mathring{y} \qquad \text{(II.6.2)}$$

We will not discuss the random deviations of stiffnesses, damping conditions etc. Attention must be paid to some special effects caused by the motion function when its random components are calculated. For the function $\Pi(\phi)$ we can write:

$$\Pi(\phi) \simeq \Pi^*(\phi_1^* + \Delta\phi) + \Delta\Pi(\phi_1^*) =$$

$$= \Pi^*(\phi_1^*) + \Pi^{*\prime}(\phi_1^*)\cdot\Delta\phi + \Delta\Pi(\phi_1^*) \qquad \text{(II.6.3)}$$

The latter component is written on the assumption that $\Delta\Pi(\phi) \simeq \Delta\Pi(\phi^*)$. Then, for the derivatives we have:

$$\Pi'(\phi) \simeq \Pi^{*\prime}(\phi_1^* + \Delta\phi) + \Delta\Pi'(\phi_1^*) = \Pi^{*\prime}(\phi_1^*) + \Pi^{*\prime\prime}(\phi_1^*)\cdot\Delta\phi + \Delta\Pi'(\phi_1^*) \qquad \text{(II.6.4)}$$

and

$$\Pi''(\phi) \simeq \Pi^{*\prime\prime}(\phi_1^* + \Delta\phi) + \Delta\Pi''(\phi_1^*) = \Pi^{*\prime\prime}(\phi_1^*) + \Pi^{*\prime\prime\prime}(\phi_1^*)\cdot\Delta\phi + \Delta\Pi''(\phi_1^*) \qquad \text{(II.6.5)}$$

To simplify the discussion we will assume, at this stage, that $\bar{\Pi} = 0$ and $\bar{\phi} = 0$. Then, $\Delta\Pi = \mathring{\Pi}$ and $\Delta\phi = \mathring{\phi}$.

For the mechanism shown in Fig. 40 and for $\Pi(\phi)$ corresponding to equation (II.5.2), we can substitute expression (II.5.2) in equations (II.6.3), (II.6.4) and (II.6.5) as follows:

$$\Pi(\phi) \simeq r\cos\frac{z_1}{z_2}\phi_1^* - r\frac{z_1}{z_2}\mathring{\phi}\sin\frac{z_1}{z_2}\phi_1^* + \mathring{\Pi}(\phi_1^*) \qquad \text{(II.6.6)}$$

$$\Pi'(\phi) \simeq -r\frac{z_1}{z_2}\sin\frac{z_1}{z_2}\phi_1^* - r(z_1/z_2)^2\mathring{\phi}\cos\frac{z_1}{z_2}\phi_1^* + \mathring{\Pi}(\phi_1^*) \qquad \text{(II.6.7)}$$

$$\Pi''(\phi) \simeq -r(z_1/z_2)^2\cos\frac{z_1}{z_2}\phi_1^* + r(z_1/z_2)^3\mathring{\phi}\sin\frac{z_1}{z_2}\phi_1^* + \mathring{\Pi}''(\phi_1^*) \qquad \text{(II.6.8)}$$

For the mechanism shown in Fig. 42 which can be described by $\Pi(\phi)$ in accordance with equation (II.5.8), we obtain:

$$\Pi(\phi) \simeq \frac{z_1 D}{2z_2}\phi_1^* + \frac{z_1 D}{2z_2}\mathring{\phi} + \mathring{\Pi}(\phi_1^*) \qquad \text{(II.6.9)}$$

$$\Pi'(\phi) \simeq \frac{z_1 D}{2z_2} + \mathring{\Pi}'(\phi_1^*) \qquad \text{(II.6.10)}$$

$$\Pi''(\phi) \simeq \mathring{\Pi}''(\phi_1^*) \qquad \text{(II.6.11)}$$

For the mechanism shown in Fig. 40 for the case a, we substitute equations (II.5.7) and (II.6.1) into equation (II.5.3) to obtain equation:

$$M = M^* + \bar{M} + \mathring{M} =$$

$$= -[\Pi^{*\prime}(\phi) + \mathring{\Pi}'(\phi_1^*)]\{F^* + \bar{F} + \mathring{F} + m[\Pi^{*\prime}(\phi) + \mathring{\Pi}''(\phi_1^*)](\dot{\phi}_1^* + \dot{\mathring{\phi}})^2\} \qquad \text{(II.6.12)}$$

From equations (II.6.9), (II.6.10) and (II.6.11) for the mechanism shown in Fig. 42, we can transform equation (II.6.12) into:

$$M = M^* + \bar{M} + \mathring{M} =$$

$$= -[\frac{z_1 D}{2z_2} + \mathring{\Pi}'(\phi_1^*)]\{F^* + \bar{F} + \mathring{F} + m[\mathring{\Pi}''(\phi_1^*)](\dot{\phi}_1^* + \dot{\mathring{\phi}})^2\} \qquad \text{(II.6.13)}$$

From equation (II.6.13) we obtain:

$$M^* = -\frac{z_1 D}{2z_2}F^* \qquad \text{(II.6.14)}$$

$$\bar{M} = -\frac{z_1 D}{2z_2}\bar{F} \qquad \text{(II.6.15)}$$

and

$$\mathring{M} \simeq -\frac{z_1 D}{2z_2}\mathring{F} - m\frac{z_1 D}{2z_2}[\mathring{\Pi}''(\phi_1^*)](\dot{\phi}_1^* + \dot{\mathring{\phi}})^2 -$$

$$-[\mathring{\Pi}'(\phi_1^*)](F^* + \bar{F} + \mathring{F}) - m[\mathring{\Pi}'(\phi_1^*)\cdot\mathring{\Pi}''(\phi_1^*)](\dot{\phi}_1^* + \dot{\mathring{\phi}})^2 \qquad \text{(II.6.16)}$$

Neglecting components of second and higher orders of infinitesimality we obtain from equation (II.6.16):

$$\mathring{M} \simeq -\frac{z_1 D}{2z_2}\mathring{F} - m\frac{z_1 D}{2z_2}(\dot{\phi}_1^*)^2\cdot\mathring{\Pi}^*(\phi_1^*) - F^*\mathring{\Pi}'(\phi_1^*) - \bar{F}\cdot\mathring{\Pi}'(\phi_1^*) \qquad \text{(II.6.17)}$$

For the motion function (II.6.6) (the mechanism shown in Fig. 40) and its derivatives (II.6.7) and (II.6.8), we obtain for the case (II.6.12) the following equation:

$$M = M^* + \bar{M} + \mathring{M} = [r\frac{z_1}{z_2}\sin\frac{z_1}{z_2}\,{}_1^* + r(z_1/z_2)^2\,\mathring{\phi}\cos\frac{z_1}{z_2}\phi_1^* + \mathring{\Pi}'(\phi_1^*)]\times$$

$$\times\{F^* + \bar{F} + \mathring{F} + m[\mathring{\Pi}''(\phi_1^*) - r(z_1/z_2)^2\cos\frac{z_1}{z_2}\phi_1^* + r(z_1/z_2)^2\mathring{\phi}\sin\frac{z_1}{z_2}\phi_1^*]\times$$

$$\times(\dot{\phi}_1^* + \dot{\mathring{\phi}})\} \qquad \text{(II.6.18)}$$

From here:

$$M^* = F^* r\frac{z_1}{z_2}\sin\frac{z_1}{z_2}\phi_1^* + mr^2(z_1/z_2)^3(\dot{\phi}_1^*)^2\sin\frac{z_1}{z_2}\phi_1^*\cos\frac{z_1}{z_2}\phi_1^*$$

$$\bar{M} = \bar{F}r\frac{z_1}{z_2}\sin\frac{z_1}{z_2}\phi_1^*$$

Neglecting the terms of second and higher orders of infinitesimality for the random components of the torque we obtain:

$$\mathring{M} \simeq \mathring{F}r\frac{z_1}{z_2}\sin\frac{z_1}{z_2}\phi_1^* + (F^* + \bar{F})[r(z_1/z_2)^2\mathring{\phi}\cos\frac{z_1}{z_2}\phi_1^* + \mathring{\Pi}'(\phi_1^*)] -$$

$$- mr^2\mathring{\phi}(\dot{\phi}_1^*)^2(z_1/z_2)^3\cos^2\frac{z_1}{z_2}\phi_1^* +$$

$$+ mr^2(\dot{\phi}_1^*)^2(z_1/z_2)^5\dot{\phi}\cos\frac{z_1}{z_2}\phi_1^*\sin\frac{z_1}{z_2}\phi_1^* \qquad \text{(II.6.19)}$$

Now let us discuss the case shown in Fig. 41b described by equation (II.5.4). Here we can rewrite the equation (II.5.4) substituting the value of $\ddot{s}$ from equation (II.5.7):

$$m\ddot{q}_2 + b_2\dot{q}_2 + c_2q_2 = -F - m\Pi''(\phi)\cdot\dot{\phi}^2 \tag{II.6.20}$$

or

$$\ddot{q}_2 + 2h\dot{q}_2 + k_2^2q_2 = -\frac{F}{m} - \Pi''(\phi)\cdot\dot{\phi}^2$$

where

$$2h = b_2/m \quad \text{and} \quad k_2^2 = c/m \tag{II.6.21}$$

Taking the random component into account we obtain:

$$\ddot{q}_2 + 2h_2\dot{q}_2 + k_2^2q_2 = -\frac{1}{m}(F^* + \bar{F} + \mathring{F}) -$$

$$- [\Pi^{*''}(\phi_1^*) + \Pi^{*'''}(\phi_1^*)\cdot\mathring{\phi} + \mathring{\Pi}''(\phi_1^*)]\cdot(\dot{\phi}_1^* + \dot{\mathring{\phi}})^2$$

Again, use the assumption made above that

$$\bar{\Pi}''(\phi) \simeq \bar{\Pi}(\phi_1^*) \quad \text{and} \quad \mathring{\Pi}''(\phi) \simeq \mathring{\Pi}(\phi_1^*) \tag{II.6.22}$$

The physical meaning of the components of the angle can be explained by the following representation:

$$\phi = \omega t = (\omega^* + \bar{\omega} + \mathring{\omega})t$$

Thus:

$$\phi_1^* = \omega_1^*t; \quad \phi^* = \omega^*t; \quad \bar{\phi} = \bar{\omega}t; \quad \mathring{\phi} = \mathring{\omega}t \tag{II.6.23}$$

If we apply equation (II.6.23) to the mechanism shown in Fig. 42 and use its motion function given by equations (II.5.8) and (II.5.9), then from equation (II.6.23), we obtain:

$$\ddot{q}_2 + 2h_2\dot{q}_2 + k_2^2q_2 \simeq -\frac{1}{m}(F^* + \bar{F} + \mathring{F}) - \mathring{\Pi}''(\phi_1^*)\cdot(\dot{\phi}_1^* + \dot{\mathring{\phi}})^2 \tag{II.6.24}$$

Since equation (II.6.20) is linear, we can use the superposition principle for solving it. By means of this principle the components of the solution can be sought in correspondence to the components of the excitation. Thus:

$$\ddot{q}_2^* + 2h_2\dot{q}_2^* + k_2^2q_2^* = -\frac{F^*}{m} \tag{II.6.25}$$

$$\ddot{\bar{q}}_2 + 2h_2\dot{\bar{q}}_2 + k_2^2\bar{q}_2 = -\frac{\bar{F}}{m} \tag{II.6.26}$$

$$\ddot{\mathring{q}}_2 + 2h_2\dot{\mathring{q}}_2 + k_2^2\mathring{q}_2 \simeq -\frac{\mathring{F}}{m} - \mathring{\Pi}''(\phi_1^*)\cdot(\dot{\phi}_1^*)^2 - 2\mathring{\Pi}''(\phi_1^*)\cdot\dot{\phi}_1^*\cdot\dot{\mathring{\phi}} - \mathring{\Pi}''(\phi_1^*)\cdot\dot{\mathring{\phi}}^2 \tag{II.6.27}$$

In this case the motion of the driven mass m is expressed in the following form:

$$y = s^* + q_2^* + \bar{q}_2 + \mathring{q}_2 \tag{II.6.28}$$

Equations (II.6.25) and (II.6.26) are trivial, and we will therefore not discuss them. From equation (II.6.23) it follows that:

$$\ddot{\mathring{q}}_2 + 2h_2\dot{\mathring{q}}_2 + k_2^2\mathring{q}_2 \simeq -\frac{\mathring{F}}{m} - \mathring{\Pi}''\omega^{*2} - 2\mathring{\Pi}''\omega^*\mathring{\omega} - \mathring{\Pi}''\mathring{\omega}^2 = Z(t) \tag{II.6.29}$$

In many cases the last component can be neglected because of its high order of infinitesimality. With regard to the component of second-order infinitesimality we have to be very careful because of the second-order derivative, i.e. even when $\mathring{\Pi}$ is very small its derivative $\mathring{\Pi}'$ and particularly its second order derivative $\mathring{\Pi}''$ can reach considerable values. The transfer function of this system may be written as follows:

$$\Phi(j\Omega) = \frac{1}{-\Omega^2 + 2h_2 j\Omega + k_2^2} \tag{II.6.30}$$

and the spectral density S_q of the random function $\mathring{q}$ can be expressed as

$$S_q(\Omega) = \frac{S_Z(\Omega)}{|k_2^2 - \Omega^2 + 2h_2 j\Omega|^2} \tag{II.6.31}$$

where S_z - spectral density of the right-hand side of equation (II.6.29).

The spectral density S_z is made up of three components:

$$S_z(\Omega) \simeq S_F(\Omega) + S_\Pi(\Omega) + S_\Omega(\Omega) \tag{II.6.32}$$

where S_F - spectral density of the random component of the external force F;

S_Π - spectral density of the random component of the function $\mathring{\Pi}''$;

S_Ω - spectral density of the random component of the function $\mathring{\Pi}''\mathring{\omega}^2$.

Thus:

$$S_q(\Omega) \simeq \frac{S_F + S_\Pi + S_\Omega}{|k_2^2 - \Omega^2 + 2h_2 j\Omega|^2} \tag{II.6.33}$$

The densities $S_F(\Omega)$ and $S_\Pi(\Omega)$ can be measured or calculated in a trivial manner. To calculate S_Ω we use the fact that the correlation function of a product of two noncorrelated variables equals the product of the correlation functions. Thus:

$$K_\Omega(\tau) = K_\Pi(\tau) \cdot K_\omega(\tau)$$

and

$$S_\Omega(\Omega) = \frac{1}{2\pi}\int_0^\infty K_\Pi(\tau)K_\omega(\tau)\cos\Omega\tau d\tau \tag{II.6.34}$$

where K_Π - correlation function of the $\mathring{\Pi}''$ variable;

K_ω - correlation function of the $\mathring{\omega}$ variable;

K_Ω - correlation function of the $\mathring{\Pi}''\mathring{\omega}^2$ variable.

As was mentioned above, we consider the function $\mathring{\Pi}''\mathring{\omega}^2 \approx 0$.

Once the components q_2^*, $\bar{q}_2$ and $\mathring{q}_2$ have been found, we can substitute them into the first equation of the system (II.5.4). We can then calculate the components of the torque:

M^*, $\bar{M}$ and $\mathring{M}$.

For the mechanism shown in Fig. 40, by substituting equations (II.6.2) and (II.6.8) into equation (II.5.4), we obtain:

$$\ddot{q}_2 + 2h_2\dot{q}_2 + k_2^2 q_2 = -\frac{F}{m} + [-r(z_1/z_2)^2\cos\frac{z_1}{z_2}\phi_1^* + r\mathring{\phi}(z_1/z_2)^3\sin\frac{z_1}{z_2}\phi_1^* + \mathring{\Pi}''(\phi_1^*)](\dot{\phi}_1^* + \dot{\mathring{\phi}})^2$$

or considering equation (II.6.23)

$$\ddot{q}_2 + 2h_2\dot{q}_2 + k_2^2 q_2 = -\frac{F}{m} + [-r(z_1/z_2)^2\cos\frac{z_1}{z_2}\omega_1^* t + r\mathring{\omega}t(z_1/z_2)^3\sin\frac{z_1}{z_2}\omega_1^* t + \mathring{\Pi}''(\omega_1^* t)](\omega_1^* + \mathring{\omega})^2 \tag{II.6.35}$$

Neglecting the components of second or higher orders of infinitesimality, we can rewrite equation (II.6.35) as:

$$\ddot{q}_2 + 2h_2\dot{q}_2 + k_2^2 \approx -\frac{F^* + \bar{F} + \mathring{F}}{m} - r\omega_1^{*2}(z_1/z_2)^2\cos\frac{z_1}{z_2}\omega_1^* t - 2r\omega_1^*\mathring{\omega}(z_1/z_2)^2\cos\frac{z_1}{z_2}\omega_1^* t + r\omega_1^{*2}\mathring{\omega}t(z_1/z_2)^3\sin\frac{z_1}{z_2}\omega_1^* t + \mathring{\Pi}''(\omega_1^* t)(\omega_1^*)^2 \tag{II.6.36}$$

This is a linear equation with a nonstationary right-hand side: by applying the superposition principle, we can express the solution in the following form:

$$\ddot{q}_2^* + 2h_2\dot{q}_2^* + k_2^2 q_2^* = -\frac{F^*}{m} + \omega_1^{*2} r(z_1/z_2)^2\cos\frac{z_1}{z_2}\omega_1^* t \tag{II.6.37}$$

$$\ddot{\bar{q}}_2 + 2h_2\dot{\bar{q}}_2 + k_2^2\bar{q}_2 = -\frac{\bar{F}}{m}$$

Obviously, the components q* and $\bar{q}$ can be calculated in a trivial way. The random component $\overset{\circ}{q}$ must be calculated from the following equation where the terms of second or higher orders of infinitesimality are neglected:

$$\ddot{\overset{\circ}{q}}_2 + 2h_2\dot{\overset{\circ}{q}}_2 + k_2^2 \simeq -2\omega_1^*\overset{\circ}{\omega}r(z_1/z_2)^2\cos\frac{z_1}{z_2}\omega_1^*t + \omega_1^{*2}\overset{\circ}{\omega}rt(z_1/z_2)^3\sin\frac{z_1}{z_2}\omega_1^*t + \overset{\circ}{\Pi}''(\omega_1^*t)(\omega_1^*)^2 \qquad (II.6.38)$$

7. DERIVATION OF THE DYNAMIC EQUATIONS (APPENDIX 1)

The equations which describe the dynamic model represented in Fig. 40 are obtained in the following way by means of a special form of the Lagrange equations. Let us use the following symbols:

T - the kinetic energy of the system

V - the potential energy of the system

q_j - generalized coordinates

Q_j - nonconservative generalized forces

λ_j, a_{ij}, a_i - some functions.

Then the Lagrange equations will take the form:

$$\frac{d}{dt}(\partial T/\partial\dot{q}_j) - \frac{\partial T}{\partial q_j} + \frac{\partial V}{\partial q_j} = Q_j + \sum_{i=1}^{n}\lambda_i a_{ij} \qquad (j = 1,\ldots,\ell) \qquad (II.7.1)$$

$$\sum_{j=1}^{s} a_{ij}\dot{q}_j + a_i = 0 \qquad (i = 1,\ldots,\ell) \qquad (II.7.2)$$

In our case the number of coordinates ℓ can be greater than the number of degrees of freedom H by the number of additional mechanical constraints n, i.e. $H = \ell - n$.

In accordance with Fig. 40 let us define:

ϕ^* - absolute angular displacement at the input of the mechanism's drive;

ϕ - absolute angular displacement at the input of the mechanism;

y - absolute displacement at the output of the mechanism;

q_1 - relative displacement on the elastic drive shaft;

q_2 - relative displacement on the elastic driven rod;

s - absolute displacement at the input of the driven rod, and obviously $s = \Pi(\phi)$.

We have chosen the following generalized coordinates q_1; q_2; $q_3 = s$; $q_4 = \phi^*$. Thus,

$$T = \frac{1}{2}m(\dot{q}_2 + \dot{x})^2 + \frac{1}{2}J(\omega + q_1)^2 + \frac{1}{2}J_o\omega^2;$$

$$V = \frac{1}{2}c_1q_1^2 + \frac{1}{2}c_2q_2^2$$

To define the generalized forces we write the work equation δW corresponding to the possible displacements q:

$$\delta W = -F\delta(q_2 + s) - b_1\dot{q}_1\delta q_1 - b_2q_2\delta q_2 + M\delta q_4$$

From here:

$$Q_1 = -b_1\dot{q}_1;\quad Q_2 = -b_2\dot{q}_2 - F;\quad Q_3 = -F;\quad Q_4 = M.$$

For the specific equations (II.7.1) and (II.7.2) for the case under consideration we obtain:

$$\begin{cases} J\ddot{q}_1 + b_1\dot{q}_1 + c_1q_1 = \lambda_1a_{11} \\ m(\ddot{s} + \ddot{q}_2) + b_2\dot{q}_2 + c_2q_2 = -F + \lambda_1a_{12} \\ m(\ddot{s} + \ddot{q}_2) = -F + \lambda_1a_{13} \\ J_o\ddot{q}_4 + J(\ddot{q}_1 + \ddot{q}_4) = M + \lambda_1a_{14} \end{cases} \tag{II.7.3}$$

One of constraint equations can be obtained from the motion functions:

$$s = \Pi(\phi) = \Pi(\omega t + q_1) \tag{II.7.4}$$

Differentiation of equation (II.7.4) gives:

$$\Pi'\dot{q}_1 + \Pi'\omega - \dot{s} = 0 \tag{II.7.5}$$

Comparing equation (II.7.5) with equation (II.7.2), we obtain:

$$a_{11} = \Pi';\quad a_{12} = 0;\quad a_{13} = -1;\quad a_{14} = \Pi'$$

Omitting the fourth equation in the system of equations (II.7.3) because coordinate q_4 can be ignored and eliminating λ_1 from the equations (II.7.3) we can rewrite the equation as:

$$\begin{cases} J\ddot{q}_1 + b_1\dot{q}_1 + c_1q_1 + [\Pi'(\omega t + q_1)](b_2\dot{q}_2 + c_2q_2) \\ m\ddot{q}_2 + b_2\dot{q}_2 + c_2q_2 = -F - m\ddot{s} \end{cases} \tag{II.7.6}$$

This equation describes model IV shown in Fig. 40.

When $c_2 \to \infty$, and because of this $q_2 = 0$, we obtain from the equation system (II.7.6) the following equations for model III:

$$\begin{cases} J\ddot{q}_1 + b_1\dot{q}_1 + c_1q_1 = -\Pi'(\omega t + q_1)P \\ P = F + m\ddot{s} \end{cases} \tag{II.7.7}$$

For model II, $c_1 \to \infty$ and $q_1 \equiv 0$:

$$\begin{cases} M = -\Pi'(\omega t)(b_2\dot{q}_2 + c_2q_2) \\ m\ddot{q}_2 + b_2\dot{q}_2 + c_2q_2 = -F - m\ddot{s}^* \end{cases} \tag{II.7.8}$$

Lastly, for model I in which $c_1 \to \infty$ and $c_2 \to \infty$, both $q_1 = q_2 = 0$. Thus,

$$\begin{cases} M = -\Pi'(\omega t)P \\ P = F + m\ddot{x}^* \end{cases} \tag{II.7.9}$$

SELECTED BIBLIOGRAPHY

1. Vulfson, I. and Kolovsky, M. Nonlinear Problems of Machine Dynamics (nelineinye zadachy dinamiki mashin) Leningrad, Mashinostroenie, 1968 (in Russian).

CHAPTER III

INFLUENCE OF DEVIATIONS IN THE CAM PROFILE ON THE ACTION OF THE CAM MECHANISM

1. INTRODUCTION

Firstly, let us delineate the reasons for deviations in the motion of the cam follower and for the regularities and dependences of these deviations. There are three basic causes of the deviations:

1. manufacturing reasons - as a result of problems connected with the manufacturing accuracy of certain parts of the cam mechanism, especially the cam profile;
2. wear and tear of conjugate surfaces during operation of the mechanisms;
3. vibrations (transversal, longitudinal or torsional) of the driving and driven elements in the mechanism caused by the elasticity of the components, by backlashes, etc.

For the first two causes, the reasons for the deviations can be investigated by commonly known methods, since errors in the dimensions of the cam profile can be detected by comparison with calculated values. In addition, for the first case the engineer has to take manufacturing restrictions into account when designing the layout of a mechanism, the optimal layout being the one in which the damage caused by profile deviations is minimized. In the second case, however, the designer must predict the shape of the profile wear and choose the layout accordingly.

The third type of deviations require a dynamic approach. Only in simplified cases are linear mathematical models suitable: in the majority of cases, nonlinear models must be applied in this analytical method. In particular, a nonlinear dynamic approach is essential when torsional vibrations of the cam shaft must be taken into consideration (see section 5 of Chapter II).

Cam profiles are manufactured by one of four methods:

1. the marking-out method, which is usually employed for the manufacture of single cams and master cams;
2. the copying method, which is used mainly in the mass production of cams such as the camshafts of internal combustion engines - in this method an enlarged "master" cam is used as the model from which smaller profiles are copied;
3. the method based on the use of cutters whose kinematics provide special trajectories;

4. the use of computerized equipment which facilitates the setting of the shape of the profile by taking the shape and the dimensions of the cutter into account: the computer can calculate the coordinates of several thousands of points on the profile.

The manufacturing accuracy obviously differs for each of the four methods. For example, for an instrument used in the single production method the errors of the radius vector of the profile may be as little as 0.02-0.03 mm. The cams of internal combustion engines are manufactured with tolerances of about ±0.02 to ±0.025 mm, the master cam having a tolerance of 0.01 mm. The accuracy of this method was neatly described by Tesar (1): "the initial student of cams is frequently quite surprised to learn that the work of the craftsman is not only faster but more accurate than the other methods. In many cases, it is also less expensive, in particular, when a small number of cams must be made from a master cam." For computerized profile cutting the accuracy is as good as 0.015 to 0.01 mm. In contrast, automatic manufacturing machines are sometimes provided with relatively crude cams whose profiles have radius vectors with tolerances of about 0.20 to 0.10 mm.

The relatively low accuracy of cam profiles sometimes leads to situations in which cam mechanisms are replaced by linkages. Linkages may be preferred because being simpler to manufacture they are more accurate even though a linkage mechanism is more complex than a cam.

This chapter deals with the problems of analysis and synthesis of the motion of the cam mechanical follower when the dynamic effects and the influence of errors in the cam profile are taken into account. The camshaft is assumed to be rotating with an ideal constant velocity except in the case when variable rotation speed is the subject of the discussion. To define the problems under discussion, let us consider the diagram given in Fig. 43. The first quadrant

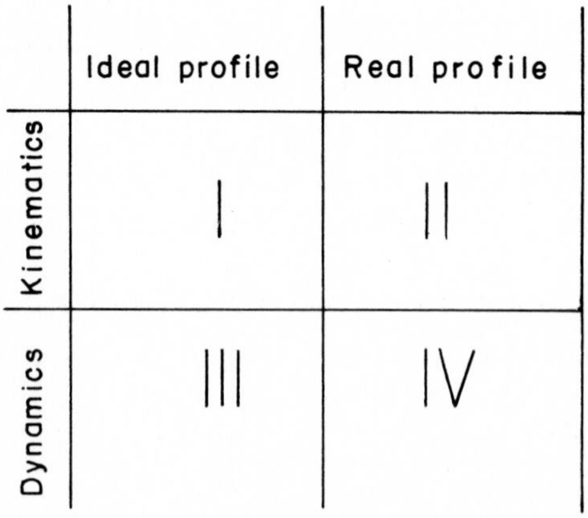

Fig. 43. Four quadrant diagram - investigation directions of cam mechanisms.

embodies the classical approach to cam mechanisms: geometric relations in the mechanism are analyzed; dynamics are not considered; and the cam profile is assumed to have been manufactured with ideal accuracy.

The second quadrant refers to the case for which the treatment remains kinematic but the real implications of the accuracy in manufacturing the profile are taken into account, i.e. the influence of profile errors on the follower motion, especially in relation to acceleration are taken into consideration.

The third quadrant covers the dynamic approach which is necessary when the mechanisms act rapidly and the driven masses are significant. In this case, the profile of the cam is considered to be ideal or accurate.

Finally, the fourth quadrant represents the most general case, in which both dynamic and profile errors are taken into account.

Cases I and III have been discussed in detail in the technical literature, for example in ref. 2. This chapter, on the other hand, aims to emphasize the situation existing in practice, i.e. cases II and IV. An attempt is made to consider both the analysis and synthesis of optimal real cam mechanisms. Experimental results illustrate practical agreement with theoretical assumptions.

2. DETERMINISTIC APPROACHES

As early as the 1950s it was realized that errors in the cam profile and their influence on the behavior of the motion of the follower are of great importance. Let us consider briefly some approaches to solving this kind of problem. The errors in the motion of the follower are represented as in Fig. 44 (the errors having been measured with an accuracy of about ±0.001 mm).

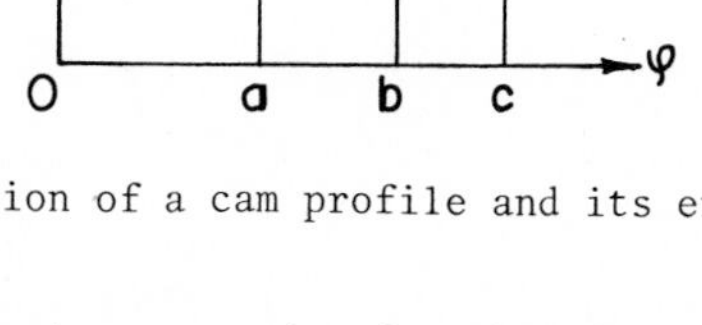

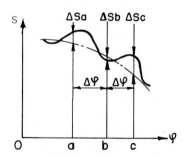

Fig. 44. A section of a cam profile and its errors.

Then, an approximate expression for the additional value of the velocity caused by these errors can be written as:

$$V_1 \simeq \frac{\Delta s_a - \Delta s_b}{\Delta t}$$

and (III.2.1)

$$V_2 \simeq \frac{\Delta s_b - \Delta s_c}{\Delta t}$$

where $\Delta t = \Delta\phi/\omega$, as is obvious from the figure, and ω = the angular velocity of the cam.

From equation (III.2.1), the additional value of the acceleration caused by the same errors can be expressed as:

$$a \simeq \pm \frac{V_2 - V_1}{\Delta t} = \pm(\Delta s_a + \Delta s_c - 2\Delta s_b)(\omega/\Delta\phi)^2 \qquad \text{(III.2.2)}$$

For the simplified case when

$$\Delta s = \Delta s_a = \Delta s_b = \Delta s_c$$

the additional acceleration is given by

$$a \simeq \pm 4\Delta s(\omega/\Delta\phi)^2 \qquad \text{(III.2.3)}$$

At this stage, we see the appearance of contradictory tendencies. On the one hand, to decrease the additional acceleration $\Delta\phi$ has to be made bigger, but on the other hand, this increase entails enlarging the cusps left by the cutter and removing the cusps will lead to additional errors.

Another source of Δs - errors in the motion of the follower - is the milling process. After the cam leaves the milling machine it has a scalloped surface. The profile is then covered with bluing and filed smooth by hand until all traces of bluing on the surface have just been removed. The form of the profile is thus controlled by the milling technique (Fig. 45). Whether the profile is

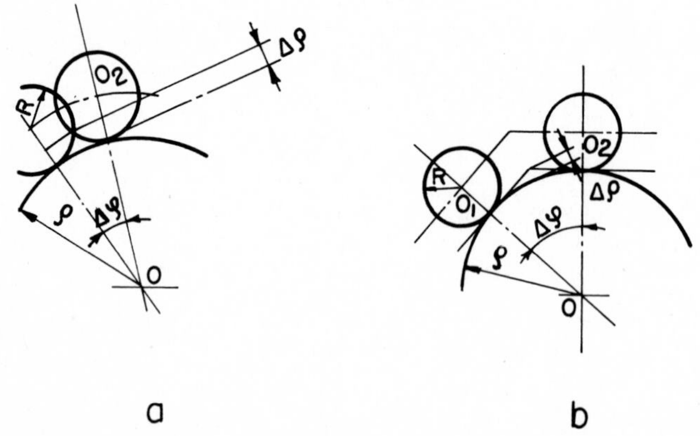

Fig. 45. Layout of the milling process for a cam profile; a) cutting fixed points; b) cutting tangential lines.

cut in accordance with fixed calculated points (Fig. 45a), or along tangential lines drawn through fixed points (Fig. 45b), or by finite steps, the question remains as to what are the allowed values of the profile errors $\Delta\rho$ and hence the allowed values of Δs, ΔV and a. In the case under discussion, $\Delta\rho$, the profile errors, are generally not equal to Δs, the errors of the motion of the follower.

For the case shown in Fig. 45a, an approximation expressing the relationship between the maximal allowed value of $\Delta\rho$ in terms of the cam parameters and the $\Delta\rho$ errors is given in the following form:

$$\Delta\phi \simeq \frac{64R^2\Delta\rho^2}{\rho} \qquad \text{(III.2.4)}$$

where R - the radius of the cutter;

ρ - the radius of the profile.

For the case shown in Fig. 45b, this expression takes the form:

$$\Delta\phi \simeq \frac{2}{\cos(1 - \frac{\Delta\rho}{\rho})} \qquad \text{(III.2.5)}$$

The following table, taken from ref. 1, provides a reliable guide to judging the quality of manufacture of a cam:

Quality of cam	Tolerance	
	Radial (mm)	Angular (seconds)
Highest	±0.0025	±2
Very good	±0.005	±3
Good	±0.01	±4
Average	±0.025	±5

It is obvious that the type of the follower affects the susceptibility of the mechanism to profile errors. The recommended values of $\Delta\phi$ are shown in the following table:

Type of follower	$\Delta\phi$ should be about:
Knife-edge	0 to 1/2°
Roller	1/2 to 1°
Flat-faced	1 to 2°

We can then substitute these recommended values of $\Delta\phi$ in expressions (III.2.2) and (III.2.3).

Rothbard (2) attempted to estimate the relationship between the law of motion of the follower and the manufacturing accuracy requirements by comparing two laws of motion. To clarify his method let us look at Fig. 46. The straight

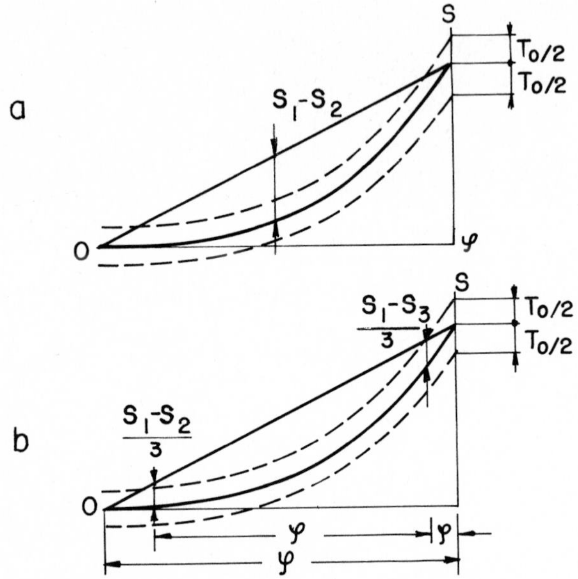

Fig. 46. Comparison of two laws of motion.

line represents a linear law of motion, while the curve represents any other law of motion, for instance a harmonic law. The difference in the ordinates s_1 and s_2 is compared with the value of the admittance T as follows:

$$\frac{s_1 - s_2}{n} > T \tag{III.2.6}$$

where n - is a constant value $1 \leqslant n \leqslant 3$.

The relationship between the cam profile angle ϕ_1 for which the condition (III.2.6) is satisfied and the whole profile angle ϕ_o reflects, to a certain extent, the percentage of profiles out of a batch of cams which corresponds to the condition (III.2.6). In Fig. III.2.3, for example, this relationship $\phi_1/\phi_o \simeq 0.85$.

We have found another criterion which reflects the dependence of the manufacturing accuracy on the law of motion which the cam profile is required to provide. Let us consider the section of the law $s(\phi)$. As is shown in Fig. 47,

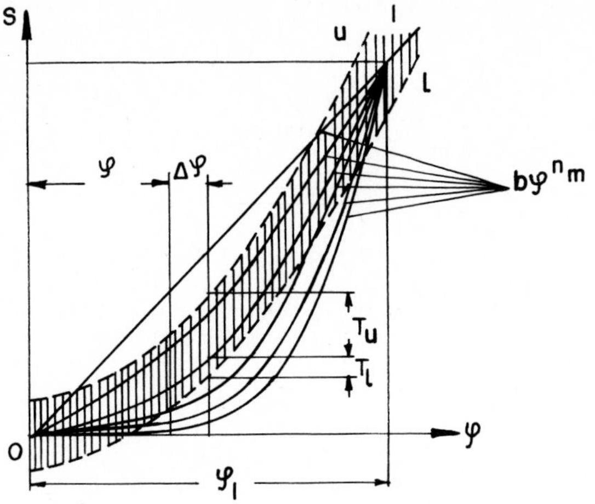

Fig. 47. Comparison of different parabolic curves for the laws of motion of a cam follower.

a number of parabolic curves pass through the points 0 and 1 in the form:

$$s_m = b\phi^{n_m} \tag{III.2.7}$$

where b = const

m = ordinal numbers of the power index.

We can designate

$$\Delta n = |n_m - n_{m-1}| \tag{III.2.8}$$

where Δn is any infinitesimal number.

A "strip" of width $\Delta\phi$ through these curves, including the border line $s = b\phi$ (the straight line passing through 0 and 1), is then cut into a definite number of segments. Let our specific curve $s_m(\phi)$ pass through 0 and 1 and let us designate by means of two parallel curves - "upper" = u and "lower = ℓ - a narrow domain of tolerance in accordance with the manufacturing accuracy of the cam. For the case under investigation, for a chosen value Δn, the number of segments K cut by the curves u and ℓ in the strip $\Delta\phi$ is a function

$$K(\phi,T) \tag{III.2.9}$$

where $T = T_u + T_\ell$ - tolerance in the direction of the ordinates,

and T_u and T_ℓ - are the upper and lower deviations of the profile, respectively.

Let us now examine this expression. From the layout shown in Fig. 47 for the strip $\Delta\phi$, it follows:

$$s_u(\phi) = T_u + s(\phi) = T_u + b\phi^n$$
$$s_\ell(\phi) = s(\phi) - T_\ell = b\phi^n - T_\ell \qquad \text{(III.2.10)}$$

From equations (III.2.8) and (III.2.7) we get:

$$s_u(\phi) = b\phi^{n+K_u\Delta n}$$
$$s_\ell(\phi) = b\phi^{n-K_\ell\Delta n} \qquad \text{(III.2.11)}$$

and from equations (III.2.10) and (III.2.11) we obtain:

$$T_u = b[\phi^{n+K_u\Delta n} - \phi^n]$$
$$T_\ell = b[\phi^n - \phi^{n-K_\ell\Delta n}] \qquad \text{(III.2.12)}$$

or

$$K_u = \frac{\ln[\frac{T_u}{s} + 1]}{\Delta n \ln \phi} \quad \text{and} \quad K_\ell = \frac{-\ln[1 - \frac{T_\ell}{s}]}{\Delta n \ln \phi} \qquad \text{(III.2.13)}$$

When $T_u = T_\ell = T$, $K = K_u + K_\ell$

$$K = \frac{\ln \frac{T + s}{s - T}}{\Delta n \ln \phi} \quad \text{for } (s > T) \qquad \text{(III.2.14)}$$

The shape of function (III.2.14) is shown in Fig. 48. If any other limit of K is desired, the curves passing from one T value to another can be changed.

The following conclusions can be drawn from our discussion:

1. It is reasonable to process the profile using different tolerances for different sections of the profile.
2. A reduction of the influence of the profile errors on the law of motion of the follower can be achieved by increasing the follower's stroke (worsening the pressure angle).
3. When there is no possibility of narrowing the tolerance domain, it is not worth using motion laws of high orders.

In their attempts to qunatify the effects resulting from profile errors, most authors superimpose some sort of waviness on the ideal desired profile and then try to build up an analytical approach for calculations. In practice, however, this approach is not suitable because the errors are very unpredictable since they depend on so many factors of the manufacturing process, such as the dynamics

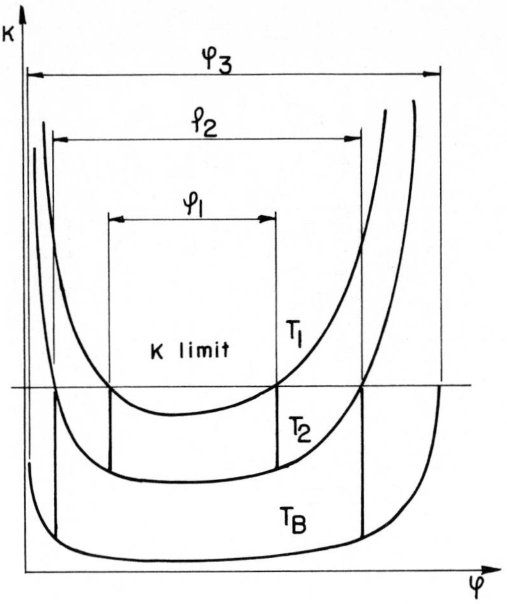

Fig. 48. Dependence of $K(\phi)$ on the admittance and cam profile angle.

of the machinery used, the "history" of the material, etc. For this reason we apply probability theory to this error problem, since the errors are generated randomly.

3. MAIN DEFINITION

Let us designate the ideal law of the follower motion as $s(\phi)$, as shown in Fig. 49. and the real motion which is realized by the mechanism as $s^*(\phi)$, where ϕ is the turning angle of the cam. Then, the displacement, velocity and acceleration errors of the follower are, respectively:

$$\Delta s = s - s^* = F_1(\Delta\rho) \quad \text{(III.3.1)}$$

$$\Delta V = \Delta\dot{s} = \dot{s} - \dot{s}^* = F_2(\Delta\rho) \quad \text{(III.3.2)}$$

$$\Delta W = \Delta\ddot{s} = \ddot{s} - \ddot{s}^* = F_3(\Delta\rho) \quad \text{(III.3.3)}$$

It can be stated that

$$\Delta\rho(\psi) = \rho(\psi) - \rho^*(\psi^*) \quad \text{(III.3.4)}$$

where

ψ - ideal angle of the cam profile

ρ - the ideal current radius of the cam profile

ρ^* - the real current radius of the cam profile

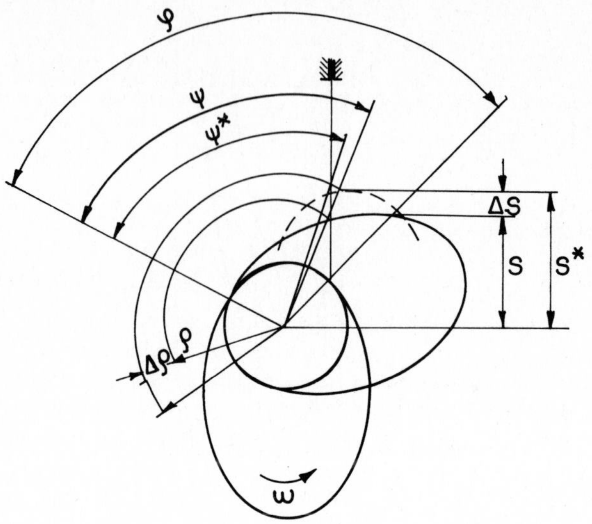

Fig. 49. Layout of a cam mechanism with an error in the profile of the cam.

ψ^* - real angle of the cam profile

$\Delta\rho$ - profile errors of the cam.

The case in quadrant II of Fig. 43 requires the study of functions F_1, F_2 and F_3, which depend on the geometry and type of the cam mechanism. In the general case, the expression for s may be written as:

$$s = s\{\rho[\psi(\phi[t])]\} \tag{III.3.5}$$

From this expression we get

$$V = \dot{s} = \frac{ds}{d\rho}\frac{d\rho}{d\psi}\frac{d\psi}{d\rho}\omega \tag{III.3.6}$$

where the angular velocity is $\omega = d\phi/dt$

and

$$W = \ddot{s} = \omega^2\left[\frac{d^2s}{d\rho^2}\left(\frac{d\rho}{d\psi}\frac{d\psi}{d\phi}\right)^2 + \frac{ds}{d\rho}\frac{d^2\rho}{d\psi^2}\left(\frac{d\psi}{d\phi}\right)^2 + \frac{ds}{d\rho}\frac{d\rho}{d\psi}\frac{d^2\psi}{d\phi^2}\right] \tag{III.3.7}$$

Let us denote

$$\frac{ds}{d\rho} = \alpha_1; \quad \frac{d\alpha_1}{d\phi} = \alpha_2; \quad \frac{d^2\alpha_1}{d\phi^2} = \alpha_3 \tag{III.3.8}$$

Based on the fact that the profile errors are small compared to the values of the radii, i.e. $\Delta\rho \ll \rho$, we can write

$$\Delta s = F_1(\Delta\rho) \simeq \alpha_1 \Delta\rho \tag{III.3.9}$$

which gives for the velocity errors:

$$\Delta V = F_2(\Delta\rho) \simeq \omega\alpha_2\Delta\rho + \alpha_1\Delta\dot{\rho} \tag{III.3.10}$$

and for the acceleration errors:

$$\Delta W = F_3(\Delta\rho) \simeq \omega^2\alpha_3\Delta\rho + 2\omega\alpha_2\Delta\dot{\rho} + \alpha_1\Delta\ddot{\rho} \tag{III.3.11}$$

The functions α_1, α_2 and α_3 can be obtained for any given cam mechanism from known data as shown, for instance, in Fig. 50.

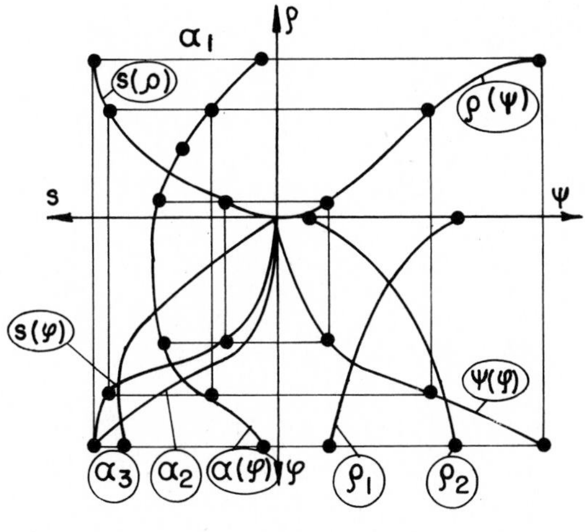

Fig. 50. Calculation of the functions α_1, α_2 and α_3.

Taking equation (III.3.5) into account, we get from equation (III.3.4)

$$\Delta\rho = \rho[\psi(\phi[t])] - \rho^*[\psi^*(\phi[t])] \tag{III.3.12}$$

Based on the previous assumption that $\Delta\rho << \rho$, we can postulate that the value of ψ does not change if we use ρ^* instead of ρ, i.e.

$$\psi \simeq \psi^* \tag{III.3.13}$$

Let us denote

$$\frac{d\psi}{d\phi} = \beta_1; \qquad \frac{d^2\psi}{d\phi^2} = \beta_2 \tag{III.3.14}$$

Then we obtain

$$\Delta\dot{\rho} \simeq \omega\beta_1\Delta\rho^1_\psi \tag{III.3.15}$$

and

$$\ddot{\Delta\rho} \approx \omega^2[\beta_1^2\Delta\rho''_\psi + \beta_2\Delta\rho'_\psi] \qquad \text{(III.3.16)}$$

Substituting equations (III.3.15) and (III.3.16) into equations (III.3.10) and (III.3.11), we obtain

$$\Delta V \approx \omega[\alpha_2\Delta\rho + \alpha_1\beta_1\Delta\rho'_\psi] \qquad \text{(III.3.17)}$$

and

$$\Delta W \approx \omega^2[\alpha_3\Delta\rho + (2\alpha_2\beta_1 + \alpha_1\beta_2)\Delta\rho'_\psi + \alpha_1\beta_1^2\Delta\rho''_\psi] \qquad \text{(III.3.18)}$$

In addition, by applying equations (III.3.8) and (III.3.14) to equation (III.3.5), we obtain

$$V = \dot{s} = \alpha_1\beta_1\omega\rho'_\psi \qquad \text{(III.3.19)}$$

and

$$W = \ddot{s} = \omega^2[\alpha_2\beta_1\rho'_\psi + \alpha_1\beta_2\rho'_\psi + \alpha_1\beta_1^2\rho''_\psi] \qquad \text{(III.3.20)}$$

4. KINEMATIC APPROACH

In the previous section, we described the relationship between profile errors and the displacement, velocity and acceleration of the follower in terms of the geometric parameters of the given cam mechanism. We did not, however, consider the analytical expressions for $\Delta\rho$ which are necessary for performing these calculations.

The essence of the problem is that profile errors have random properties; this is the reason that statistical methods will be used for describing the errors. This statistical approach is also more realistic for the mass production of cams. The innovation in our approach thus lies in the fact that elements of the theory of random functions will be applied, and the dependence $\rho^*(\psi)$ will be considered from this standpoint. Therefore, $\rho^*(\psi)$ can be represented as a random function as follows:

$$\rho^* = \rho + \bar{\rho} + \overset{\circ}{\rho} \qquad \text{(III.4.1)}$$

or, applying equation (III.3.4) as:

$$\Delta\rho = \bar{\rho} + \overset{\circ}{\rho} \qquad \text{(III.4.2)}$$

where $\bar{\rho}(\psi)$ - the estimation of the mathematical expectation of the random errors of the profile radius;

$\overset{\circ}{\rho}(\psi)$ - the random (centralized) component of the profile radius.

To obtain the probability characteristics of the errors we have to measure the profile radii ρ^* for a number of cams.

Then, we will have

$$\bar{\rho}(\chi) \quad \frac{\sum_{i=1}^{n} \rho_i^*(\psi)}{n} - \rho(\psi) \qquad \text{(III.4.3)}$$

where n - the number of cams measured.

If the following assumptions are made:

1. the errors $\Delta\rho$ are stationary: their properties do not depend on the location of the profile;
2. the errors can be described adequately by means of the normal distribution;

then, for a description of the random component it is necessary to know only the value of σ [the mean root square deviation (MRSD) of the random value]. To apply the formulas (III.3.7), (III.3.15) and (III.3.16), we have to express the MRSD for $\Delta\rho$, $\Delta\rho'$ and $\Delta\rho''$, respectively, and the resulting expressions are:

$$\sigma_S^2 \simeq \alpha_1^2\sigma_\rho^2 \qquad \text{(III.4.4)}$$

$$\sigma_V^2 \simeq \omega^2[\alpha_2^2\sigma_\rho^2 + \alpha_1^2\beta_1^2\sigma_{\rho'}^2] \qquad \text{(III.4.5)}$$

$$\sigma_W^2 \simeq \omega^4[\alpha_s^2\sigma_\rho^2 + (2\alpha_2\beta_1 + \alpha_1\beta_2)^2\sigma_{\rho'}^2 + \beta_1^4\alpha_1^2\sigma_{\rho''}^2] \qquad \text{(III.4.6)}$$

Note: We propose to calculate $\sigma_{\rho'}$ and $\sigma_{\rho''}$ by a procedure which is based on the following two statements:

1. If a correlation function $K_\rho(\psi)$ of a stationary process $\rho(\psi)$ is given, then

$$\sigma_\rho^2 = K_\rho(0)$$

2. If $\rho' = d\rho/d\psi$ and $K_{\rho'}$ is the correlation function of the random process ρ'_ψ, then

$$K_{\rho''} \simeq -\frac{d^2K_\rho(\psi)}{d\psi^2}$$

$$K_{\rho''} \simeq \frac{d^4K_\rho(\psi)}{d\psi^4}$$

(See I.31.5).

Therefore, we have

$$\sigma_{\rho'}^2 = K_{\rho'}(0)$$

and

$$\sigma^2_{\rho''} = K_{\rho''}(0) \qquad \text{(III.4.7)}$$

Expressions (III.4.4) to (III.4.6) show that the values of the MRSD of the errors σ^2_S, σ^2_V and σ^2_W of the follower motion are functions of the value of the rotation angle ϕ because of their dependence on functions α_1, α_2, α_3, β_1 and β_2 which, in turn, depend on this angle. Therefore, the designer has to decide at what interval of the ϕ angle he wants to minimize the MRSD values of the errors of the follower motion and then evaluate the results for different variations of the cam mechanism and choose the best one.

In some cases, the designer has not only to define the tolerances of the cam profile radii but also to limit the difference in the values of two adjacent radii $[\Delta\rho]$. Using the expressions obtained, he can calculate this required difference $[\Delta\rho]$ when the allowed values of the velocity $[\Delta V/V]$ or acceleration $[\Delta W/W]$ errors are given. For instance, let us describe the cam profile by polar coordinates. Then, because of small values of the angle $\Delta\psi$ between adjacent radii, it can be assumed that the allowed value of the $[\Delta\rho]$ error can be expressed in the following manner:

$$[\Delta\rho] = A\Delta\psi \qquad \text{(III.4.8)}$$

where A = const.

Then

$$\Delta\rho' = A \quad \text{and} \quad \Delta\rho'' = 0 \qquad \text{(III.4.9)}$$

From equations (III.3.10), (III.3.11), (III.4.8) and (III.4.9), we obtain

$$[\Delta\rho] = \frac{[\Delta V/V]V\Delta\psi}{\omega(\alpha_1\Delta\psi + \alpha_1\beta_1)} \qquad \text{(III.4.10)}$$

or

$$[\Delta\rho] = \frac{[\Delta W/W]W\Delta\psi}{\omega^2(\alpha_3\Delta\psi + 2\alpha_2\beta_1 + \alpha_1\beta_2)} \qquad \text{(III.4.11)}$$

In other words, the required or allowed kinematic accuracy of manufacturing can be predicted at the design stage.

Obviously, the considerations described in this paragraph correspond to the first and second quadrants of Fig. 43.

In many cases the correlation function can be sufficiently well approximated by expressions such as:

$$K_\rho = \sigma^2_\rho e^{-\gamma^2\psi^2} \qquad \text{(III.4.12)}$$

or

$$K_\rho = \sigma_\rho^2 e^{-\gamma^2\psi^2} \cos\eta\psi \qquad \text{(III.4.13)}$$

where γ and η are constant coefficients.

From equations (III.4.7), (III.4.12), and equation (III.4.13), respectively, we obtain the expressions for the variances of $\Delta\rho'$ and $\Delta\rho''$ in the following forms:

$$\sigma_{\rho'}^2 = 2\gamma^2\sigma_\rho^2$$
$$\text{(III.4.14)}$$
$$\sigma_{\rho'}^2 = (2\gamma^2 + \eta^2)\sigma_\rho^2$$

and

$$\sigma_{\rho''}^2 = 12\gamma^4\sigma_\rho^2$$
$$\text{(III.4.15)}$$
$$\sigma_{\rho''}^2 = (12\gamma^4 + 12\gamma^2\eta^2 + \eta^2)\sigma_\rho^2$$

The advantage of using the correlation function as a criterion of the profile accuracy lies in the simplification of the measuring conditions. The usual methods of measuring the cam profile are comparison with a high-accuracy pattern or measurement of the absolute values of the profile radius. With the method that we recommend, i.e. application of the correlation function, it is possible to compare two cam profiles from the same manufacturer (see section 9). From the measured differences between the two profiles, we can calculate the correlation function according to expression (I.28.3). It is clear from the statistical standpoint that the values obtained for σ_ρ^2 in this case will be twice those measured by conventional means.

Let us illustrate this calculation method with an example based on the analysis of the cams of a Diesel engine. The profile of these cams consists of three conjugate arcs of different radii, as shown in Fig. 51. The three sections of the profile may be described as follows:

I. $0° \leq \psi_1 \leq 9°21'$

$$\rho_1 = 17.66 \cos\psi_1 + \sqrt{4.6^2 - 17.66^2(1 - \cos^2\psi_1)}$$

$$\text{(III.4.16)}$$

II. $9°21' \leq \psi_2 \leq 46°45'$

$$\rho_2 = -76\cos(55°30' - \psi_2) + \sqrt{91.26^2 - 76^2[1 - \cos(55°30' - \psi_2)]}$$

III. $46°45' \leq \psi_3 \leq 66°56'$

$$\rho_3 = -16.71\cos(66°56' - \psi_3) + \sqrt{31.71^2 - 76^2[1 - \cos(66°56' - \psi_3)]}$$

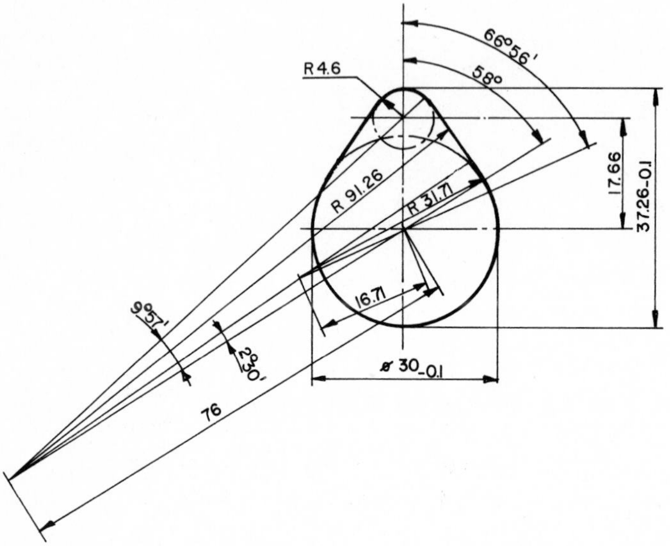

Fig. 51. Cam of a Diesel engine.

Twenty-two cam profiles were measured. The measurements were carried out on the device shown in Fig. 52, which consists of a base 1 on which an optical dividing head 2 and a support 3 are installed. The follower 5 is allowed to move in its guide 4 to actuate the indicator 6. Thus, the device measures the real value of the follower motion s*.

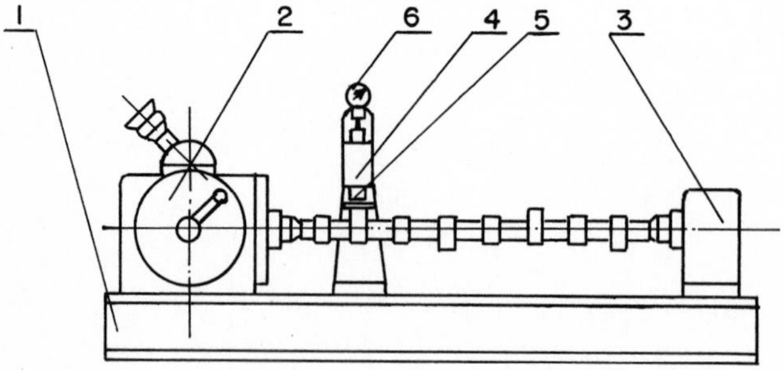

Fig. 52. The device for profile measurements.

The ideal motion of the follower may be described as follows:

I. For the rotating angle ϕ from 0° to 48°03' - 58°-9°57' and $0° \leq \phi_1 \leq 48°03'$

$$s_1 = 17.66(1 - \cos\phi_1) \tag{III.4.17}$$

and

$$s_{1max} = 17.66(1 - \cos 48°03') = 5.85$$

II. For the rotating angle ϕ from 48°03' to 55°30' = 58°-2°30' and $0° \leq \phi_2 \leq 7°27'$

where ϕ_{2max} = 9°57'-2°30' = 7°27' corresponding to the profile.

$$s_2 = s_{1max} + 76[\cos(9°57' - \phi_2) - \cos 9°57']$$

and

$$s_{2max} = s_{1max} + 76[\cos(9°57' - 7°27') - \cos 9°57'] = 6{,}92$$

III. For the rotating angle ϕ from 55°30' to 66°56' where $0° \leq \phi_3 \leq 11°26'$

where ϕ_{3max} = 66°56' - 55°30' = 11°26'

$$s_3 = s_{2max} + 16.71[\cos(11°26' - \phi_3) - \cos 11°26']$$

Functions $s(\phi)$ and $\rho(\psi)$ are shown in Fig. 53. Using the auxiliary lines, we

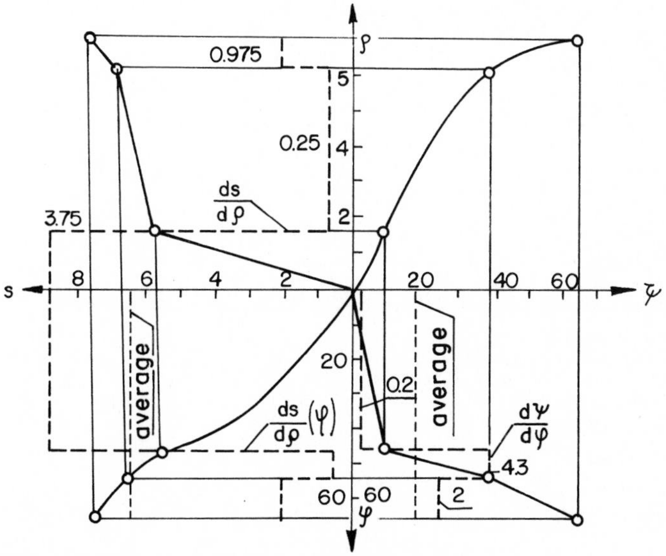

Fig. 53. Calculation of the functions α and β.

can find the functions α_1, α_2 and α_3 in accordance with equation (III.3.8) and the functions β_1 and β_2, in accordance with equation (III.3.14). In our case, obviously, $\alpha_2 \simeq 0$, $\alpha_3 \simeq 0$ and $\beta_2 \simeq 0$ because $\alpha_1 \simeq$ const and $\beta_1 \simeq$ const.

The measured correlation function of the ρ errors is given in Fig. 54.

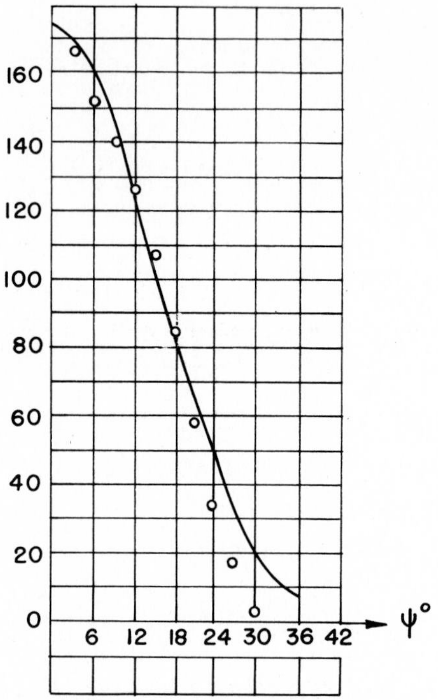

Fig. 54. The correlation function at the measured cam profile errors.

This correlation function is approximated by the expression:

$$K_\rho = 13.2^2 \exp[-3^2\psi^2]\,\mu m^2 \qquad \text{(III.4.18)}$$

From equations (III.4.7) and (III.4.14) we obtain:

$$\sigma_\rho^2 \simeq 175\ \mu m^2$$

$$\sigma_{\rho'}^2 \simeq 2\gamma^2\sigma_\rho^2 \simeq 3150\ \mu m^2/rad^2$$

$$\sigma_{\rho''}^2 \simeq 12\gamma^4\sigma_\rho^2 \simeq 170000\ \mu m^2/rad^2$$

Therefore, from equations (III.4.4), (III.4.5) and (III.4.6) it is now possible to calculate the values of σ_S^2, σ_V^2 and σ_W^2. For this calculation we will use the average values of α_1 and β_1 which are, respectively:

$\bar{\alpha}_1 \simeq 2.76$ $\qquad\qquad$ $\bar{\beta}_1 \simeq 1.08$

For a cam-shaft-rotation velocity of $\omega = 150$ rad/sec, the following values are obtained:

$$\sigma_S^2 \simeq \bar{\alpha}_1^{-2}\sigma_\rho^2 = 1350\ \mu m^2$$

$$\sigma_V^2 \simeq \omega^2\bar{\alpha}_1^{-2}\bar{\beta}_1^{-2}\sigma_{\rho'}^2 = 6150000\ \mu m^2/sec^2$$

$$\sigma_W^2 \simeq \omega^4\bar{\alpha}_1^{-2}\bar{\beta}_1^{-2}\sigma_{\rho''}^2 = 85\cdot 10^{10}\ \mu m^2/sec^4$$

The next step is the determination of the tolerances of the displacement, velocity and acceleration of the follower. This goal is achieved by the $\pm 3\sigma$ rule:

$$T_S = 6\sigma_S = 6\cdot 36.74 = 220\ \mu m$$

$$T_V = 6\sigma_V = 6\cdot 2480 = 14.879\ mm/sec$$

$$T_A = 6\sigma_W = 6\cdot 9.2\cdot 10^5 = 5520\ mm/sec$$

5. DYNAMIC APPROACH

At this point, we have to take into consideration the effects which appear as a result of the real properties of the elasticity of the follower mechanism. A large number of publications have been devoted to elastic follower motion in cam mechanisms. One of the classic works - that of Wolfson and Kolovsky (5) - treats this problem within the framework of a general nonlinear case. Our approach, on the other hand, will be statistical, since we consider the problem to be one of accuracy. If we assume that the mechanical system of the follower is linear or can be linearized, we can describe this system by its transfer function $\Phi(j\Omega)$. Then, we can apply the superposition principle, and the solution can be represented as a sum

$$y = y_o + y_1 + \bar{y} + \mathring{y} \qquad \text{(III.5.1)}$$

where

y_o - the solution of the homogeneous equation;

y_1 - the solution for the ideal shape of the profile;

$\bar{y}$ - the solution which agrees with the mathematical expectations in the input of the follower system;

$\overset{\circ}{y}$ - the solution which agrees with the random part of the motion in the input.

To find the output follower motion, we apply the concept of spectral density of a random process. For a dynamic system, the connection between the spectral density of the input process S_s and the spectral density of the output process S_y takes the form:

$$S_y = |\Phi(j\Omega)|^2 S_s \tag{III.5.2}$$

It is also known that the MRSD of any process depends on its spectral density, so that:

$$\sigma_y^2 = \int_0^\infty S_y d\Omega \tag{III.5.3}$$

Substituting equation (III.5.2) into equation (III.5.3), we obtain:

$$\sigma_y^2 = \int_0^\infty |\Phi(j\Omega)|^2 S_s d\Omega \tag{III.5.4}$$

And, as follows from the spectral theory of stationary random functions

$$\sigma_{\dot{y}}^2 = \int_0^\infty |\Phi(j\Omega)|^2 \Omega^2 S_s d\Omega \tag{III.5.5}$$

and

$$\sigma_{\ddot{y}}^2 = \int_0^\infty |\Phi(j\Omega)|^2 \Omega^4 S_s d\Omega \tag{III.5.6}$$

where $\dot{y}$ and $\ddot{y}$ - speed and acceleration of the driven link, respectively.

The procedure described above agrees with a stationary process on the input of this system. But, s can be assumed to be a stationary process only in the case in which the follower has a point contact with the cam profile and its line of motion passes through the rotation center of the cam. Then α_1 = const. Despite this consideration, it is possible to expand the field of use of expressions (III.5.2), (III.5.4) and (III.5.5), at least for practical purposes, as described below.

We begin with the fact that we know how to solve linear differential equations (6) when the input acts as a nonstationary process χ, in the following form:

$$\chi = \xi(t)s(t)$$

where

$\xi(t)$ - some function; in our case, according to equations (III.3.9) and (III. (III.4.4), this function is $\alpha_1(t)$;

$s(t)$ - our input into the follower system; this function agrees with the above-described assumption (section 2) of stationarity.

For purposes of convenience, we simplify the expression for χ by taking the average value of $\bar{\alpha}_1$ and using it as a constant.

It should be noted that for a more complete treatment of the conditions of linearity, the expressions (III.5.4), (III.5.5) and (III.5.6) are applicable to some nonlinear problems (using, for instance, the statistical linearization method). The limited scope of this chapter does not allow us to elaborate on this idea (see Chapter V).

The dynamic approach must be based on the use of dependences (III.5.4), (III.5.5) and (III.5.6). As will be seen, two factors influence the values σ_y, $\sigma_{\dot{y}}$ or $\sigma_{\ddot{y}}$: the spectral density S_s of the input of the dynamic system, and the properties of the dynamic system itself - $\Phi(j\Omega)$.

We have already discussed how to improve s, if possible. There are, however, many more ways of influencing the accuracy of the follower motion when $\Phi(j\Omega)$ is used as a tool for changing σ_y, $\sigma_{\dot{y}}$ and $\sigma_{\ddot{y}}$; for example:

i) by choosing better values for the mass, stiffness and dissipative damping; or

ii) by choosing a better layout for the dynamic system.

Let us consider, as an example, the same cam as that described in the previous paragraph. The mechanism is shown in Fig. 55, and the simplified dynamic model

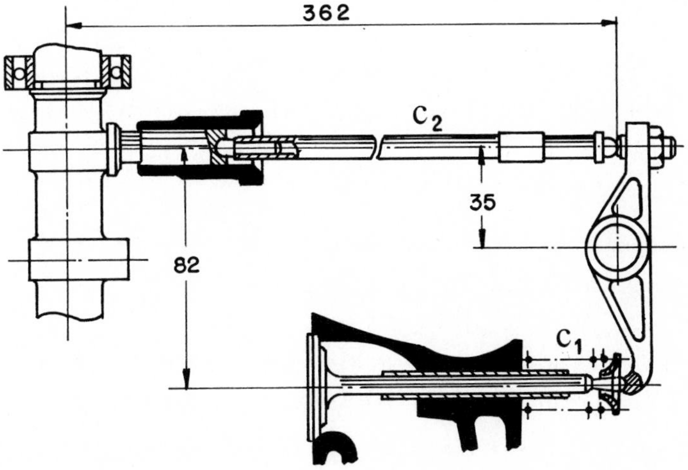

Fig. 55. Valve mechanism of a Diesel engine.

is represented in Fig. 56. In this layout, c_1 and c_2 represent the stiffnesses, b_1 and b_2, the damping coefficients and M, the mass. On the assumption that the system is linear, the output motion equation may be expressed as follows:

$$m\ddot{y} + (b_1 + b_2)\dot{y} + (c_1 + c_2)y = c_2 s + b_2\dot{s} - F_o \qquad \text{(III.5.7)}$$

where

y - the displacement of the driven mass

F_o - the initial force of the spring.

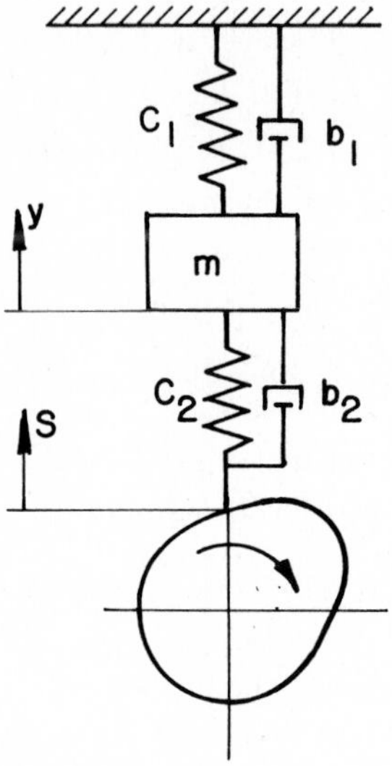

Fig. 56. A simplified dynamic model of the mechanism shown in Fig. 55.

Since we are dealing with a lumped cam mechanism, the stiffnesses and damping coefficients are reduced to the driven mass. As the system is linear, the superposition principle is applicable. Then, the solution can be represented as the sum

$$y = y_o + y_1 + \bar{y} + \mathring{y} \qquad \text{(III.5.8)}$$

where

y_o - the solution of the homogeneous equation;

y_1 - the solution for the ideal shape of the profile;

$\bar{y}$ - the solution which agrees with the mathematical expectations in the input;

$\mathring{y}$ - the solution which agrees with the random part of the motion in the input.

We are interested only in the solution $\mathring{y}$, because the solutions for non-random parts are trivial.

For this purpose we apply the concept of the spectral density S of a random process.

Taking into consideration that

$$\Phi(j\Omega) = \frac{b_2 j\Omega + c_2}{m(j\Omega)^2 + (b_1 + b_2)j\Omega + c_1 + c_2}$$

we have

$$\sigma_y^2 = \int_0^\infty \left| \frac{b_2 j\Omega + c_2}{-m\Omega^2 + (b_1 + b_2)j\Omega + c_1 + c_2} \right|^2 S_s d\Omega \qquad \text{(III.5.9)}$$

For $\sigma_{\dot{y}}^2$ and $\sigma_{\ddot{y}}^2$ we have

$$\sigma_{\dot{y}}^2 = \int_0^\infty |\Phi(j\Omega)|^2 \Omega^2 S_s d\Omega$$

and

$$\sigma_{\ddot{y}}^2 = \int_0^\infty |\Phi(j\Omega)|^2 \Omega^4 S_s d\Omega$$

If we substitute the following data, c_1 the lumped stifnesses of the mechanism $= 2\cdot 10^7$ N/m; $c_2 = 10^4$ N/m; m = 80 g; $b_1 = 3$ Nsec/m; and $b_2 = 1$ Nsec/m; we obtain:

$$\sigma_y^2 \simeq 2400\ \mu m^2$$

$$\sigma_{\dot{y}}^2 \simeq 11\cdot 10^6\ \mu m^2/sec^2$$

$$\sigma_{\ddot{y}}^2 \simeq 140\cdot 10^{10}\ \mu m^2/sec^4$$

In this example, for the correlation function expressed by equations (III.4.12) and (III.4.18), we use the following formula (see I.34) for the spectral density;

$$S_s(\Omega) = \frac{\sigma_s^2}{4\gamma\sqrt{\pi}} \exp[-\Omega^2/2\gamma^2] \qquad \text{(III.5.10)}$$

for $\sigma_s \simeq 13.2$ μm and $\gamma = 3$ we therefore obtain:

$$S_s(\Omega) = 8.192 \exp[-\Omega^2/18] \qquad \text{(III.5.11)}$$

which we then substitute in equation (III.5.9).

The tolerances of the displacement, velocity and acceleration are:

$T_y \simeq 6\sigma_y = 294\ \mu m$

$T_{\dot{y}} \simeq 6\sigma_{\dot{y}} = 20\ mm/sec$

$T_{\ddot{y}} \simeq 6\sigma_{\ddot{y}} = 7100\ mm/sec^2$

6. SYNTHESIS PROBLEM

The synthesis of an optimal cam mechanism during the design stage is both desirable and important. We will try to show how this is applicable to dynamic optimization of cam mechanisms according to quadrants III and IV of Fig. 43.

In general, the optimization of systems may be defined as follows: The determination of the layouts and the values of their parameters which give the minimum RMSV for the deviations of the displacement, velocity and acceleration of the follower.

Quadrant III

Expression (III.5.2) is the basic equation we use for optimization purposes. If s is the input motion of the dynamic system [and is also the desirable output motion-law of the follower motion] and y_1 is the summary output motion which includes the dynamic deviations, then the output deviations are given by $Y = y_1 - s$. This concept can be expressed in Laplace variables as:

$$y_1 = |\Phi(p)|s \tag{III.6.1}$$

and

$$Y(p) = |\Phi(p) - 1|s(p) \tag{III.6.2}$$

Therefore, for equation (III.6.2) we obtain:

$$\sigma_Y^2 = \int_0^\infty |\Phi(j\Omega) - 1|^2 S_s(\Omega)d\Omega \tag{III.6.3}$$

Application of this kind of $\Phi(j\Omega)$ function, which minimizes the value of σ_y, can solve the optimization problem for the case described in quadrant III.

Quadrant IV

In this case, in addition to the above-described considerations, we have to take into account the dynamic influence of the profile errors. When the dynamic system can be assumed to be linear, the superposition principle can be used, i.e. to equation (III.6.3) must be added the value of σ_y^2 which represents the

Fig. 57. General view of the experimental device.

influence of the profile error component of the output deviations. This value can be calculated directly from expression (III.5.2). When the spectral density of the profile errors $S_{\Delta s}$ is added, then the expression appears in the following form:

$$\sigma^2_{Y_*} = \sigma^2_Y + \sigma^2_y = \int_0^\infty \{|\Phi(j\Omega) - 1|^2 S_s + |\Phi(j\Omega)|^2 S_{\Delta s}\} d\Omega \qquad \text{(III.6.4)}$$

When the RMSV of the acceleration is sought, expression (III.6.4) becomes:

$$\sigma^2_{\ddot{Y}_*} = \int_0^\infty \{|\Phi(j\Omega) - 1|^2 S_s + |\Phi(j\Omega)|^2 S_{\Delta s}\} \Omega^4 d\Omega \qquad \text{(III.6.5)}$$

To examine the validity of the theoretical results rerived so far, the experimental equipment illustrated in Fig. 57 was built. The layout of this device is shown in Fig. 58 and the dynamic model, in Fig. 59. The equipment

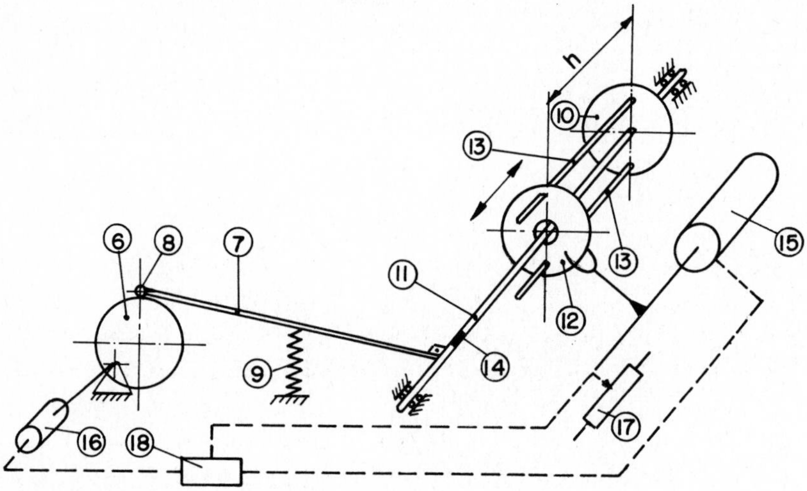

Fig. 58. Layout of the device shown in Fig. 57.

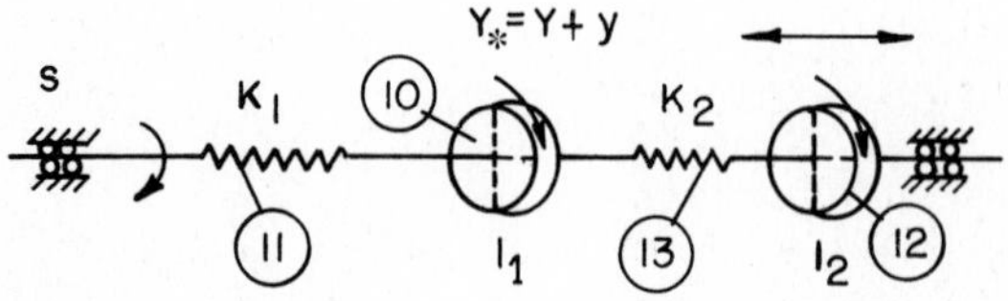

Fig. 59. Simplified dynamic model of the device shown in Fig. 57.

consists of a base 1, an electromotor 2 (1.5 kW, 1435 rpm), and a belt drive 3 with a variator 4, which transmits the motion from the motor 2 via camshaft 5 to the cam 6. By means of the variator 4, the rotation speed of the cam 6 can be varied from 150 to 500 rpm. The cam 6 drives an oscillating follower 7, provided with a roller 8. The contact between the cam and the follower is provided by a spring 9. The follower 7 drives a mass 10 ($I_1 = 1.8 \times 10^{-2}$ kgm^2) which is fastened to a shaft (of stiffness $k_1 = 930$ N/m); the mass represents that part of the mechanism whose motion is under consideration. To examine the possibility of optimization, a second mass 12 ($I_2 = 3.6 \times 10^{-2}$ kg^2) is connected to the mass 10 by means of two pivots 13. This mass can be moved along the pivots 13, thus changing their stiffness. A set 14 of strain gauges is glued to the head of the shaft 11. In our experiments, the acceleration of the mass 10 was measured for several positions of the mass 12 along the pivots 13 which are 24 cm long. The displacement of the mass 12 along the pivots is denoted by h. In this section, we present results for h = 4 cm, 12 cm and 21 cm; the latter being almost at the optimal position.

This dynamic model can be described by the following equations:

$$\begin{cases} I_1\ddot{\theta}_1 + k_1(\theta_1 - \theta_o) + k_2(\theta_1 - \theta_2) = 0 \\ I_2\ddot{\theta}_2 + k_2(\theta_2 - \theta_1) = 0 \end{cases} \qquad \text{(III.6.6)}$$

Our experiment showed that in this case the damping can be neglected.

Two cams were tested. Cam A was manufactured with relatively high accuracy; while cam B was produced manually with a file. For this purpose, the profile of each cam was chosen in the form of a circle with a radius R = 80 and fastened on the camshaft with an eccentricity of e = 20 mm. The errors of cam B were compared with those of cam A, and the correlation function K for these errors was calculated as a function of the profile angle. Fig. 60 shows this measured correlation function (the circles) and its analytical approximation (the curve) in the form:

$$K_\rho(\psi) \simeq 530\, e^{-4\psi^2} \cos 0.327\psi \times 10^{-6}\ cm^2 \qquad \text{(III.6.7)}$$

Note:

1. When profile errors are measured, the shape of the pick-up has to be the same as that of the follower edge.
2. The correlation function must be periodic because of the rotation of the cam. However, as can be seen, at a cam profile angle of close to 40°, this function becomes negligible. This is the reason that the graph has been cut off at this point. Since roller 8 of the follower 7 has a comparatively

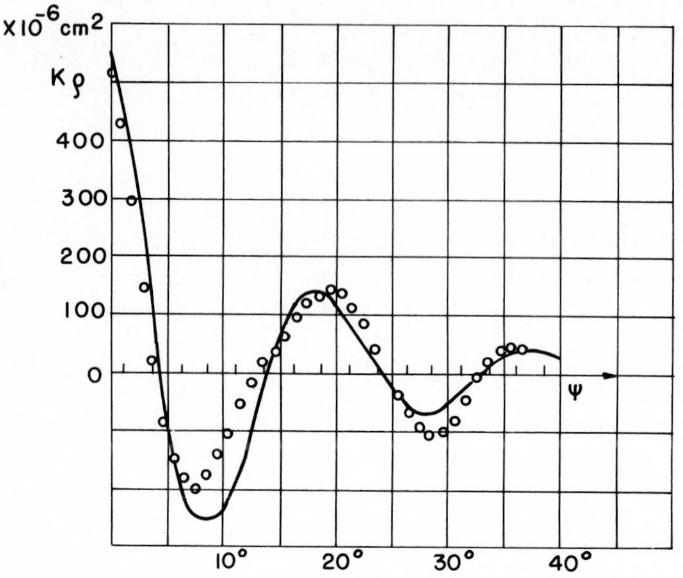

Fig. 60. The correlation function of the cam profile errors.

small radius and since the follower is relatively long, it can be assumed for equations (III.3.8) and (III.3.14) that:

$\alpha_1 \simeq 1; \quad \alpha_2 = \alpha_3 \simeq 0; \quad \beta_1 \simeq 1; \quad \beta_2 \simeq 0,$

or for equation (III.3.9) that:

$$\Delta s \simeq \Delta\rho$$

and (III.6.8)

$$\phi \simeq \psi$$

From equation (III.3.14), we obtain:

$$\psi \simeq \omega t \qquad \text{(III.6.9)}$$

where ω - the angular velocity of the cam shaft.

For correlation function (III.6.7), the spectral density S_s can be written in the following form (for ω = 26.18 1/sec):

$$S_{\Delta s}(\Omega) = 0.88 \times 10^{-6}\left(\frac{1}{10966 + (3.56 + \Omega)^2} + \frac{1}{10966 + (3.56 - \Omega)^2}\right)[\text{sec m}^2]$$

(III.6.10)

The motion law for the follower of the experimental device may be described in the following way:

$$s^* = 2(-\cos\phi + \sqrt{\cos^2\phi + 15})10^{-2}[m] \tag{III.6.11}$$

which, after being extended in a Fourier series, gives for the spectral density S_S the expression:

$$S_s \approx \sum_{n=1}^{\infty} \frac{\delta(\Omega - n\omega)}{n^3} \tag{III.6.12}$$

where δ - Dirac impulse function.

From expression (III.6.6) the transfer function in our two-mass dynamic system can be given as:

$$\Phi(j\Omega) = \frac{k_1(k_2 - I_2\Omega^2)}{I_1I_2\Omega^4 - (I_1k_2 + I_2k_2 + I_2k_1)\Omega^2 + k_1k_2} \tag{III.6.13}$$

(Here all the parameters are in agreement with Fig. 59. Dissipative damping is neglected.)

Substituting the given values in equation (III.6.13), we obtain:

$$\Phi(j\Omega) = \frac{930k_2 - 33.5\Omega^2}{6.5\cdot 10^{-4}\Omega^4 - (0.054k_2 + 33.5)\Omega^2 + 930k_2} \tag{III.6.14}$$

Fig. 61 illustrates the behavior of $\sigma^2_{\ddot{y}}$ as a function of the stiffness k_2. (The angular velocity of the camshaft was ω = 26.18 1/sec.) The graph shows five minima of $\sigma^2_{\ddot{y}}$. The k_2 values which agree with these minima also agree with

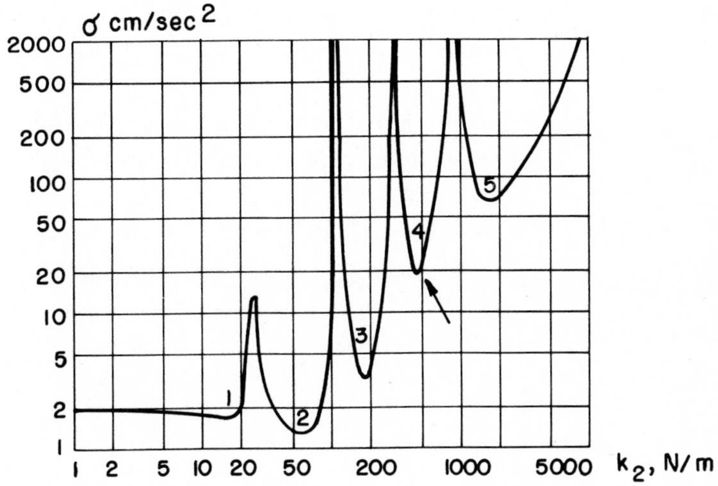

Fig. 61. The RMSV of the follower's acceleration corresponding to the stiffness k_2.

the displacement of the mass I_2 (Fig. 57, 58 and 59) along the pivots 13, as mentioned above. This dependence is given in Fig. 62. We can see that the fourth minimum on the graph (Fig. 61) corresponds to the case in which the mass I_2 is situated at a distance of 21 cm from mass I_1.

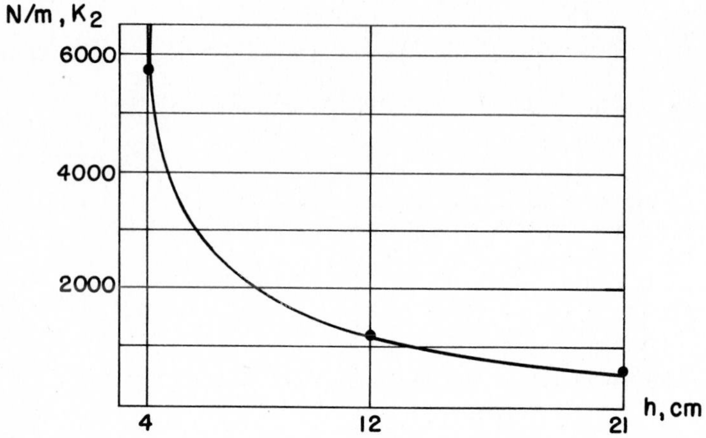

Fig. 62. The stiffness k_2 as a function of the length h of the rods.

Note: We consider only the fourth minimum for the following reason: Obviously, we are interested in the lowest values of the acceleration, but the first, second and third minima require too low values of k_2 (or too large values of h), and the fifth minimum gives bigger values of the amplitude.

The right-hand side of Fig. 63 shows the oscillographs of accelerations of mass I_1 for h = 4 cm, 12 cm and 21 cm when cam A drives mass I_1. It is obvious that the third case is the "quietest."

The left hand side of Fig. 63 shows the acceleration of the same mass I_1, when cam B is mounted on the camshaft. Now, the difference between cases h = 12 cm and h = 21 cm is not so clear. Evidently, the minimum in this case has moved in the direction of higher values of the stiffness k_2, i.e. nearer to the mass I_1. The calculation shows that in this case the optimal value of k_2 is approximately equal to k_2 = 700 N/m.

To obtain a quantitative criterion for the described measurements, the RMSV of the acceleration was measured by means of a Frequency Analyser (Bruel & Kjer

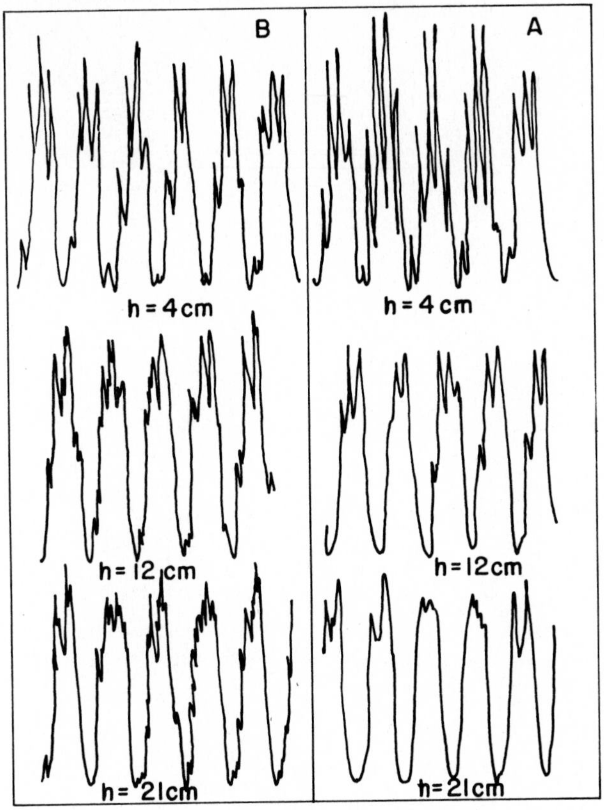

Fig. 63. Comparison of the acceleration of the follower driven by accurate and rough cams for different values of h.

Type 2120). The results are given in Fig. 64a), b) and c). These measurements were then processed and are presented in Fig. 65. In this Figure we can see the relative values of the RMSV of the acceleration for the six cases presented in Fig. 63.

The value of the ordinate for any chosen frequency on the curves shows the RMSV of the acceleration which corresponds to the interval from the chosen frequency to infinity.

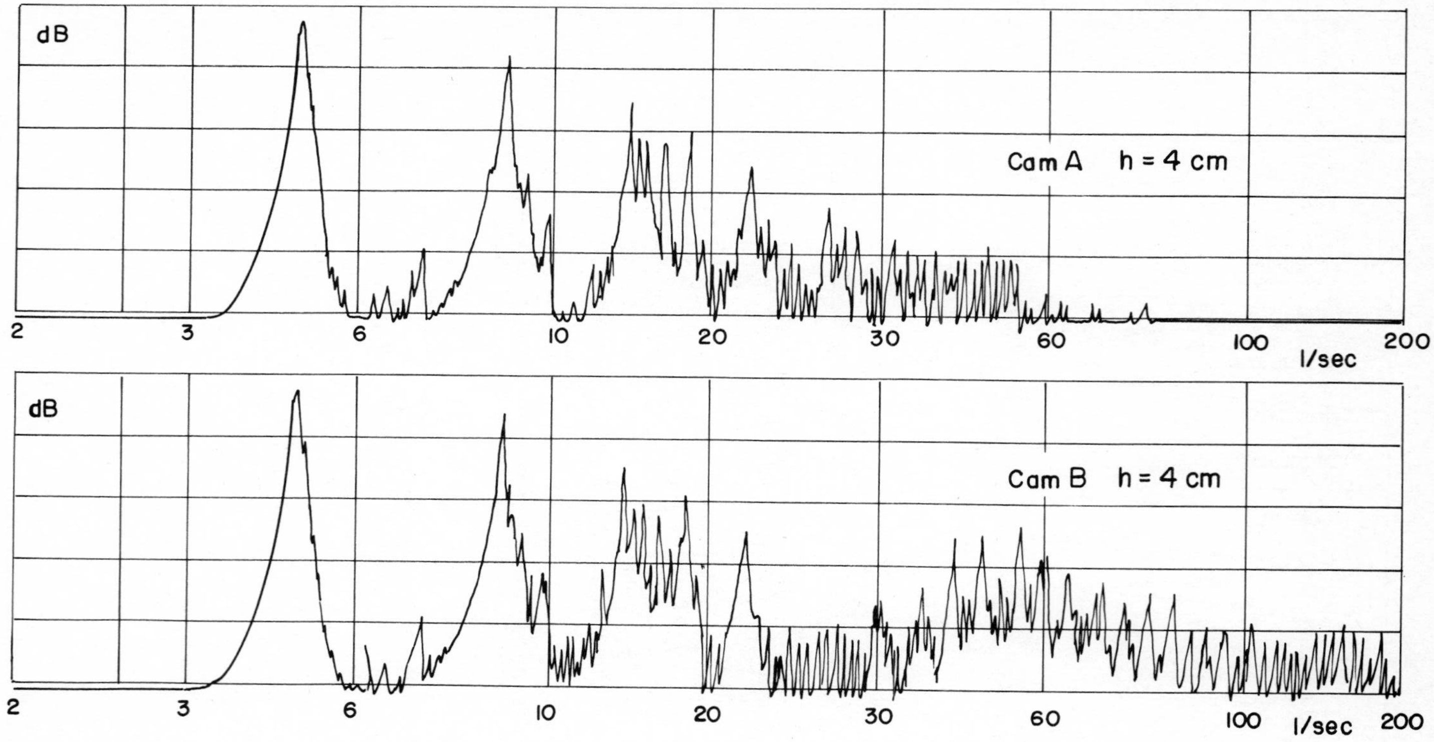

Fig. 64. a) The acceleration spectrum of the motion of the follower vs. frequency for h = 4 cm.

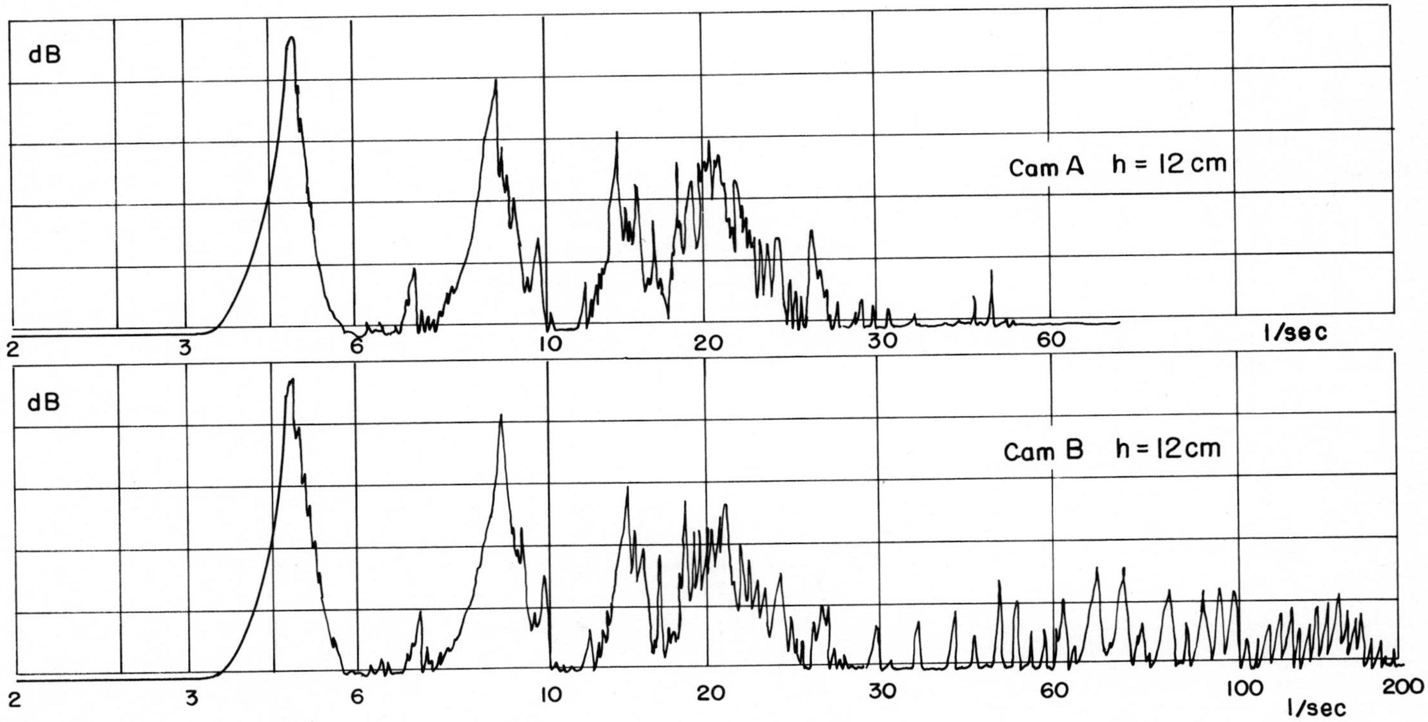

Fig. 64. b) The acceleration spectrum of the motion of the follower vs. frequency for h = 12cm.

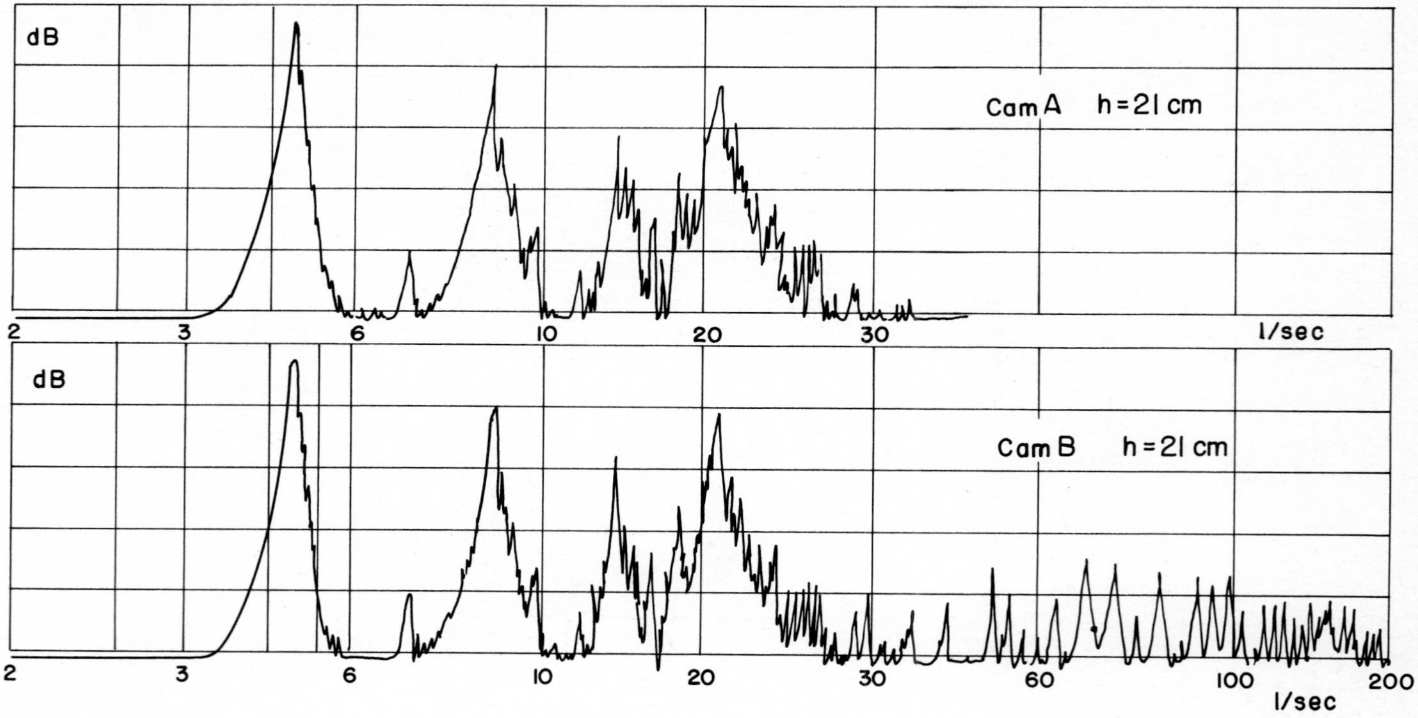

Fig. 64. c) The acceleration spectrum of the motion of the follower vs. frequency for h = 21 cm.

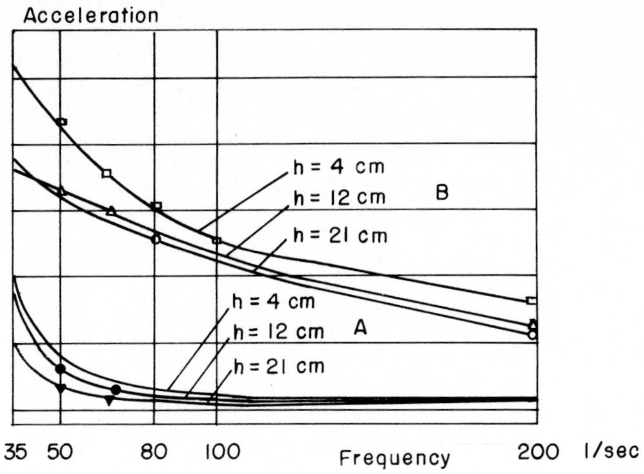

Fig. 65. Comparison of the RMSV of the follower's acceleration for different cams and h values.

Conclusions

1. The dynamic and kinematic properties of cam mechanisms can be improved by choosing a more suitable structure for the follower and more suitable values of the mechanism parameters, both dynamic and kinematic.
2. It is possible to decrease the influence of cam profile errors on the accuracy of the follower motion by means of dynamic damping.
3. For each camshaft velocity there is an optimal combination of parameters which provides the minimum of nondesired deviations of the follower motion.
4. It is possible to change a particular parameter, either manually of automatically, in order to provide more-or-less optimal actuation of the cam mechanism over a wide range of camshaft velocities.

7. UNIFORMITY OF ROTATION OF THE CAMSHAFT

Let us suppose that the profile of the cam under consideration is perfect, which means $\rho^* = \rho$ and $\Delta\rho = 0$. The camshaft rotates with a speed ω such that

$$\omega = \bar{\omega} + \mathring{\omega} \qquad (III.7.1)$$

The question we formulate at this stage is:
What are the motion errors of the follower, or what are the values of $\mathring{V}$, $\mathring{W}$ and $\mathring{s}$ when the value of $\mathring{\omega}$ is known and the law of motion of the follower is given.

From equation (III.3.6) we have:

$$V = \bar{V} + \mathring{V} = \frac{ds}{d\phi}\frac{d\phi}{dt} = \frac{ds}{d\phi}(\bar{\omega} + \mathring{\omega}) \qquad (III.7.2)$$

where V - the real velocity of the follower

$\bar{V}$ - the expectation (or ideal, calculated value of the velocity).

The average value of the rotation speed $\bar{\omega}$ includes the ideal speed ω and the constant systematic error.

From equation (III.7.2) we define:

$$\bar{V} = \frac{ds}{d\phi}\bar{\omega} \quad \text{which gives} \quad \frac{ds}{d\phi} = \frac{\bar{V}}{\bar{\omega}} \tag{III.7.3}$$

and $\overset{\circ}{V} = \frac{ds}{d\phi}\overset{\circ}{\omega}$ or, taking equation (III.7.3) into account,

$$\overset{\circ}{V} = \frac{\bar{V}}{\bar{\omega}}\overset{\circ}{\omega} \tag{III.7.4}$$

where $\bar{V}$ is a variable value and $\bar{\omega}$ is constant.

Denoting $\overset{\circ}{\varepsilon} = \frac{d\overset{\circ}{\omega}}{dt}$

we obtain the acceleration of the follower by differentiating equation (III.7.1) as follows:

$$W = \bar{W} + \overset{\circ}{W} = \frac{dV}{dt} = \frac{d^2s}{d\phi^2}(\bar{\omega} + \overset{\circ}{\omega})^2 + \frac{ds}{d\phi}\overset{\circ}{\varepsilon} \tag{III.7.5}$$

where W - the real acceleration of the follower

$\bar{W}$ - the expectation (the ideal, calculated value of the acceleration).

Thus,

$$\bar{W} = \frac{d^2s}{d\phi^2}\bar{\omega}^2 \quad \text{or} \quad \frac{d^2s}{d\phi^2} = \frac{\bar{W}}{\bar{\omega}^2} \tag{III.7.6}$$

and

$$\overset{\circ}{W} = 2\frac{d^2s}{d\phi^2}\bar{\omega}\overset{\circ}{\omega} + \frac{d^2s}{d\phi^2}\overset{\circ}{\omega}^2 + \frac{ds}{d\phi}\overset{\circ}{\varepsilon} \tag{III.7.7}$$

Neglecting the members of the second order of infinitesimality and simplifying equation (III.7.7) by using equation (III.7.6), we obtain

$$\overset{\circ}{W} \simeq 2\frac{\bar{W}}{\bar{\omega}}\overset{\circ}{\omega} + \frac{\bar{V}}{\bar{\omega}}\overset{\circ}{\varepsilon} \tag{III.7.8}$$

At this point, we have obtained formulas for the relationship between the errors of the camshaft motion and those of the cam follower. If the functions $\overset{\circ}{\omega}(t)$ and $\overset{\circ}{\varepsilon}(t)$ are known, they can be substituted in expressions (III.7.4) and

(III.7.8), and the motion errors $\mathring{V}(t)$ and $\mathring{W}(t)$ can be calculated. Since the functions $\mathring{\omega}(t)$ and $\mathring{\varepsilon}(t)$ are usually of a strictly probabilistic nature, we feel the probabilistic approach to be very useful in this case. We will consider $\mathring{\omega}$ and $\mathring{\varepsilon}$ to be random functions. Indeed, these functions or motion errors are caused by a number of factors acting in a drive transmission, such as the deviations in the pitches on gear wheels, changes in loads acting on the shaft and transmission, deviations in the electric network (frequency, voltage), and effects of elasticity of the drive elements. These factors are in practice independent of one another. Thus the influence of each factor taken separately is modest, but together they cause a typically random effect with an approximately normal distribution low.

The random functions $\mathring{\omega}$ and $\mathring{\varepsilon}$ are stationary when the mechanism is considered acting with the average speed which has become settled after the transient processes are finished. To describe the random function $\mathring{\omega}$ we need to know its correlation function $K_\omega(\tau)$. Then, as we know [see section I.31], the random function $\mathring{\varepsilon}$ is described by a correlation function $K_\varepsilon(\tau)$ which is calculated as follows:

$$K_\varepsilon(\tau) = -\frac{d^2K_\omega(\tau)}{d\tau^2} \quad \text{and} \quad \sigma_\varepsilon^2 = K_\varepsilon(0)$$

The form of the approximation expression that we choose for the correlation function must be such that it can be differentiated. For instance, for

$$K_\omega = \sigma_\omega^2 \exp[-\alpha^2\tau^2]$$

we have (III.7.9)

$$\sigma_\varepsilon^2 = 2\sigma_\omega^2\alpha^2$$

Taking expression (III.7.9) into account, we obtain from equation (III.7.4) and (III.7.8), respectively:

$$\sigma_V^2 = (\bar{V}/\bar{\omega})^2\sigma_\omega^2 \qquad \text{(III.7.10)}$$

and

$$\sigma_W^2 = 4(\bar{W}/\bar{\omega})^2\sigma_\omega^2 + 2\alpha^2(\bar{V}/\bar{\omega})^2\sigma_\omega^2 \qquad \text{(III.7.11)}$$

Obviously, using the "±3σ low", we can determine the tolerances of the follower's speed and accelerations caused by the uniformity of the speed of the camshaft in the form:

$$T_V \simeq 6\sigma_V \quad \text{and} \quad T_W \simeq 6\sigma_W \qquad \text{(III.7.12)}$$

We now have to determine the deviations of the displacement of the follower s caused by $\mathring{\omega}$. In accordance with the definition:

$$s = \bar{s} + \mathring{s}$$

and

$$s = \int_0^t V dt = \int_0^t \bar{V} dt + \int_0^t \mathring{V} dt$$

By applying equation (III.7.4), we obtain for $\bar{s}$ and $\mathring{s}$:

$$\bar{s} = \int_0^t \bar{V} dt \qquad \text{(III.7.13)}$$

and

$$\mathring{s} = \frac{1}{\bar{\omega}} \int_0^t \bar{V}\mathring{\omega} dt \qquad \text{(III.7.14)}$$

Sometimes to facilitate the integration of expression (III.7.14) it is possible to simplify the equation by taking into account the fact that $\mathring{\omega}$ is usually relatively small in comparison with $\bar{\omega}$, i.e.:

$$\mathring{\omega} << \bar{\omega} \qquad \text{(III.7.15)}$$

on this assumption, we obtain from equation (III.7.3):

$$\mathring{s} \simeq \frac{\bar{V}}{\bar{\omega}} \mathring{\phi}$$

and because

$$\mathring{\phi} = \int_0^t \mathring{\omega} dt \qquad \text{(III.7.16)}$$

we obtain

$$\mathring{s} \simeq \frac{\bar{V}}{\bar{\omega}} \int_0^t \mathring{\omega} dt \qquad \text{(III.7.17)}$$

This expression can be more conveniently manipulated than equation (III.7.14).

When the correlation function of the random function $\mathring{\omega}$ is known and its analytical approximation K_ω is given, we can calculate the correlation function K_s of the random function $\mathring{s}$ in accordance with (I.30) in the following manner:

$$K_s = (\bar{V}/\bar{\omega})^2 \int_0^t \int K_\omega dt dt'$$

We have now reached a suitable stage to show the effects of the nonuniformity of the rotation of a camshaft by deterministic methods. Such effects are typical for mechanisms working in nonstationary regimes, for instance, auxiliary control shafts in automatic machines. The rotation of such shafts is interrupted during each cycle; this entails acceleration and deceleration of the movement of the cams driven by the shaft and thus nonuniformity of the cam's rotation.

Let us deal here with two possible approaches to the problem of nonuniformity of the camshaft rotation:

(1) Definition of the movement of the follower driven by a given nonuniformely rotating cam when the cam profile has been designed to provide a certain law of motion by means of uniform cam rotation;

(2) Design of the cam profile in such a way as to compensate for the nonuniform rotation of the camshaft to provide the desired motion of the follower.

Let us denote:

ω = var. - the nonuniform angular velocity of the cam shaft;

ω_o = const. - the uniform angular velocity of the cam shaft;

s_o = the law of motion of the follower driven by a cam rotating with velocity ω_o;

s = the law of motion of the follower driven by a cam rotating with velocity ω;

V_o and W_o = the speed and acceleration respectively of a follower driven by the motion law s_o;

V and W = the speed and acceleration respectively, of a follower driven by the motion law s;

ϕ = the angle of rotation of the cam;

t = time;

t_o = initial moment;

then, in analogy with expression (III.7.2), we obtain the dependence:

$$V = \frac{ds_o}{d\phi}\omega \tag{III.7.18}$$

and for V_o

$$V_o = \frac{ds_o}{d\phi}\omega_o \tag{III.7.19}$$

from which it follows that

$$V = \frac{V_o}{\omega_o}\omega \tag{III.7.20}$$

Then

$$s = \frac{1}{\omega_o}\int_{t_o}^{t} V_o \omega dt \tag{III.7.21}$$

Here, the simplification made in equation (III.7.17) is not applicable, because of the absence of condition (III.7.15). Obviously, for acceleration we have

$$W = W_o \frac{\omega}{\omega_o} + \frac{V_o}{\omega_o}\frac{d\omega}{dt} \tag{III.7.22}$$

Expressions (III.7.20), (III.7.21) and (III.7.22) answer the first problem formulated above. The second problem can be answered by inversion of expression (III.7.20).

Thus:

$$V_o = \frac{V}{\omega}\omega_o \tag{III.7.23}$$

then

$$s_o = \omega_o \int_{t_o}^{t} \frac{V}{\omega} dt \tag{III.7.24}$$

and

$$W_o = \frac{W}{\omega}\omega_o - \frac{V\varepsilon}{\omega^2}\omega_o \tag{III.7.25}$$

Let us now consider the example of an indexing table driven by a cam which is provided with an Archimedes profile and is actuated every cycle. Often, the transient acceleration process of the cam is so short that it does not reach a constant speed of rotation. The nonuniform speed of rotation ω can be approximated in the form:

$$\omega = \omega_o(1 - e^{-at}) \qquad \text{where } a = \text{const.} \tag{III.7.26}$$

Now let us try to define the law of motion of the follower, in this case the table. If the cam were to rotate with a constant speed ω_o for the given profile we would have:

$$s_o = B\omega_o t \qquad V_o = B\omega_o \qquad \text{and} \qquad W_o = 0 \qquad \text{where} \quad B = \text{const.}$$

By applying expressions (III.7.20), (III.7.21) and (III.7.22) and assuming that the profile begins to move the follower at time t_o, we obtain:

$$s = B\omega_o(t - t_o + \frac{1}{a}[e^{-at} - e^{-at_o}])$$

$$V = B\omega_o(1 - e^{-at}) \tag{III.7.27}$$

$$A = B\omega_o ae^{-at}$$

Now to calculate the motion law s_o so as to provide constant speed for the table, i.e. V = const., for

$$s = B\omega_o t; \quad V = B\omega_o; \quad W = 0 \quad \text{and } \omega = \omega_o(1 - e^{-at})$$

we obtain from equations (III.7.23), (III.7.27) and (III.7.25):

$$s_o = \frac{B\omega_o}{a} [t - t_o + \ln \frac{1 - e^{-at}}{1 - a^{-at_o}}]$$

$$V_o = \frac{B\omega_o}{a} [t + \frac{ae^{-at}}{(1 - e^{-at_o})(1 - e^{-at})}]$$

$$W_o = B\omega_o a \frac{e^{-at} - 2e^{-2at}}{(1 - e^{-at_o})(1 - a^{-at})^2}$$

8. PROBABILISTIC DESCRIPTION OF A ROLLING FOLLOWER

In the problems discussed above we considered methods of taking into account cam profile errors and transforming them into the errors of the motion of the follower. We almost neglected the fact that there is an additional factor which effects the transmission of the motion from the profile to the follower, as will be discussed below.

Let us consider the process of the contact between a roller and the cam profile. The layout of this process is shown in Fig. 66. When the roller rolls

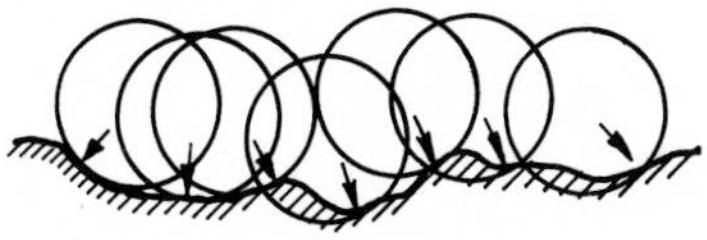

Fig. 66. Layout of the process of a roller contact with a non-accurate cam profile.

on the convex parts of the microprofile caused by errors, there is no additional error. Similarly, when it rolls on the concave parts where the radius of the roller R is smaller than the microprofile curvature radius r, i.e. R > r, there is also no problem. However, when this condition changes such that

$$R \leqslant r \tag{III.8.1}$$

the rolling is not longer smooth. We will set out to investigate this phenomenon in this section. For this purpose we will try to find the probability P (r < R) for given probabilistic characteristics of the profile deviations. Let us consider the profile of the cam $\rho(\psi)$ as the sum:

$$\rho = \bar{\rho} + \mathring{\rho}$$

Let us assume the deviations of the profile to be conjugate arcs as is shown in Fig. 67 for a section of the profile. From the Figure, it follows that:

$$\overline{CB} = \mathring{\rho}; \quad \overline{OC} = r - \mathring{\rho} \qquad \text{(III.8.2)}$$

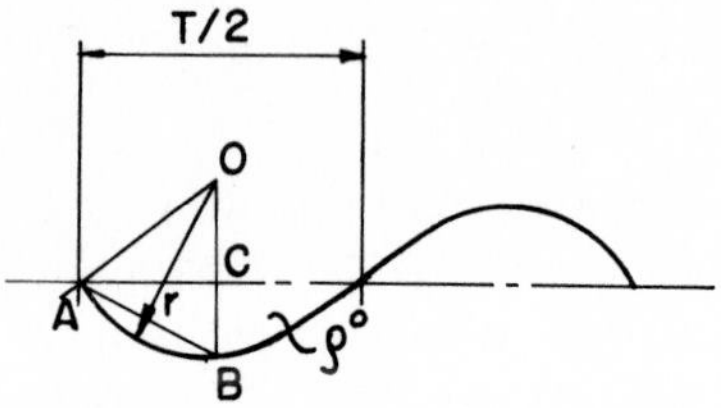

Fig. 67. Assumed arced deviations of the profile.

For the triangle ACO we can state:

$$\overline{OC}^2 = r^2 - (T/4)^2 \qquad \text{(III.8.3)}$$

Substituting expression (III.8.2) into equation (III.8.2), we obtain:

$$r^2 - (T/4)^2 = (r - \mathring{\rho})^2$$

or

$$\mathring{\rho}^2 - 2r\mathring{\rho} + \frac{T^2}{16} = 0$$

Neglecting the second order infinitesimality, we can rewrite this expression as:

$$r \simeq \frac{T^2}{32\mathring{\rho}} \qquad \text{(III.8.4)}$$

Let us denote $T^2 = \theta$ then instead of equation (III.8.4), we obtain

$$r \simeq \frac{\theta}{32\mathring{\rho}} \qquad \text{(III.8.5)}$$

It is now possible to find the distribution function F_r [see (I.20.4] of the curvature radii of the cam profile errors:

$$F_r = \int_D\int f(\mathring{\rho},\theta)\,d\mathring{\rho}\,d\theta \qquad \text{(III.8.6)}$$

where D - the integration domain which is defined by expression (III.8.5);

f - density distribution law of the two random variables $\mathring{\rho}$ and θ.

The next step is the calculation of the probability P (R > r) that the roller of the follower will meet a concave error with a curvature greater than its own:

$$P(R > r) \;=\; F_r(r = R) \qquad \text{(III.8.7)}$$

Since the measurement and definition of the density distribution of a two-variable system is a cumbersome task, we make the rough assumption that the random variables $\mathring{\rho}$ and θ are independent, being described by density distributions f_ρ and f_θ, respectively.

Thus:

$$f(\mathring{\rho},\theta) = f_\rho \cdot f_\theta \qquad \text{(III.8.8)}$$

Then, instead of expression (III.8.6) we can write:

$$F_r = \int_{-\infty}^{\infty}\int_{0}^{32^\circ r} f_\rho \cdot f_\theta \, d\theta \, d\mathring{\rho} \qquad \text{(III.8.9)}$$

Suppose the random variable $\mathring{\rho}$ has a normal distribution and is characterized by the density distribution:

$$f_\rho \simeq \frac{1}{\sigma_\rho\sqrt{2\pi}} \exp[-\mathring{\rho}^2/2\sigma_\rho^2] \qquad \text{(III.8.10)}$$

In turn, we can determine the density distribution f_θ in, say, the following manner. The recording shown in Fig. 68 is the cam profile measurement of an

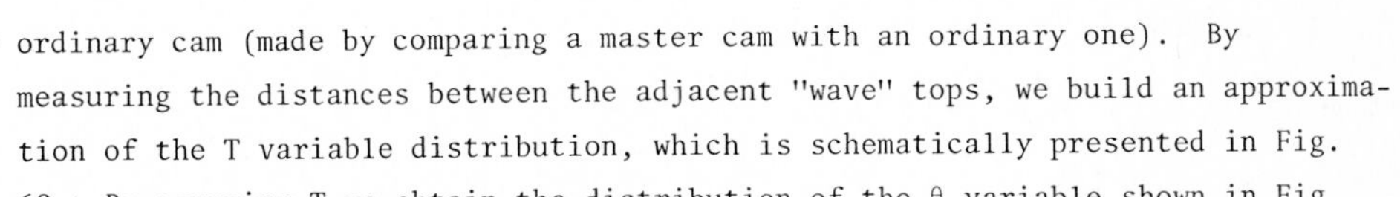

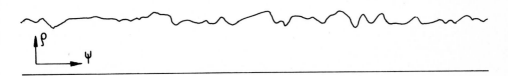

Fig. 68. An example of recorded cam profile errors.

ordinary cam (made by comparing a master cam with an ordinary one). By measuring the distances between the adjacent "wave" tops, we build an approximation of the T variable distribution, which is schematically presented in Fig. 69. By squaring T we obtain the distribution of the θ variable shown in Fig. 70. This figure shows that a uniform density distribution is a satisfactory

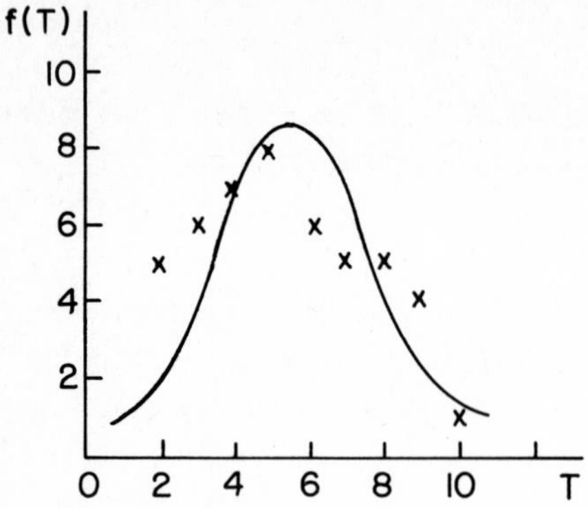

Fig. 69. Distribution law of the T values for the profile recorded in Fig. 68.

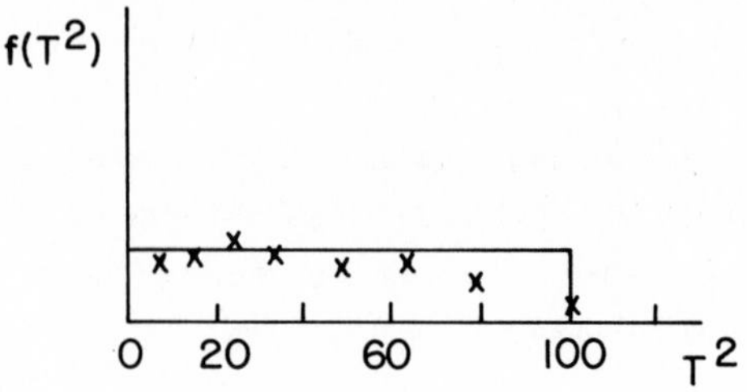

Fig. 70. Distribution law of T^2 values.

approximation for the θ variable. Thus, for f_θ we have:

$$f_\theta \simeq \frac{1}{\theta_1 - \theta_o} \tag{III.8.11}$$

where

θ_o and θ_1 - interval limits.

We can now rewrite expression (III.8.8):

$$F_r \simeq \frac{1}{\sigma_\rho \sqrt{2\pi}\,(\theta_1 - \theta_o)} \int_{-\infty}^{\infty} \int_{o}^{32\mathring{\rho} r} \exp[-\mathring{\rho}^2/2\sigma_\rho^2]\, d\theta\, d\mathring{\rho} \tag{III.8.12}$$

After the first integration with respect to θ and changing the lower limit of ρ we obtain:

$$F_r \simeq \frac{64r}{\sqrt{2\pi}\,\sigma_\rho (\theta_1 - \theta_o)} \int_{o}^{\infty} \mathring{\rho} \exp[-\mathring{\rho}^2/2\sigma_\rho^2]\, d\mathring{\rho} \tag{III.8.13}$$

Thus:

$$F_r \simeq \frac{128r\,\sigma_\rho}{\sqrt{2\pi}\,(\theta_1 - \theta_o)} \; ; \quad 0 < r \lesssim \frac{2\pi(\theta_1 - \theta_o)}{128\,\sigma_\rho} \tag{III.8.14}$$

and

$$P(r < R) = \frac{128\sigma_\rho R}{\sqrt{2\pi}\,(\theta_1 - \theta_o)} \tag{III.8.15}$$

9. SOME IDEAS FOR MEASURING CAM PROFILE ERRORS

The usual way of calculating cam profile errors is by measuring the radii of the profile as a function of the angle. In practice, this entails the rotation of the cam for an angular step, say every 2°, by means of a special device and the measurement at each step of the value of the radii. By comparing these measurements with the calculated values, we obtain the errors of the profile. Another possibility is the comparison of the measured cam profile with that of a master cam which is manufactured with high degrees of accuracy. Fig. 71 shows the layout of a mechanical device which can be used for this purpose.

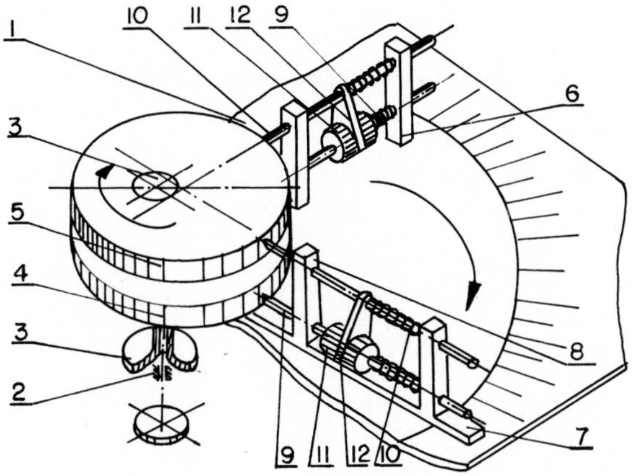

Fig. 71. Layout of a correlometer.

This device also facilitates the measurement of the information necessary to perform calculation of the correlation function. The device consists of a base 1 on which bearings 2 for the shaft 3 are installed. Cam 4, the cam whose profile errors are to be measured, and cam 5 the master cam, are fastened to shaft 3. A pair of supports 6 are attached to the base 1. Another pair of supports 8 are fastened to a lathe 7 which is arranged such that it can rotate around the shaft 3. Probes 9 and 10 are fitted to supports 6 and 8, respectively. The bodies 11 of the inductive displacement sensors are fastened to probe 9 and the armatures 12 of these sensors are attached to probe 10. Thus, each sensor measures the error or the difference between the master cam and the "measured" one. Rotating the movable sensor for specific angles ϕ relative to the immovable sensor, we obtain simultaneously the errors for two sections separated by an angle ϕ. Obviously, this information can be used for calculation of the correlation function. This measuring method has one inherent drawback, namely, the necessity for a master cam: the production of a master cam is expensive and may sometimes entail a degree of accuracy exceeding that possible in practice.

For this reason, we present an alternative method for measuring cam profile errors: the method is based on the comparison of two ordinary cams.

Let us denote:

ρ_1' - the radius of the first cam in the first position by probe 9;

ρ_1'' - radius of the second cam in the first position measured by probe 10;

ρ_2' - the radius of the first cam in the second position measured by the probe 9 on the movable lathe 7;

ρ_2'' - radius of the second cam in the second position measured by the probe 10 on the movable lathe 7.

Thus, the sensor on the immovable supports 6 measures $(\rho_1' - \rho_1'')$ and the movable sensor measures $(\rho_2' - \rho_2'')$. Remembering, that

$$\rho^* = \rho + \bar{\rho} + \mathring{\rho} \qquad \text{(see III.4.1)}$$

we obtain

$$r_1 = \rho_1^{*\prime} - \rho_1^{*\prime\prime} = \rho_1' + \bar{\rho}_1' + \mathring{\rho}_1' - \rho_1'' - \bar{\rho}_1'' - \mathring{\rho}_1'' = \bar{\rho}_1' - \mathring{\rho}_1'' \qquad \text{(III.9.1)}$$

and

$$r_2 = \rho_2^{*\prime} - \rho_2^{*\prime\prime} = \rho_2' + \bar{\rho}_2' + \mathring{\rho}_2' - \rho_2'' - \bar{\rho}_2'' - \mathring{\rho}_2'' = \bar{\rho}_2' - \mathring{\rho}_2''$$

Expressions (III.9.1) are derived from the obvious equalities:

$$\rho_1' - \rho_1'' = 0; \quad \rho_2' - \rho_2'' = 0 \qquad \text{(III.9.2)}$$

For the case in which the two cams originate from the same batch, we have

$$\bar{\rho}_1' - \bar{\rho}_1'' = 0; \quad \bar{\rho}_2' - \bar{\rho}_2'' = 0. \qquad \text{(III.9.3)}$$

Using equations (III.9.1), we can express the correlation function K_m linking the two random values r_1 and r_2 in the following way:

$$K_m = \frac{1}{\phi}\int_0^{\phi} r_1 r_2 d\phi = \frac{1}{\phi}\int_0^{\phi} (\mathring{\rho}_1' - \mathring{\rho}_1'')(\mathring{\rho}_2' - \mathring{\rho}_2'')d\phi =$$

$$\text{(III.9.4)}$$

$$= \frac{1}{\phi}\{ \int_0^{\phi} \mathring{\rho}_1' \mathring{\rho}_2' d\phi - \int_0^{\phi} \mathring{\rho}_1' \mathring{\rho}_2'' d - \int_0^{\phi} \mathring{\rho}_1'' \mathring{\rho}_2' d\phi + \int_0^{\phi} \mathring{\rho}_1'' \mathring{\rho}_2'' d\phi = K_1 + K_2 - K_{12} - K_{21}$$

where

K_1 - auto-correlation function of the first cam;

K_2 - auto-correlation function of the second cam;

K_{21} and K_{12} - cross-correlation functions of the two profiles.

Since the two profiles are independent random functions, the cross-correlation equals zero, i.e.:

$$K_{12} = K_{21} = 0 \qquad \text{(III.9.5)}$$

As a result, from equation (III.9.4) we obtain:

$$K_m = (K_1 + K_2) \qquad \text{(III.9.6)}$$

Because the profiles under consideration are those of two cams produced in the same batch:

$$K_1 = K_2 = K \qquad \text{(III.9.7)}$$

Thus

$$K_m = 2K \qquad \text{(III.9.8)}$$

We have thus obtained the desired result by measuring the profiles without comparison with a pattern which requires a high degree of manufacturing accuracy for a master cam. Reliable results can be obtained by measuring in the described manner a number of cam pairs and calculating the average K_m value.

The device described above supplies information in an electrical form as voltages proportional to the random variables r_1 and r_2. There is no difficulty in digitizing this information and feeding it into a computer for correlation computation. An alternative, a perhaps preferable, method makes use of an analog correlator: a dynamometer wattmeter can be used for this purpose. This device consists of an immovable coil and a rotating coil driving the pointer. The torque which actuates the pointer is defined as:

$$M = c_m r_1 \cdot r_2 \qquad \text{(III.9.9)}$$

where c_m - a proportionality coefficient.

Because of the inertia of the pointer's mass, its rotation angle is calculated as:

$$\theta = \frac{c_\theta}{T} \int_0^T M(t)dt \qquad \text{(III.9.10)}$$

where T - time;

c_θ - coefficient of proportionality.

Substituting equation (III.9.9) into equation (III.9.10), we obtain

$$\theta = \frac{c_m c_\theta}{T} \int_0^T r_1 r_2 dt \qquad \text{(III.9.11)}$$

If the cams rotate with a constant angular speed, ω = const, we can write:

$$t = \frac{\phi}{\omega} \quad \text{and} \quad T = \frac{\phi}{\omega}$$

Then, from equation (III.9.11), we have:

$$\theta = K(\phi) = \frac{c_m c_\theta}{\omega} \int_0^t r_1 r_2 d\phi \qquad \text{(III.9.12)}$$

Thus, the deviation of the pointer of this correlator is proportional to the correlation function $K(\phi)$ of the profile.

To illustrate our proposed method, we prepared three groups of cam with equivalent profiles but with different profile finishing techniques as described below. Each profile is circular disk of diameter 100 mm whose axis is located 10 mm from its geometric center.

The first group of steel cams, designated 1 and 2 were hardened to RC = 52-55 and polished by lapping to a surface roughness corresponding to N6 with Ra (arithmetic mean deviation of the surface microwaves) about 0.8-1 μm. The second group of steel cams, designated 3, 4 and 5 were hardened to RC = 50-52 and finished by grinding to a surface roughness corresponding to N9 with Ra about 6-10 μm. The third group of raw steel cams, designated 6, 7 and 8, were milled to a surface roughness corresponding to N11 with Ra = 20-25 μm. In Fig. 72 we show the normalized correlation function for cams 3, 4 and 5 which can be

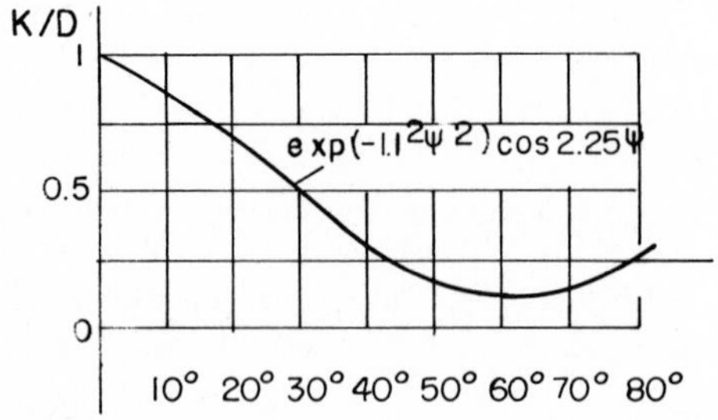

Fig. 72. Correlation function of grinded cam profile errors.

approximated by the analytical expression:

$$\exp[-1.1^2\psi^2]\cos 2.25 \tag{III.9.13}$$

Fig. 73 shows the normalized correlation function for cams 6, 7 and 8 which can be approximated by the analytical expression:

$$\exp[-5.46^2\psi^2] \tag{III.9.14}$$

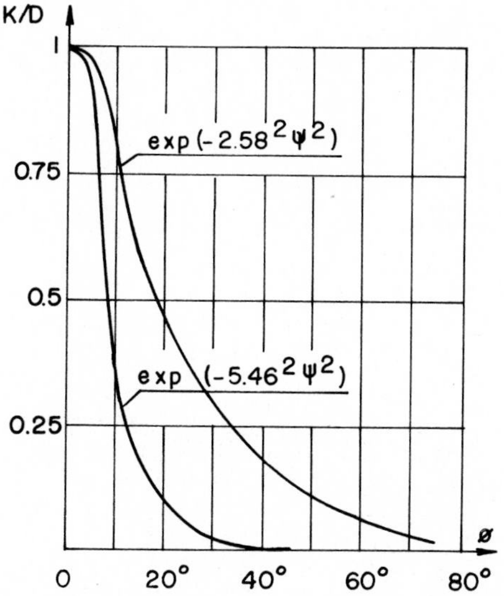

Fig. 73. Correlation function of milled and manually filed cam profile errors.

In this figure we also show the normalized correlation function of three cams manufactured manually with a low degree of accuracy (Ra = 100-150 μm). The analytical approximation is given by

$$\exp[-2.58^2\psi^2] \tag{III.9.15}$$

SELECTED BIBLIOGRAPHY

1. Tesar, D. and Matthew, G.K., The Dynamic Synthesis, Analysis and Design of Modeled Cam Systems, Gainesville, Mechanical Engineering University of Florida, 1973.

2. Rothbart, H.A., Cams, New York, John Wiley & Sons Inc., 1956.

CHAPTER IV

GEAR TRANSMISSIONS

1. MAIN DEFINITIONS

The importance of the gear drive in machines and apparatuses cannot be sufficiently stressed. In the design and manufacture of gear wheels the accuracy of the gear trains is one of the main problems. Solutions thus have to be found for both the dynamic and the kinematic behavior of gear drives.

The accuracy of the gear wheel is dependent on:

(a) errors in the profile of the teeth

(b) errors in the pitch of the teeth

(c) the eccentricity of the wheel.

Of course, in a working gear drive, there are many other sources of error, such as, teeth deflections, profile wear, dirt in the train and deflection of the shafts. To estimate the accuracy, we have first to define the criteria for the accuracy and then to have at our disposal the means for measuring them; see for example, ref. 1-5.

A typical picture of gear-tooth errors generated in a transmission is shown in Fig. 74. This figure is adapted from AGMA, Gear Handbook Volume 1 (AGMA

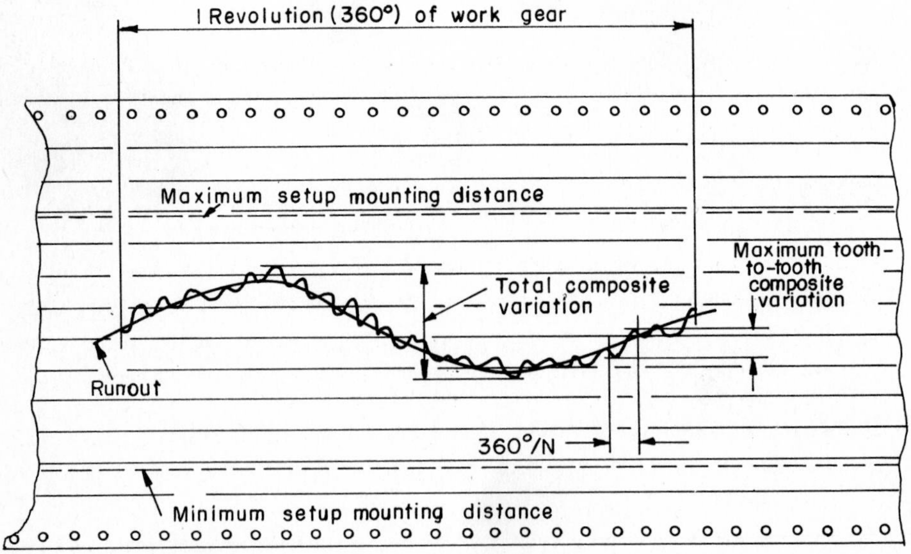

Fig. 74. Gear-tooth errors generated in a transmission.

380.03 Jan. 1981). During one revolution of the work, the eccentricity of the gear wheel is the cause of the big sin-like wave on which the small deviations are located. The small deviations are caused by the engagement of the teeth. In addition, errors in the profiles of the teeth are generally a result of the level of manufacturing accuracy and, especially, of wear and tear. A good example of profile deviations of gear teeth may be found in the paper of Masao [6].

This chapter deals with a special statistical approach to the field of gear-wheel accuracy. The approach is based on two main premises:

(1) Because of the random character of the errors, we can use a stochastic approach for defining the criteria of accuracy and for calculating the influence of the errors on the drive's kinematic and dynamic behavior;

(2) To apply the stochastic approach, we must supply the relevant information on methods of measuring the errors and processing the data.

Now, let us explain the above-mentioned kinematic and dynamic accuracy of the gear drive with the aid of the example shown in Fig. 75. In this figure we can

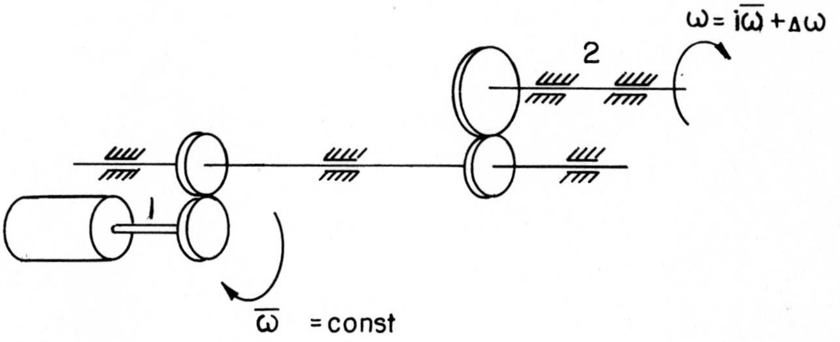

Fig. 75. Example of a gear-drive.

see an input motion source (an electric motor), which drives a shaft 1 with a constant rotation velocity $\bar{\omega}$. As a result of the above-described errors, the output shaft 2 rotates with a variable velocity ω so that we can write:

$$\omega = i\bar{\omega} + \Delta\omega \qquad \text{(IV.1.1)}$$

where ω = const

i = ratio of the drive gearing

$\Delta\omega$ = the error of the velocity.

From this equation, the acceleration ε in this mechanism can be described by:

$$\varepsilon = \frac{d\Delta\omega}{dt} \tag{IV.1.2}$$

And the dependence between the rotating angles of the input shaft 1 and the output shaft 2 can be expressed in the following form:

$$\phi = i\bar{\phi} + \Delta\phi \tag{IV.1.3}$$

where $\bar{\phi}$ - is the initial rotating angle of the driving gear wheel, when $\bar{\phi} = \bar{\omega}t$

$\Delta\phi$ - is the angular error of the driven wheel resulting from nonaccurate manufacturing and other above-mentioned reasons.

When kinematic accuracy is being discussed, expressions (IV.1.2) and (IV.1.3) are used. The errors $\Delta\phi$ and velocity deviations $\Delta\omega$ are responsible for decreasing the quality of the drive. Angular errors are of particular importance in the gear mechanisms used in watches, tuning systems, etc.

When investigating the problem of dynamic accuracy, the stiffnesses of the teeth, shafts and keys as well as the masses of the rotating parts and damping factors have to be considered. In gearing, dynamic loads are of the same order of magnitude as the static loads. The dynamic approach is particularly useful for analyzing resonance phenomena in gear drives. It is these dynamic effects that we will consider in the following paragraphs.

In the first stage of the investigation, let us consider a gear train with basic radii R_1 and R_2. Because of the errors, the real values of the radii can be expressed as

$$\begin{aligned} R_1 &= \bar{R}_1 + \Delta R_1 \\ R_2 &= \bar{R}_2 + \Delta R_2 \end{aligned} \tag{IV.1.4}$$

where the bar denotes the ideal theoretical value and Δ, the errors. The R errors are caused by eccentricity of wheel (relative to its central opening), the eccentricity of the shaft on which this opening is mounted and the quality of assembling. To obtain the equations (IV.1.4) we reasoned as follows. The errors in the motion of the driven wheel result from the fact that metching teeth profile points do not meet at ideal locations irrespective of the sources of the deviations. Each deviation, whatever the origin, can be considered to result from a deviation of the basic radius which causes the deviation of the tooth profile involute which, in turn, brings the profiles into nonaccurate interaction.

Since it is difficult to measure ΔR and, moreover, since this parameter is not the only one which influences errors in the gear ratio, we require more potent criteria for defining the accuracy. We therefore suggest using (and later show how to measure) the statistical characteristics of the ratio errors Δi for describing the gear accuracy directly.

Let us denote $i = \bar{i} + \Delta i$, where $i = R_1/R_2$, then

$$\Delta i = \frac{R_1}{R_2} - \frac{\bar{R}_1}{\bar{R}_2} = \frac{\bar{R}_1 + \Delta R_1}{\bar{R}_2 + \Delta R_2} - \frac{\bar{R}_1}{\bar{R}_2} \qquad (IV.1.5)$$

After simplifying equation (IV.1.5) and neglecting $\Delta R_1 \Delta R_2$ (second order of infinitesimality) we obtain:

$$\Delta i \simeq \bar{i}\left(\frac{\Delta R_1}{\bar{R}_1} - \frac{\Delta R_2}{\bar{R}_2} \right) \qquad (IV.1.6)$$

Let us denote the root mean square value (RMSV) of the ratio $\Delta R/R$ as D_r. Then, from equation (IV.1.6), we obtain:

$$D_i \simeq \bar{i}^2 (D_{r_1} + D_{r_2}) \qquad (IV.1.7)$$

Now, if we consider two equal wheels (from the same series)

$$\bar{i} = 1; \quad \bar{R}_1 = \bar{R}_2 = \bar{R}; \quad D_{r_1} = D_{r_2} = D_r \qquad (IV.1.8)$$

This gives

$$D_i = 2D_r \qquad (IV.1.9)$$

or, for a single wheel

$$D_i^* = D_r = D_i/2 \qquad (IV.1.10)$$

In section 3 of this chapter we will use the value D_i^* for describing the accuracy. Expressions (IV.1.7) - (IV.1.10) are of paramount importance in the development of a measurement technique.

From the condition of continuity of the engagement in the gear drive we obtain:

$$R_1\omega_1 = R_2\omega_2 \qquad (IV.1.11)$$

Substituting expressions (IV.1.4) and (IV.1.1) in equation (IV.1.11),we derive:

$$\bar{R}_1\bar{\omega}_1 + \Delta R_1\bar{\omega}_1 + \bar{R}_1\Delta\omega_1 + \Delta R_1\Delta\omega_1 =$$
$$= \bar{R}_2\bar{\omega}_2 + \Delta R_2\bar{\omega}_2 + \bar{R}_2\Delta\omega_2 + \Delta R_2\Delta\omega_2 \qquad (IV.1.12)$$

Neglecting $\Delta R_1\Delta\omega_1$ and $\Delta R_2\Delta\omega_2$ because of their second order of infinitesimality and remembering that

$$\bar{R}_1\bar{\omega}_1 = \bar{R}_2\bar{\omega}_2$$

We can simplify equation (IV.1.12) to:

$$\Delta\omega_2 = \frac{\Delta R_1\bar{\omega}_1 + \bar{R}_1\Delta\omega_1 - \Delta R_2\,\omega_2}{\bar{R}_2}$$

or (IV.1.13)

$$\Delta\omega_2 = \bar{\omega}_1\frac{\bar{R}_1}{\bar{R}_2}\left(\frac{\Delta R_1}{\bar{R}_1} - \frac{\Delta R_2}{\bar{R}_2}\right) + \frac{\bar{R}_1}{\bar{R}_2}\Delta\omega_1$$

which equals

$$\Delta\omega_2 = \bar{\omega}_1\bar{i}\left(\frac{\Delta R_1}{\bar{R}_1} - \frac{\Delta R_2}{\bar{R}_2}\right) + \bar{i}\Delta\omega_1 \qquad \text{(IV.1.14)}$$

Note: since expression (IV.1.13) is symmetrical with respect to ω_1 and ω_2, we can deduce this expression irrespective of which wheel is being driven and which wheel is driving.

To calculate the errors of the angular acceleration of the wheels and shafts caused by the deviations of the geometrical dimensions of wheels, we must differentiate formula (IV.1.14); thus:

$$\Delta\varepsilon_2 = \bar{\omega}_1\bar{i}[d(\Delta R_1/\bar{R}_1)/dt - d(\Delta R_2/\bar{R}_2)/dt] + \bar{i}\Delta\varepsilon_1 \qquad \text{(IV.1.15)}$$

By analogy, to find the errors of the rotation in accordance with equation (IV.1.3), we must integrate expression (IV.1.14):

$$\Delta\phi = \bar{\omega}_1\bar{i}\int_o^t\left(\frac{\Delta R_1}{\bar{R}_1} - \frac{\Delta R_2}{\bar{R}_2}\right)dt + \bar{i}\int_o^t\Delta\omega_1 dt \qquad \text{(IV.1.16)}$$

Of course, there is no sense in taking t bigger than one whole period t_p of the rotation of the slowest wheel, i.e.

$$0 < t \leq t_p$$

Let us now consider a number of specific cases

1. When the first wheel is made more accurately than the second and rotates with constant speed so that $\Delta\omega_1 \simeq 0$ which can be achieved by high inertial masses on its shaft, high power drive and constant load, then:

   $$\Delta\omega_2 = \bar{\omega}_1\bar{i}\,\Delta R_2/\bar{R}_2$$

   and

   $$\Delta\varepsilon_2 = \bar{\omega}_1\bar{i}\,d(\Delta R_2/\bar{R}_2)/dt$$

2. When the same wheel rotates with speed deviations $\Delta\omega_1$, then:

$$\Delta\omega_2 = \bar{\omega}_1 \bar{i}\ \Delta R_2/\bar{R}_2 + \Delta\omega_1 \bar{i}$$

and

$$\Delta\varepsilon_2 = \bar{\omega}_1 \bar{i}\ d(\Delta R_2/\bar{R}_2)/dt + \bar{i}\Delta\varepsilon_1$$

3. When first and second wheels are made with the same accuracy, but the rotation of the first is uniform, then:

$$\Delta\omega_2 = \bar{\omega}_1 \bar{i}\left(\frac{\Delta R_1}{\bar{R}_1} - \frac{\Delta R_2}{\bar{R}_2} \right)$$

and

$$\Delta\varepsilon_2 = \bar{\omega}_1 \bar{i}[d(\Delta R_1/\bar{R}_1)/dt - d(\Delta R_2/\bar{R}_2)/dt]$$

2. PROBABILISTIC APPROACH

By now it is clear that the only practical way of dealing with the formulas obtained above is the probabilistic approach. In applying this approach, we will make some assumptions.

(i) The errors of the wheels are of a stationary nature. This assumption is based on physical observations, although strictly speaking, the process of generating motion errors in a gear transmission is pseudostationary because of periodicity of the wheels' rotation. However, the average values of the errors are, of course, constant. Thus, the accumulated error per revolution obviously equals 0.

(ii) The correlation functions of the errors in the radii K_r and the rotation speed K_ω can be measured and approximated by certain analytical expressions, say those given below:

$$K_r \approx D_r e^{-\alpha_r^2 t^2}$$

and (IV.2.1)

$$K_\omega \approx D_\omega e^{-\alpha_\omega^2 t^2}$$

where $D_r = \sigma_r^2$ and $D_\omega = \sigma_\omega^2$ $\qquad r = \Delta R/R$

There are no restrictions on the choice of other approximations, should the experiment require it.

From (I.31) it follows that for the derivatives $\dot{r}$ and $\dot{\omega} = \varepsilon$:

$$D_{\dot{r}} \simeq 2\alpha_r^2 D_r \qquad \text{(IV.2.2)}$$

and

$$D_{\varepsilon} \simeq 2\alpha_{\omega}^2 D_{\omega}$$

where $D_{\dot{r}}$ - variance of $\dot{r} = d(\Delta R/R)/dt$ of the wheels;

D_{ε} - variance of the angular acceleration ε of the shaft rotation.

We can now formulate the expression for the errors of the angular speed of the driven shaft, on the basis of equation (IV.1.14), in the following form:

$$D_{\omega_2} = \bar{\omega}_1^2 \bar{i}^2 (D_{r_1} + D_{r_2}) + \bar{i}^2 D_{\omega_1} \qquad \text{(IV.2.3)}$$

By analogy, we obtain from equation (IV.1.15), the following expression for the variance in the acceleration:

$$D_{\varepsilon_2} = 2\bar{\omega}_1^2 \bar{i}^2 (\alpha_{r_1}^2 D_{r_1} + \alpha_{r_2}^2 D_{r_2}) + 2\bar{i}^2 \alpha_{\omega}^2 D_{\omega_1} \qquad \text{(IV.2.4)}$$

With regard to the rotation angles of the shafts, we offer the following consideration for the definition of the variance.

Let us denote:

D_{ϕ} - angular variance
m - modulus of the engagement
z - number of teeth
$\bar{\psi}$ - the ideal pitch angle, which equals the average angular pitch;
$\Delta\psi$ - angular pitch error;
then, obviously:

$$\frac{2\pi(\bar{R} + \Delta R)}{z} = \bar{\psi} + \Delta\psi \qquad \text{(IV.2.5)}$$

thus

$$\Delta\psi = \frac{2\pi\Delta R}{z} \qquad \text{(IV.2.6)}$$

Remembering that $R = \dfrac{mz}{2}$

we obtain $z = \dfrac{2R}{m}$

Substituting the latter expression into equation (IV.2.6) we obtain:

$$\Delta\psi = \pi m \Delta r \qquad \text{(IV.2.7)}$$

Then

$$D_{\psi} = \pi^2 m^2 D_r \tag{IV.2.8}$$

Let us consider the gear chain shown in Fig. 76. In this figure, the numbering of the wheels is begun from the driving shaft. Thus, in the transmission we have n wheels, n/2 engagements and n/2+1 shafts. It follows from

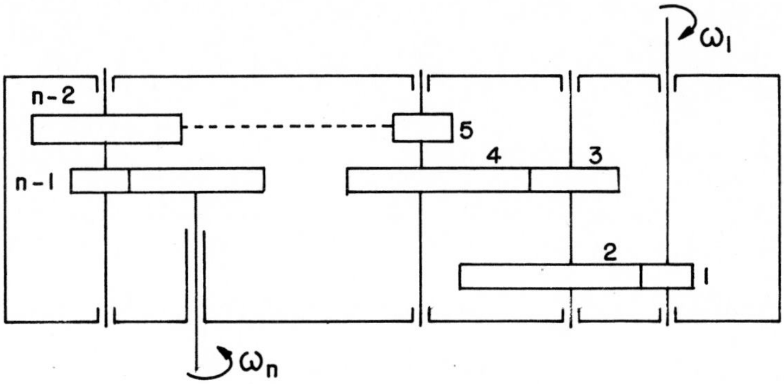

Fig. 76. Gear chain.

this figure that:

$$D_{\omega_2} = D_{\omega_3}; \quad D_{\omega_4} = D_{\omega_5}; \quad \ldots ; \quad D_{\omega_{n-2}} = D_{\omega_{n-1}} \tag{IV.2.9}$$

and

$$\bar{\omega}_3 = \bar{\omega}_1 i_{12}; \quad \bar{\omega}_5 = \bar{\omega}_1 i_{12} \cdot i_{34}; \quad \bar{\omega}_{n-1} = \bar{\omega}_1 i_{12} \cdot i_{34} \ldots i_{(n-3)(n-2)} \tag{IV.2.10}$$

Using expression (IV.2.3) sequentially for a number of gear wheels, we can obtain the D_{ω_n} value for this gear chain and for the driven shaft:

$$D_{\omega_2} = \bar{\omega}_1^{-2} i_{12}^2 (D_{r_1} + D_{r_2}) + i_{12}^2 D_{\omega_1};$$

$$D_{\omega_4} = \bar{\omega}_3^{-2} i_{34}^2 (D_{r_3} + D_{r_4}) + i_{34}^2 D_{\omega_3};$$

$$D_{\omega_6} = \bar{\omega}_5^{-2} i_{56}^2 (D_{r_5} + D_{r_6}) + i_{56}^2 D_{\omega_5};$$

. . . .

$$D_{\omega_n} = \bar{\omega}_{n-1}^{-2} i_{(n-1)n}^2 (D_{r_{n-1}} + D_{r_n}) + i_{(n-1)n}^2 D_{\omega_{n-1}}. \tag{IV.2.11}$$

Using expressions (IV.2.9) and (IV.2.10) and making sequential substitutions, we obtain from equation (IV.2.11):

$$D_{\omega_n} = \omega_1^{-2}[i^2_{(n-1)n}\ldots i^2_{12}(D_{r_n} + D_{r_{n-1}} + D_{r_{n-2}} + D_{r_{n-3}}) +$$

$$+ i^2_{(n-3)(n-2)}\ldots i^2_{12}(D_{r_{n-5}} + D_{r_{n-4}}) + \ldots$$

$$\ldots + i^2_{[n-(n-3)][n-(n-4)]}i^2_{[n-(n-1)][n-(n-2)]}(D_{r_{[n-(n-2)]}} +$$

$$+ D_{r_{[n-(n-1)]}})] + i^2_{12}D_{\omega_1} \; . \qquad \text{(IV.2.12)}$$

In the same manner, from equation (IV.2.4) we can obtain an expression for D_ε of the driven wheel:

$$D_{\varepsilon_n} = 2\omega_1^{-2}[i^2_{(n-1)n}\ldots i^2_{12}(\alpha_{r_n}D_{r_n} + \alpha_{r_{n-1}}D_{r_{n-1}} + \alpha_{r_{n-2}}D_{r_{n-2}} +$$

$$+ \alpha_{r_{n-3}}D_{r_{n-3}}) + i^2_{(n-3)(n-2)}\ldots i^2_{12}(\alpha_{r_{n-5}}D_{r_{n-5}} + \alpha_{r_{n-4}}D_{r_{n-4}}) + \ldots$$

$$\ldots + i^2_{[n-(n-3)][n-(n-4)]}i^2_{[n-(n-1)][n-(n-2)]}(\alpha_{r_{[n-(n-2)]}}D_{r_{[n-(n-2)]}} +$$

$$+ \alpha_{r_{[n-(n-1)]}}D_{r_{[n-(n-1)]}})] + 2i^2_{12}\alpha^2_\omega D_{\omega_1} \; . \qquad \text{(IV.2.13)}$$

If the conditions permit us to assume

$$D_{r_1} = D_{r_2} = \ldots = D_{r_n} \qquad \text{(IV.2.14)}$$

and

$$\alpha_{r_1} = \alpha_{r_2} = \ldots = \alpha_{r_n}$$

then, the expressions (IV.2.12) and (IV.2.13) can be simplified.

3. MEASUREMENTS

Let us now return to expressions (IV.1.7) and (IV.1.10): from these equations, the variance of the ratio error D_i of wheel pair can be expressed as:

$$D_i \simeq i^2(D_{r_1} + D_{r_2}) \qquad \text{(IV.3.1)}$$

and for $i = 1$ and $D_{r_1} = D_{r_2}$ we obtain: $D_i = 2D_r$ (IV.3.2)

For a single wheel, we introduced the criterion

$$D_i^* = \frac{D_i}{2} = D_r$$

Of course, if a frequential picture of the errors is of importance, we can obtain such a transformation from equation (IV.1.6) by the use of correlation functions (CF), such that:

$$K_i(\phi) \simeq i^2[K_{r_1}(\phi) + K_{r_2}(\phi)] \qquad (IV.3.3)$$

and for the same conditions for equal wheels, according to expression (IV.1.8)

$$K_i = 2K_r \qquad (IV.3.4)$$

or, for a single wheel, according to the definition (IV.1.10):

$$K_i^* = K_r \qquad (IV.3.5)$$

where ϕ - is the angle of wheel which, in the case of uniform rotation of the drive wheel, can be expressed in terms of the angle of the velocity ω as:

$$\phi = \bar{\omega}t \qquad (IV.3.6)$$

In this way, substituting equation (IV.3.6) into equations (IV.1.10) and (IV.1.11), we can obtain these expressions as functions of time. A similar frequential approach is necessary for the dynamic analysis of gear drives, as shown in ref. 6 and 7. The dynamic system can be described by means of its transfer function $\Phi(j\Omega)$ (where $j = \sqrt{-1}$; Ω - frequency). [this TF can be used in both linear or nonlinear cases (if linearized)]. Then, we can use the well known dependence (I.35.1):

$$S_y = |\Phi(j\Omega)|^2 S_x$$

where S_x - is the spectral density in the input of the gear;

S_y - is the spectral density in the output of the gear.

Thus, Fourier transforms of the correlation functions will provide the spectral density (and vice versa).

We will now discuss a method and apparatus for measuring the statistical characteristics of a gear wheel. The layout of the measuring device is shown in Fig. 77 as follows. The device consists of a shaft 1 on which a pulley 2 is mounted by means of bearings. The pulley is driven by synchronous motor 3 via a belt 4 with a rotation velocity of approximately 2 rpm. On the shaft 1, two equal gears 5 and 6 (from the same manufacturing series) are mounted by

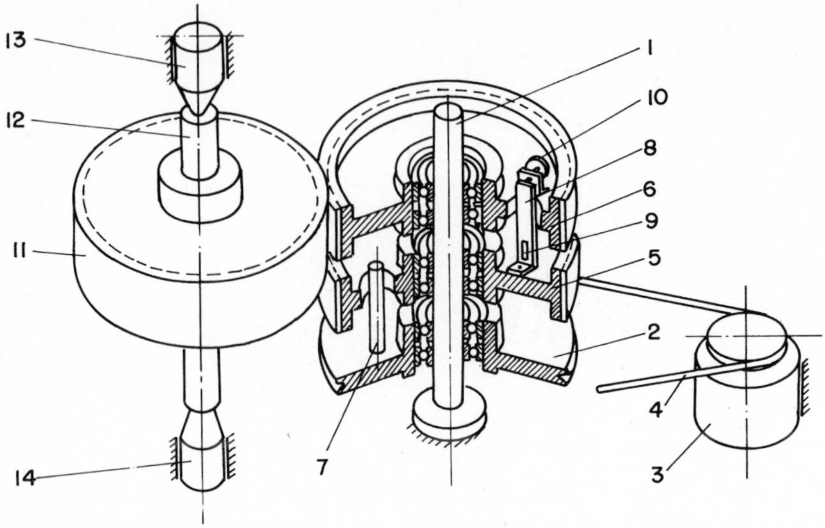

Fig. 77. Layout of the device for measuring gear errors.

means of bearings in such a way that the rotation of the two wheels is completely independent. The lower wheel is driven with a rotation speed of 1 rpm by the pulley 2 via a pin 7. To the wheel 5 is fastened a lamellar spring 8, on which a set of strain gauges 9 is glued. On the wheel 6 is fastened an adjustable screw 10 which is brought into contact with the spring 8. The measured wheel 11 is fastened to a shaft 12, which is placed between two conical supports 13 and 14, and is allowed to engage with the two wheels 5 and 6. Therefore, the motion passes from wheel 5, to wheel 11, to wheel 6, and the deformation of the spring γ measures the general error of the transmission of the three wheels. A photograph of the device is given in Fig. 78.

The general ratio of the described device i_{13} is

$$i_{13} = i_{12} \cdot i_{23} \tag{IV.3.7}$$

where

$$i_{12} = \bar{i}_{12} + \Delta i_{12}$$
$$i_{23} = \bar{i}_{23} + \Delta i_{23} \tag{IV.3.8}$$

By substituting equation (IV.3.8) in equation (IV.3.7), we obtain:

$$i_{13} = \bar{i}_{13} + \Delta i_{13} \simeq \bar{i}_{12} \cdot i_{23} + \bar{i}_{12}\Delta i_{23} + \bar{i}_{23}\Delta i_{12} \tag{IV.3.9}$$

$$\Delta i_{13} \simeq \bar{i}_{12}\Delta i_{23} + \bar{i}_{23}\Delta i_{12} \tag{IV.3.10}$$

Fig. 78. A general view of the device for measuring gear errors (prototype).

For this device we have:

$$z_1 = z_3 = z; \quad \bar{i}_{12} = \frac{z}{z_2}; \quad \bar{i}_{23} = \frac{z_2}{z}; \quad D_{i_{12}} = D_{i_{23}} = D_i \qquad \text{(IV.3.11)}$$

and in terms of RMSV:

$$D_{13} = D_i(\bar{i}_{12}^2 + \bar{i}_{23}^2) = D_i \frac{z^4 + z_2^4}{z^2 z_2^2} \qquad \text{(IV.3.12)}$$

If $z_2 = z$ and if the measured wheel is from the same series, we have

$$D_{13} = 2D_i \qquad \text{(IV.3.12)}$$

To exclude the errors of the device and find the accuracy of the measured wheel we have to estimate the RMSV of the two wheels which belong to the device, i.e. we have to be able to answer the question: what is the constant error?

By substituting equation (IV.1.10) in equation (IV.3.13), we obtain for the case $z_2 = z$

$$D_{13} = 4D_i^* \tag{IV.3.14}$$

And for a single wheel, in this specific case, which is convenient for the estimation of the device's errors we obtain:

$$D_i^* = \frac{D_{13}}{4} \tag{IV.3.15}$$

Therefore, the constant RMSV of the device is

$$D = 2D_i^* \tag{IV.3.16}$$

To obtain the frequential picture of the constant wheels of the device we can use expressions (IV.3.10) with the specific conditions (IV.3.11):

$$K_{13} = 2K_i \tag{IV.3.17}$$

and for $z_2 = z$

$$K_{13} = 4K_i^* \tag{IV.3.18}$$

and finally

$$K = 2K_i^* \tag{IV.3.19}$$

as the constant characteristics of the device.

We can see here that a "master wheel" is not necessary for this kind of measurement. High-precision wheels can also be compared in the same manner without the need for a higher precision "master wheel". We feel that this fact constitutes an important advantage in the proposed method.

By measurement, we obtain the variance D_{13} - which includes the constant error of the device and is described by D_1 - and the specific variance D^* of the wheel. However, the latter is included twice because of two engagements. Thus, to express D^* in the general case we must calculate:

$$D^* = \frac{D_{13} - D}{2} \tag{IV.3.20}$$

As an example, three gear wheels, $z_2 = 24$, $z_2 = 48$ and $z_2 = 54$ with modules m = 2 mm were measured, and the latter one was used for determination of the constant errors of the device. Fig. 79 shows three typical curves of the general errors during one revolution, one curve for each of the three wheels.

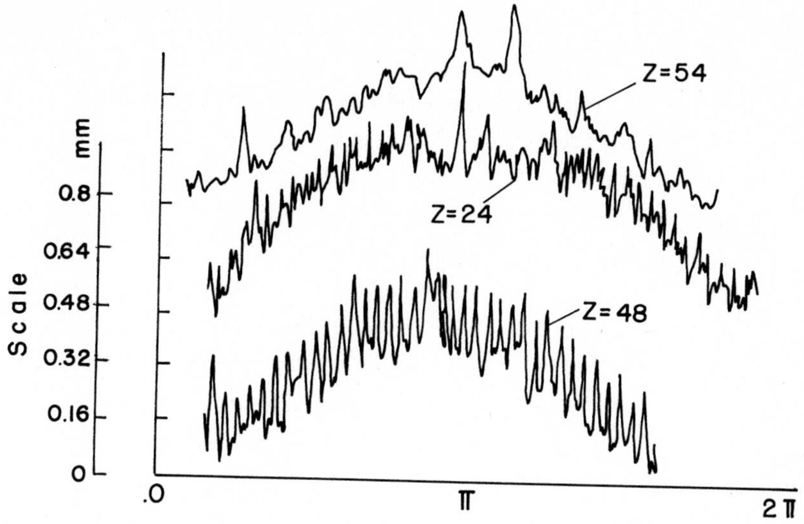

Fig. 79. Gear error curves measured by the proposed device.

Here we measure in millimeters the relative displacement of the constant wheels (gear wheels 5 and 6 of Fig. 77). Analysis of the errors recorded for the measured gear wheels gives for:

$$z = 54 \quad D_{13/54} \simeq 5.8 \cdot 10^{-5}\ \mathrm{mm}^2$$

$$z = 48 \quad D_{13/48} \simeq 6.9 \cdot 10^{-4}\ \mathrm{mm}^2$$

$$z = 24 \quad D_{13/24} \simeq 2.9 \cdot 10^{-4}\ \mathrm{mm}^2$$

The constant wheels of the device have 54 teeth. Thus, from expressions (IV.3.16) and (IV.3.15) we obtain:

$$D = \frac{D_{13}}{2} \simeq \frac{5.8 \cdot 10^{-5}}{2} \simeq 2.9 \cdot 10^{-5}\ \mathrm{mm}^2$$

Now if we substitute these figures in equation (IV.3.20), we obtain:

$$D^*_{54} \simeq \frac{5.8 \cdot 10^{-5} - 2.9 \cdot 10^{-5}}{2} = 1.45 \cdot 10^{-5}\ \mathrm{mm}^2$$

$$D^*_{48} \simeq \frac{6.9 \cdot 10^{-4} - 2.9 \cdot 10^{-5}}{2} = 33.05 \cdot 10^{-5}\ \mathrm{mm}^2$$

$$D^*_{24} \simeq \frac{2.9 \cdot 10^{-4} - 2.9 \cdot 10^{-5}}{2} \simeq 13.05 \cdot 10^{-5} \text{ mm}^2$$

To translate these linear errors into angular errors, we have to make allowance for the radii of the wheels and the location of the gauges. The spectral density of the above-described errors is shown in Fig. 80. It is evident that, for instance, for wheel z = 48 there is an obvious peak near the frequency of 1 Hz. For a rotation velocity of 1 rpm (see the description of the measuring device) and for the number of teeth = 54, the interchange between the teeth takes place at the above-mentioned frequency, i.e. 1 Hz. This finding implies that the main source of errors is the pitch of the measured wheel. (For the wheel z = 54 teeth, one sees, on the contrary, a very smooth curve of error distribution.)

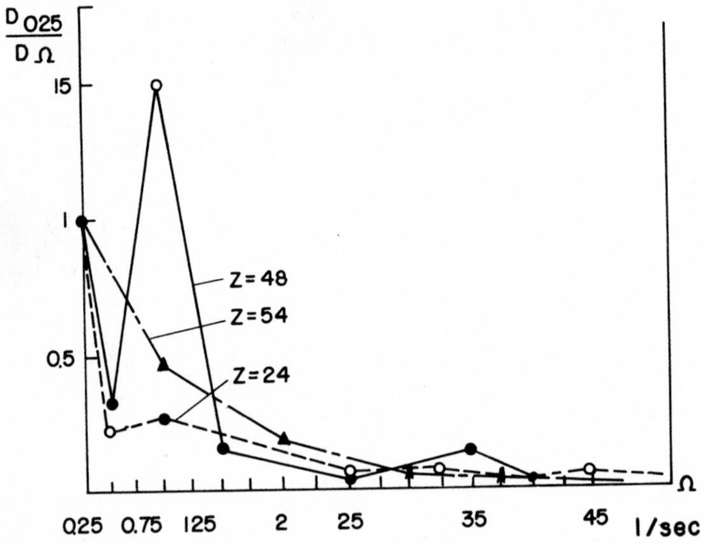

Fig. 80. Spectral density of the teeth errors.

Conclusions

1. A statistical approach to the measurement of the gear wheels permits a general estimation of the wheel's accuracy.
2. Spectral analysis of the errors enables us to determine the source of the error (for instance, pitch error, eccentricity, etc.)
3. The proposed measuring device offers a fast and relatively cheap method of obtaining information about the accuracy of the gear wheel.
4. With the described approach it is not necessary to use a "master wheel."

4. DYNAMICS OF GEAR TRANSMISSION

Let us consider the gear shown in Fig. 81. The eccentricity of the wheels on the shafts (as a result of restricted accuracy during manufacturing and assembling) and the pitch errors excite vibrations in the dynamic system. It is clear that the dynamic properties of the mechanism depend on the number z of teeth on the wheels when the common ratio i of the gearing is defined.

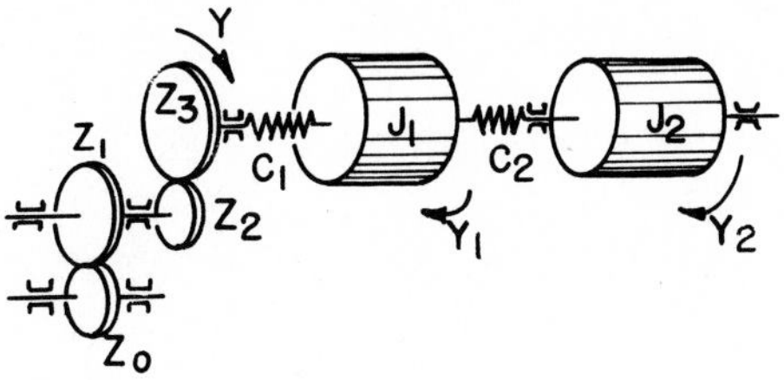

Fig. 81. Dynamic model of a gear transmission.

In the general case, some motion Y of a mechanism element can be considered as the sum:

$$Y = Y_o + y_o + y_d + y_r \tag{IV.4.1}$$

where

y_o - uniform motion (which may in some instances be absent);

Y_o - periodic motion with a period according to the relevant law;

y_d - determined dynamic constituent of the error;

y_r - random dynamic constituent of the error.

Obviously, y_o does not influence the dynamics, and we shall therefore not consider it any further in our discussion. By comparing the desired (or designed) motion Y_o with components y_d and y_r, we can see that they constitute the deviation of the motion error. We shall thus designate the sum

$$y_d + y_r = y \tag{IV.4.2}$$

and thus, taking the above-mentioned considerations into account, we obtain from equation (IV.4.1):

$$Y = Y_o + y \tag{IV.4.3}$$

Furthermore, we are interested only in the value Y(t) that describes the real motion. For the estimation of the motion Y(t) it is convenient to use the criterion:

$$\sigma_Y^2 = \frac{1}{T}\int_0^T Y^2 dt \qquad T \to \infty \tag{IV.4.4}$$

Obviously, σ_Y^2 is the variance. The use of such a criterion does not depend on the presence of a random component in the sum Y. It is known that the variance of any stationary process can be expressed in terms of its spectral density, i.e.:

$$\sigma_Y^2 = \int_0^\infty S_Y(\Omega)d\Omega \tag{IV.4.5}$$

where S_Y - spectral density of the process Y.

Ω - frequency.

There is, in turn, a connection between the spectral density of the input process S_o and the spectral density of the output process S_Y. This connection can be expressed in the form

$$S_Y = |\Phi(j\Omega)|^2 S_o \tag{IV.4.6}$$

where $\Phi(j\Omega)$ is equal to the complex frequency function (CFF) of the linear system under consideration. As is known, the CFF can be extracted by replacing in the Laplace transfer function (TF) $\Phi(p)$ the symbol p by the expression $j\Omega$. Substituting equation (IV.4.6) into equation (IV.4.5) we obtain:

$$\sigma_Y^2 = \int_0^\infty |\Phi(j\Omega)|^2 S_o d\Omega \tag{IV.4.7}$$

To obtain the spectral density of a particular process, we can use Dirac impulse functions in the form:

$$S_o \simeq \frac{1}{2}\sum_{k=o}^{n} A_k^2 \delta(\Omega - \omega_k) \tag{IV.4.8}$$

where A_k - amplitude of harmonic motion with a frequency equal to ω_k. In this case [i.e. substituting equation (IV.4.8) into equation (IV.4.7)], the integration of the expression is considerably simplified:

$$\sigma_Y^2 = \frac{1}{2}\sum_{k=o}^{n} A_k^2 |\Phi(j\omega_k)|^2 \tag{IV.4.9}$$

The transfer function of this dynamic system (damping being neglected) takes the form

$$\Phi(j\Omega) = \frac{c_1(c_2 - J_2\Omega^2)}{(c_1 + c_2 - J_1\Omega^2)(c_2 - J_2\Omega^2) - c_2^2} \tag{IV.4.10}$$

Thus, the errors can now be described in terms of their spectral density $S_o(\Omega)$. According to Arai and Ishikawa [2] and Maruyama and Nakada [3] the motion errors Δ can be approximated as:

$$\Delta = \Delta_e + \Delta_T \tag{IV.4.11}$$

where the errors Δ_e on the third shaft are influenced by the eccentricity of the wheels, and the errors Δ_T on the third shaft are influenced by deviations in the pitch of the teeth.

Here, the following assumptions are made:

1. The errors are harmonic (this assumption is based on experimental data: even though this description is, of course, not complete, it is sufficient to furnish an idea of the problem under consideration.)
2. The tolerances of the eccentricity e are equal for all the wheels.
3. The tolerances of the pitch deviations T are also equal for all the wheels.
4. The speed of the input motion ω is constant.

Then, the spectral density depending on wheel's eccentricity takes the following form:

$$S_e = 2(e\frac{z_2}{z_3})^2 \{\delta[\Omega - \frac{\omega z_o z_2}{2\pi z_1}] + \delta[\Omega - \frac{\omega z_o}{2\pi}]\} \tag{IV.4.12}$$

and, the spectral density depending on pitch errors takes the form:

$$S_T = (T_i)^2/2\ \delta[\Omega - \frac{\omega}{2}] + 2(T\frac{z_2}{z_3})^2\ \delta[\Omega - \frac{\omega z_o}{2\pi}] + \frac{T}{2}\ \delta[\Omega - \frac{\omega}{2\pi} i] \tag{IV.4.13}$$

The spectral density of the entire input, thus takes the form

$$S = S_T + E_e \tag{IV.4.14}$$

where T - the amplitude of the error of the teeth pitch, and e - wheel eccentricity on the shafts.

In the general case a random item can be added which must be described by means of an analytical approximation S_r. Then, from equation (IV.4.14) we obtain

$$S_o = S_T + S_e + S_r \tag{IV.4.15}$$

Further, by substituting equations (IV.4.15) and (IV.4.10) into equation (IV.4.7) we can calculate σ_Y^2. Thus, for this linear case the problem is trivial enough. However, it seems to us that this is the place toformulate an important optimization problem.

The amplitude-frequency of any mechanism depends on the frequency and the values of parameters x_n. In mechanical cases these parameters are mass, stiffness and damping properties. When the minimum of σ_Y^2 is desired, it is necessary to find the optimal combination of parameters x_n, i.e., for instance, we can formulate an optimization problem to choose the best combination of z_o, z_1, z_2 which minimizes vibrations of some mass (say, J_1), when all other parameters are defined. Obviously,

$$z_3 = \frac{z_o z_2}{z_1 i} \qquad \text{(IV.4.16)}$$

Therefore we have described a simple parametric optimization problem. Where σ^2 is the objective function of n parameters x_η $(\eta = 1,\ldots,n)$

$$\sigma^2 = f(x_1, x_2, \ldots, x_n) \qquad \text{(IV.4.17)}$$

The mechanical problems with which we are dealing from the optimization point of view can be characterized by the following properties:

1. The motion of the parts of the mechanism is practically continuous because of damping, elasticity of the parts.
2. Technology- and construction-imposed restrictions do not permit us to change the parameters of masses, elasticity, damping over a wide range.
3. The number of changeable parameters is not very large.

In practice, at the design stage we have to estimate the approximate values of the parameters which give the minimal (maximal) value of the objective function under consideration. Often, we have to be satisfied with the use of a local optimum. Thus, we may have to choose the best of several local minima. In many cases, conventional optimization methods are not best suited to such purposes. Because of the complexity of the problem, a computer is usually employed for this operation: the randomized methods allow the computer to "jump" over the extremes and in this way to reveal several minima.

In general, real mechanisms, when dynamically analyzed, are represented by idealized and simplified mathematical models. For this reason the picture we have so far obtained of the behavior of systems allows us to estimate only approximately both the main qualitative properties and the quantitative characteristics, i.e. the agreement between the model and the real mechanism is only approximate because of a series of assumptions made before modelling. This fact justifies the use of an approximate optimization procedure (at least, from the practical point of view).

The elements of a mechanism oscillate as a result of their dynamic properties. When designing a layout, we must therefore choose parameters of the system which will ensure minimum vibrations of the most important element. For example, in a gear train, a possible optimization problem can be formulated so as to minimize the output vibrations ψ_1 of the mass J_1 of the mechanism, i.e. to minimize the value of σ_ψ^2.

5. OPTIMIZATION ALGORITHM

The theory of optimization has been developed over the past 40 years. Short historical reviews of this process can be found in the publications of Fiacco and McCormich [7] and Hadley [8]. It is possible to separate the known optimization techniques into two branches - determinate and statistical. It is impossible to say which technique is better: in any real situation, we are interested in choosing that optimization policy which is less costly. Sometimes statistical algorithms are superior to regular (determined) algorithms. Of the criteria that can be used to compare different optimization techniques, we will mention only two:

1. If $\min_{x^* \in X} f(x) = f^*(x^*)$

and the minimization algorithm number r gives $f_r(x_r)$ as the minimized value of the objective function, then $\Delta = |f^*(x^*) - f_r(x_r)|$ can be taken as criterion of optimization accuracy.

2. <u>Execution time in seconds</u>. Let us suppose that the minimal value of an objective function $f(x_1, x_2, \ldots, x_n)$ is the desired value. Then, we have to seek the best combination of parameters $x_1, x_2, \ldots, x_n$ which will provide such a minimal value of the given function.

The limits of the parameter space can be expressed in any form:

$$x_{\eta o} < x_\eta < x_{\eta *} \qquad \eta = 1, \ldots, n \qquad \text{(IV.5.1)}$$

where the limits x_o and x_* can be functions or constant values.

The first step in the proposed algorithm involves dividing the intervals (IV.5.1) by two:

$$\bar{x}_\eta = \frac{x_{\eta o} + x_{\eta *}}{2} \qquad \text{and} \qquad \Delta x_\eta = \frac{x_{\eta *} - x_{\eta o}}{2} \qquad \text{(IV.5.2)}$$

Obviously, $\bar{x}$ = the middle of the interval and Δx = half of the interval.

Let us designate the number α of each parametric "cube" in binary code such that

$$\alpha = (\alpha_1, \ldots, \alpha_q, \ldots, \alpha_n) \qquad \text{(IV.5.3)}$$

where

$$\alpha_q = \begin{cases} 0 \\ 1 \end{cases}$$

Let "0" designate the left part of the interval and "1" the right part. For each fixed α take a series of n uniform $\overline{0.1}$ random numbers

$$h_1^{(j)}, \ldots, h_n^{(j)} \qquad j = 1, \ldots, k$$

Note: it is possible to calculate the values of the objective function f_j which agree with each j group of the randomized parameters.

$$f_\eta(x^{(j)}) = f_\eta(x_{no} + \Delta x_1[\alpha_1 + h_1^{(j)}], \ldots, x_{no} + \Delta x_n[\alpha_n + h_n^{(j)}]) \tag{IV.5.4}$$

where k is the number of randomized parameter groups we have to "throw" to cover the space of one "cube" with sufficient density. For each of m cubes we have to compute k values of the objective function using, each time, randomized parameters according to equation (IV.5.3). We can now select the "cube" in which we obtain the minimal value of the objective function and note the coordinates of this "cube". This reduced n-dimensional parametric "cube" can now be used to define the new parametric space instead of equation (IV.4.7) or (IV.4.9). We then repeat the procedure ℓ times until we obtain:

$$\Delta x_\eta^\ell < \varepsilon_\eta$$

The value ε_η defines the permissible or desirable calculation accuracy for each η-th parameter. The calculation accuracy for parameter number η can be determined as

$$\varepsilon_\eta = \frac{x_{\eta*} - x_{\eta o}}{2^\ell}$$

Obviously, we have to calculate the value of the objective function 2_k^n times during one cycle and $N = 2^{\ell+kn}$ times during the complete calculation. It must be pointed out that to arrive at some minima (maxima) one has to repeat the same calculation s times.

The sensitivity of the above-described algorithm depends on the form of the function. Let us consider the following special cases.

1. If the function changes slowly and forms a "flat" surface, as is shown in Fig. 82a, we cannot expect a solution of high accuracy: from a practical

point of view, however, this does not matter, since the minimal value of the objective function is almost reached.

2. In the function shown in Fig. 82b the probability of "hitting" in the "pit" is very small, so that the minimum can be missed.
3. If the function has the form shown in Fig. 82c, we need too many "throwings" to get an accurate result.

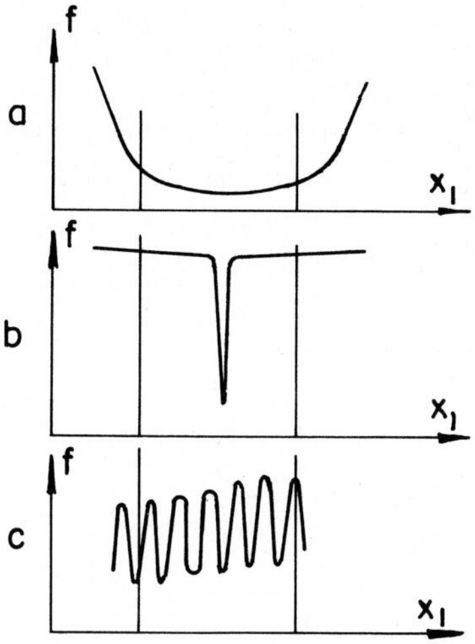

Fig. 82. a) Example of a "flat" minima; b) Example of a minimum with the shape of a narrow "pit"; c) Example of a function with a multiple of minima.

The flow diagram of the proposed algorithm is shown in Fig. 83. To examine the algorithm, we can apply some of the test problems given by Aoki [10]:

1. <u>Rosenbrock's (1960) problem</u>

$$y = 100(z - x^2)^2 + (a - x)^2$$

has the exact minimum y = 0 at the point x = 1 and z = 1. The area $-2 \lesssim x \lesssim 2$ and $-1 \lesssim z \lesssim 4$ was used for calculation. The calculations gave x = 1, z = 0.992188 and y = 0.006103. Here was k = 200, s = 3, ℓ = 7.

2. <u>Witte and Holst's (1964) problem</u>

$$y = (z - x^2)^2 + (1 - x)^2$$

has the exact minimum y = 0 at the point x = 1 and z = 1. The area $0 \lesssim x \lesssim 4$ and $0 \lesssim z \lesssim 9$ was considered. By calculation x = 1, z = 0.984, y = 0.00024 were obtained. Here was k = 50, s = 3, ℓ = 7.

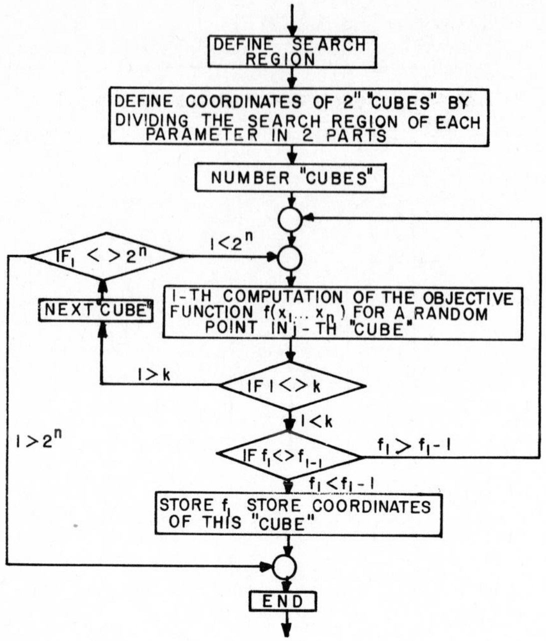

Fig. 83. Flow diagram of the optimization algorithm.

3. Our own test problem in the following form:

$$y = A\sin(az + \alpha) + B\sin(bz + \beta) + C\sin(cx + \xi) + D\sin(dx + \delta)$$

By changing the constants in this expression, we can study the behavior of the proposed algorithm in several difficult situations.

For the parameter area $0 \leq z \leq 9$ and $0 \leq x \leq 4$ and

$A = 10$	$a = 1$	$\alpha = 0$
$B = 5$	$b = 3$	$\beta = \pi/4$
$C = 20$	$c = 2$	$\xi = \pi/3$
$D = 5$	$d = 5$	$\delta = \pi/5$

we get $x = 3.3.125$, $z = 5.34375$, $y = -37.5273$ as a first minimum and $x = 1.0625$, $z = 5.34375$, $y = -31.9876$ as a second minimum. Here $k = 25$, $s = 5$, $\ell = 7$.

Let us now apply this algorithm for gear train dynamic optimization. Here we simplify the problem and content ourselves with expressions (IV.4.14), (IV.4.12) and (IV.2.13) (without a pure random item). According to Fig. 81 the dynamic system has three unknown parameters and a nonlinear boundary condition (IV.4.16). For the following data

$e = 0.01$ cm, $T = 0.002$ cm, $c_1 = 10^6$ Kgcm/rad, $c_2 = 2.10^6$ Kgcm/rad, $J_1 = 5$ Kg cms^2, $J_2 = 10$ Kg cms^2, $i = 0.333$ and

$$18 \leq z_o \leq 36$$

$$20 \leq z_1 \leq 100$$

$$18 \leq z_2 \leq 36$$

$$18 \leq z_3 \leq 50$$

we get, for example, by using 60 "throws" the next optimal combination

$$z_o = 29 \qquad z_1 = 60 \qquad z_2 = 18 \qquad z_3 = 25$$

(obviously we have used only whole numbers). We obtain the value of $\sigma^2_{\psi 1} = 0.412 \cdot 10^{-3}$ rad^2. If we change the permitted limits, for instance, for only one parameter, for instance

$$18 \leq z_3 \leq 100$$

we will obtain

$$z_o = 29 \qquad z_1 = 29 \qquad z_2 = 27 \qquad z_3 = 86$$

then $\sigma^2_{\psi_1} = 0.487 \cdot 10^{-5}$ rad^2.

Attention must be drawn to the fact that in the latter case to decrease the vibration of the mass J_1 the first gearing pair has to increase the velocity a little before decreasing it, as opposed to the usual design requirement for all the gearing pairs to reduce the velocities.

Conclusions

1. Spectral theory permits, in a comparatively easy way, the synthesis of an optimal (from the dynamic standpoint) mechanical system, at least in linear or linearized cases.
2. Selection of combinations of mechanical parameters (mass, stiffness, and damping) enables us to improve significantly the dynamic properties of a mechanical system.
3. By choosing the correct (or a more suitable) combination of frequencies of disturbance (number of teeth in a gearing), we can decrease the output errors without increasing manufacturing accuracy of the system.
4. A randomized algorithm is applicable for this type of dynamic optimization.

6. GEAR CALCULATION RELIABILITY

> There are about as many rules for computing the power of a gear as there are manufacturers of gears, each foundryman having a rule, the only good one, which he has found in some book, and with which he will figure the power down to so many horses and hundredths of a horse as confidently as he will count the teeth or weigh the casting.
>
> George B. Grant's "Gearing" (quoted by Darle W. Dudley, The Evolution of the Gear Art, published by AGMA, Washington DC, 1969).

Let us denote:

a_1, b_i - the limits of the range;

D - integration domain;

g, f - density function (DF);

$f(x_1,x_2)$ - joint DF;

Q - calculated function;

ΔQ - deviation of the calculated function;

G - distribution function;

i, j, k, l, n - numbers;

m, z, y - parameters or constraints describing different properties of the subject under consideration;

p - probability;

S - calculated value;

ΔS - deviation of the calculated value;

x - parameter;

$\bar{x}$ - mathematical expectation of the parameter;

Δx - deviation of the parameter;

P, X, Z, S - dimensionless values;

σ_x - the root mean square value of the parameter;

ϕ - symbol of the Laplace function.

The calculations with which the industrial designer has to deal are often based on the use of standardized methods or recommendations. Sometimes, the same value can be calculated by different methods, and the results will then differ. For instance, one can calculate gear ratings following AGMA [13] or ISO [14] recommendations or use several handbooks, etc. So we can write:

$$S_A = Q_A(\ldots, x_i, \ldots) \qquad S_B = Q_B(\ldots, y_i, \ldots) \qquad \text{(IV.6.1)}$$

$$i = 1, \ldots, k \qquad i = 1, \ldots, \ell$$

corresponding to method A or B, respectively. In most cases, the analytical expressions that the designer uses take the following form:

$$S = \prod_{i=1}^{n} x_i^{m_i} \qquad (IV.6.2)$$

He then has to figure out or find out the values of the parameters from tables or monograms. The estimation of these values is based on many years of experience in manufacturing and application of the subject, on successes and failures. The value chosen for each particular parameter has a certain "reliability" p_i. This "reliability" influences the trustiness of each calculated value S which can be described by its "reliability" p_S.

At this stage, we will make an attempt to estimate this reliability quantitatively and to compare the recommended calculation methods for gear ratings. The different calculation methods are based on two contradictory tendencies. On the one hand, accuracy is improved by taking into account the maximum possible properties describing the subject of investigation. On the other hand, accuracy and reliability of the calculated results is lost as a result of the inclusion of a large number of parameters, the values of which are not known exactly. Each additional parameter included implies that all the parameters used in the calculations have to be known with higher accuracy in order to maintain the desired level of accuracy of the result.

Since the choice of parameters is usually made in a partially random manner, we can describe the parameters by means of density function (DF) f_i:

$$f_i(x_i, \bar{x}_i, \sigma_{x_i})$$

Then, the probability that "exact" value of a parameter is within the desired range can be expressed by:

$$p(a_i < x_i < b_i) = \int_{a_i}^{b_i} f_i(x_i)dx_i \qquad (IV.6.3)$$

The specific forms (IV.6.1) and (IV.6.2) provide us with the possibility of finding, at least in principle, the DF g(S) of the computed value S and this also the probability of "hitting" the S value in a definite range of S values:

$$p(S_1 < S < S_2) = \int_{S_1}^{S_2} g(S)dS \qquad (IV.6.4)$$

As the values of p become smaller, the reliability of the calculations decreases as does the reliability of the result.

We can now estimate either the probability of covering the calculated value by the given range, or the range required to provide the desired probability (or reliability) of covering the calculated value. A knowledge of the value p helps us to answer the following questions:

(1) which computation method is more reliable and therefore preferable;

(2) which parameters have the greatest influence on the accuracy of the calculated value;

(3) in which range of the calculated value are the results more reliable;

(4) what is the optimal number of parameters required to give a trustworthy result;

(5) what level of accuracy must be provided when choosing the values of the parameters in order to get the desired reliability of the result.

In special cases when the errors of the parameters are relatively small, the comparison of the methods and the estimation of the accuracy of the calculations of the S value can be achieved by the following procedure:

$$S \simeq Q(\bar{x}_i) \pm \sqrt{\sum_{i=1}^{k} (\partial\theta/\partial x_i)^2_{x_i=\bar{x}_i} \cdot \Delta x_i^2} = Q \pm \Delta Q \qquad \text{(IV.6.5)}$$

The bigger the value of ΔQ, the worse the method. Sometimes, the errors in the choice of the parameters x_i are not so small to justify application of the expression (IV.6.5).

If normal distribution can be assumed for ΔQ, the reliability p_S of this calculation $S = Q(x_i)$ can be estimated in the conventional manner. We determine the root mean square value as:

$$\sigma_s \simeq \Delta\theta/3$$

The expression

$$p_S \simeq \Phi[(\Delta S-\bar{S}) \; / \; \sqrt{2}\sigma_S] \qquad \text{(IV.6.6)}$$

gives us the probability of the "right" value "hitting" in the range ΔS. To proceed, we have to recall some dependencies used in the probability theory. These dependencies will be used to analyze equation (IV.6.2).

(1) If $z = x^n$, and $f(x)$ is the DF of the random value x, then the DF of another random value z will take the form:

$$g(z) = \frac{1}{n} f(z^{1/n}) \cdot z^{(1/n - 1)} \qquad \text{(IV.6.7)}$$

Applying equation (IV.6.7) in some specific cases, we obtain the following results:

for $z = x^2$ $\qquad g(z) = \frac{1}{2\sqrt{z}} f(\sqrt{z})$ (IV.6.8)

for $z = 1/x$ $\qquad g(z) = -f(1/z)/z^2$ (IV.6.9)

for $z = 1/x^2$ $\qquad g(z) = -f(1/\sqrt{z})/2\sqrt{z^3}$

(2) If $z = A^x$ where A = const, then:

$$g(z) = f(\log_A z)/z \ln A \qquad \text{(IV.6.11)}$$

(3) If $z = x_1 \cdot x_2$ (see Fig. 84) and if we can assume that x_1 and x_2 are independent values, we can write:

$$f(x_1, x_2) = f_1(x_1) \cdot f_2(x_2) \qquad \text{(IV.6.12)}$$

where $f(x_1,x_2)$ is the joint DF of random values x_1 and x_2. Now, using equations (IV.6.4) and (IV.6.14), we can compute the "reliability" of the results. Then,

$$G(z) = \int_D \int f_1(x_1) \cdot f_2(x_2) dx_1 dx_2 \qquad \text{(IV.6.13)}$$

$$g(z) = d[G(z)]/dz \qquad \text{(IV.6.14)}$$

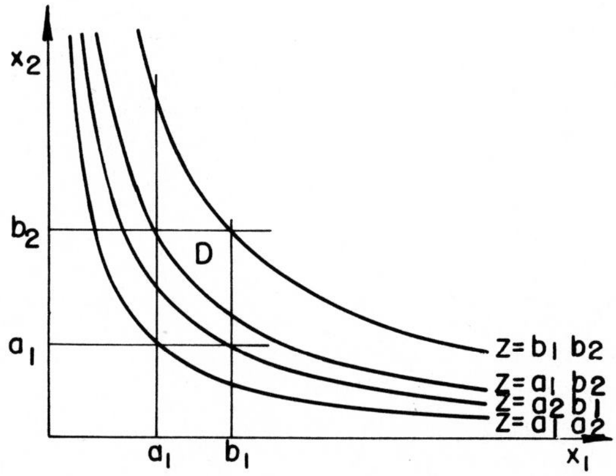

Fig. 84. Graphic interpretation of the function $z = x_1 \cdot x_2$ and the integration domain.

For our purposes, it is more convenient to use dimensionless relative parameters. We will define them as the ratio between the random value and the chosen one:

$$X_i = \frac{x_i}{\bar{x}_i} \qquad \text{(IV.6.15)}$$

The chosen value $\bar{x}_i$ is taken as the average value of x_i so that the average value of X_i equals 1. Then, the calculated values (at any calculation stage) can be expressed in a dimensionless form as follows:

$$Z_j = \frac{z_j}{\bar{z}_j} \quad \text{and} \quad S = \frac{S}{\bar{S}} \qquad \text{(IV.6.16)}$$

The values of $\bar{z}_j$ and $\bar{S}$ are obtained by substituting $\bar{x}_i$ in corresponding formulas of equation (IV.6.1).

In our discussion, the nondimensional values will be denoted by italics. Dimensionless transformations of the parameters enable us to compare the calculation methods even when the absolute calculation results differ. But this simplification is of value only if equation (IV.6.2) can be applied.

As a typical example of the comparison of calculation methods, we will consider the gear power rating for the calculation of the durability of spur gears. Let us apply two different currently used methods - one proposed by AGMA and the second - by ISO - and one "old fashioned" method - Box's rule recommended by George B. Grant in his book "gearing" [1] published in 1907. (The latter method is included only as an illustration of the calculation technique.)

1. AGMA method [2]:

$$P = \frac{n_p d^2 F I S_{ac}^2 C_L^2 C_v m_G}{12600\, C_m C_p^2 C_{SF} (m_G + 1)} \qquad \text{(IV.6.17)}$$

where

P - power, HP;

n_p - pinion speed, rpm;

d - operating pitch diameter of the pinion, inches;

F - net face width of the narrowest of the mating gears;

I - geometry factor;

S_{ac} - allowable contact stress number for steel;

C_L - life factor;

C_V - dynamic factor;

C_m - load distribution factor;

C_p - elastic coefficient for gear material;

C_{SF} - service factor;

m_G - gear ratio, $m_G > 1$.

2. ISO method [3]:

$$P = \frac{0.523nd_1bu[Z_NZ_vZ_xZ_LZ_RZ_W]^2\delta_{Hlim}}{(u+1)[Z_HZ_EZ_\varepsilon Z_B]^2K_{H\alpha}K_{H\beta}K_AK_vS^2} \quad \text{(IV.6.18)}$$

where

P - power, HP;

n - pinion speed, rpm;

d_1 - operating diameter of the pinion;

b - face width;

u - gear ratio, $u > 1$;

Z_N - life factor for contact stresses;

Z_V - speed factor;

Z_X - size factor;

Z_L - lubrication factor;

Z_R - roughness factor for contact stresses;

Z_W - work hardening factor;

Z_H - zone factor;

Z_E - elasticity factor;

Z_ε - contact ratio factor;

Z_B - helix angle factor;

Z_H - transverse load distribution factor;

K_A - application factor;

K_V - dynamic factor;

S - safety factor;

δ_{Hlim} - endurance limit for contact stress;

K_H - angle factors.

3. Box's rule [1] (as a simple calculation example):

$$P = \frac{12c^2\ f\ \sqrt{dn}}{1000} \quad \text{(IV.6.19)}$$

where

c - circular pitch;

f - the face, inches;

d - diameter, inches;

n - rpm

P - power, HP.

Obviously, the exact values of some of the factors and parameters in each method (such as ratio, diameters, face width, etc.) are, in practice, known and cannot cause errors in the calculation of the results. On the other hand, other parameters (for instance, application, safety or surface roughness factors) have different confidence levels because of their nature and our skill. Therefore, in the first step we have to decide which parameters will be considered as random, i.e. which contain random items causing errors in their estimation. In the second step we have to transform the factors with which we are dealing to dimensionless forms. For this purpose, each parameter in formulas (IV.6.17) to (IV.6.19) has to be divided by the average value thus transforming the three equations into the following expressions (IV.6.20) to (IV.6.22), respectively:

$$P = \frac{\mathrm{P}}{\bar{\mathrm{P}}} = \frac{[Z_N Z_v Z_L Z_R Z_W]^2 \, \delta_{\mathrm{Hlim}}}{[Z_H Z_E]^2 K_{\mathrm{H\alpha}} K_{\mathrm{H\beta}} K_A K_v \, S^2} \qquad \text{(IV.6.20)}$$

$$P = \frac{J C_v C_L^2 S_{ac}^2}{C_m C_p^2 C_{SF}} \qquad \text{(IV.6.21)}$$

$$P = X\sqrt{n} \qquad \text{(VI.6.22)}$$

where X is the fraction 12/1000 containing information about material properties and tooth shape.

Table IV.1 summarizes the assumed confidence level of the factors used in the three calculation methods under consideration. From the Table we can see which parameters can cause deviations of the calculated results for each method and the supposed deviations of each item. The nondimensional parameters which are not given in the Table equal 1, i.e. in practice, their values are known very accurately.

Table IV.1. Proposed accuracy classification

±ΔX	±1%	±2%		±5%	±7.5%	±10%		±15%		±20%	±40%
Method	ISO	AGMA	ISO	ISO	AGMA	ISO	AGMA	ISO	AGMA	BOX	BOX
x_i	Z_H Z_E	I	Z_N Z_v	$K_{H\alpha}$ $K_{H\beta}$ Z_L Z_R Z_W	C_m C_L	δ_{Hlim} K_V	S_{ac} C_V C_p	K_A S	C_{SF}	n	x

To illustrate the proposed procedures for the estimation of reliability we will lokk at Box's rule in detail. (For the AGMA and ISO methods only the final results will be shown.) In nondimensional form Box's rule takes the form of expression (IV.6.22). At first, we will use the procedure described by expression (IV.6.5). In this case, the calculated value S equals P. Obviously, in this nondimensional situation:

$$\bar{Q}(\bar{X}_i) = 1 \qquad \bar{X}_i = 1 \tag{IV.6.23}$$

$$(\partial Q/\partial X)_{x=\bar{x}} = \sqrt{\bar{n}} = 1$$

$$(\partial Q/\partial n)_{n=\bar{n}} = \frac{X}{2\sqrt{\bar{n}}} = \frac{1}{2}$$

Because of the illustrative character of these calculations, let us for this case consider n as a random variable. According to Table IV.1:

$$0.8 < n < 1.2 \qquad \Delta n = \pm 0.2$$
$$0.6 < X < 1.4 \qquad \Delta X = \pm 0.4 \tag{IV.6.24}$$

Substituting expressions (IV.6.23) and (IV.6.24) into equation (IV.6.5), we obtain:

$$Q \simeq 1 \pm \sqrt{1 \cdot 0.4^2 + 0.2^2/2^2} = 1 \pm 0.41$$

$$\Delta Q = \pm 0.41 \qquad \sigma_Q \simeq \frac{2 \cdot 0.41}{6} = 0.137$$

Assuming for Q a normal distribution (for instance), we can calculate the reliability as the probability of p "hitting" in the 10% range:

$$p(0.9 < P < 1.1) = \phi\left(\frac{0.1}{\sqrt{2}\,\sigma_Q}\right) = \phi\left(\frac{0.1}{\sqrt{2}\cdot 0.137}\right) \simeq 0.536 \tag{IV.6.26}$$

where ϕ - Laplace function.

(For a uniform DF, p = 0.244. This result is obtained from:

$$p(0.9 < P < 1.1) = \int_{-0.1}^{+0.1} \frac{dx}{b-a} \simeq \int_{-0.1}^{+0.1} \frac{dx}{0.41+0.41} = \frac{x}{0.82}\Bigg|_{-0.1}^{+0.1} = 0.244$$

where a = -0.41 and b = +0.41 as follows from $\Delta Q = \pm 0.41$.)

The second procedure is based on the knowledge of the DF of the parameter x_i. For example, we assume that the DF are uniform, and then according to the Table IV.1 we obtain

$$f(n) = \frac{1}{b_1 - a_1} = \frac{1}{1.2 - 0.8}$$

$$f(X) = \frac{1}{b_2 - a_2} = \frac{1}{1.4 - 0.6} \qquad \text{(IV.6.27)}$$

For $Z_1 = \sqrt{n}$ the DF, according to equation (IV.6.7), is:

$$g_1(Z_1) = \frac{2Z_1}{b_1 - a_1} = \frac{1}{0.2} \quad \text{for } \sqrt{a_1} < Z_1 < \sqrt{b_1} \quad \text{or} \quad 0.894 < Z_1 < 1.095$$

For $Z_2 = Z_1X$ for DF g_2 must be calculated in accordance with equations (IV.6.12), (IV.6.13) and (IV.6.14).

$$\sqrt{a_1}\cdot a_2 < Z_2 < a_2\cdot\sqrt{b_1}$$

$$0.537 < Z_2 < 0.657$$

$$G_2(Z_2) = \frac{2}{(b_1 - a_1)(b_2 - a_2)} \left[\frac{Z_2^2}{2a_2} - Z_2\sqrt{a_1} + \frac{a_1a_2}{2} \right] \qquad \text{(IV.6.28)}$$

$$g_2(Z_2) = \frac{2}{(b_1 - a_1)(b_2 - a_2)} \left[\frac{Z_2}{a_2} - \sqrt{a_1} \right]$$

$$a_2\sqrt{b_2} < Z_2 < \sqrt{a_1}\cdot b_2$$

$$0.657 < Z_2 < 1.252$$

$$G_2(Z_2) = \frac{2}{(b_1 - a_1)(b_2 - a_2)} \left[Z_2(\sqrt{b_1} - \sqrt{a_1}) - \frac{a_2}{2} (b_1 - a_1)\right) \qquad \text{(IV.6.29)}$$

$$g_2(Z_2) = \frac{2(\sqrt{b_1} - \sqrt{a_1})}{(b_1 - a_1)(b_2 - a_2)}$$

$$\sqrt{a_1}\cdot b_2 < Z_2 < \sqrt{b_1}\cdot b_2$$

$$1.252 < Z_2 < 1.533$$

$$G_2(Z_2) = \frac{2}{(b_1 - a_1)(b_2 - a_2)} \left[Z_2\sqrt{b_1} - \frac{a_2}{2} (b_1 - a_1) \frac{Z_2^2}{2b_2} - \frac{a_1b}{2} \right] \qquad \text{(IV.6.30)}$$

$$g_2(Z_2) = \frac{2}{(b_1 - a_1)(b_2 - a_2)} \left[\sqrt{b_1} - \frac{Z_2}{b_2} \right]$$

Fig. 84 explains the origin of the integration limits of the above-mentioned domains [see equation (IV.6.13) and expressions (IV.6.28), (IV.6.29) and (IV.6.30)]. In this figure the integration domain is restricted for x_1 and x_2 by the ranges a_1b_1 and a_2b_2, respectively, so that $Z = x_1x_2$:

(1) $Z < a_1a_2$ $\qquad G(Z) = 0$

(2) $a_1a_2 < Z < a_2b_1$

$$G(Z) = \int_{a_1}^{Z/a_2} \int_{a_2}^{Z/x_1} f_1(x_1)\cdot f_2(x_2)dx_1dx_2$$

(3) $a_2b_1 < Z < a_1b_2$

$$G(Z) = \int_{a_1}^{b_1} \int_{a_2}^{Z/x_1} f_1(x_1)\cdot f_2(x_2)dx_1dx_2$$

(4) $a_1b_2 < Z < b_1b_2$

$$G(Z) = \int_{a_1}^{b_1} \int_{a_2}^{Z/x_1} f_1(x_1)\cdot f_2(x_2)dx_1dx_2 - \int_{a_1}^{Z/b_2} \int_{b_2}^{Z/x_1} f_1(x_1)\cdot f_2(x_2)dx_1dx_2$$

(5) $b_1b_2 < Z$ $\qquad G(Z) = 1$

It should be noted that the choice of x_1 and x_2 must provide $a_2b_1 < a_1b_2$. When $a_2b_1 = a_1b_2$, the step (3) does not exist.

Now, we can calculate the reliability of "hitting," say, in the ±10% range. As can be seen from equation (IV.6.29) and Fig. 85, where the DF is shown corresponding to these expressions (IV.6.28)-(IV.6.30), the limits form the boundary of this range. Therefore, the reliability can be determined by the use of G_2 in the following way:

$$p(0.9 < P < 1.1) = G_2(1.1) - G_2(0.9) \simeq 0.25 \qquad \text{(IV.6.31)}$$

This result is very close to that shown above for uniform DF.

The difference in the results (IV.6.26) and (IV.6.31) is caused by different DF being assumed for the parameters under consideration. In addition, the first procedure (IV.6.26) is not really suitable for such wide deviations of the parameters.

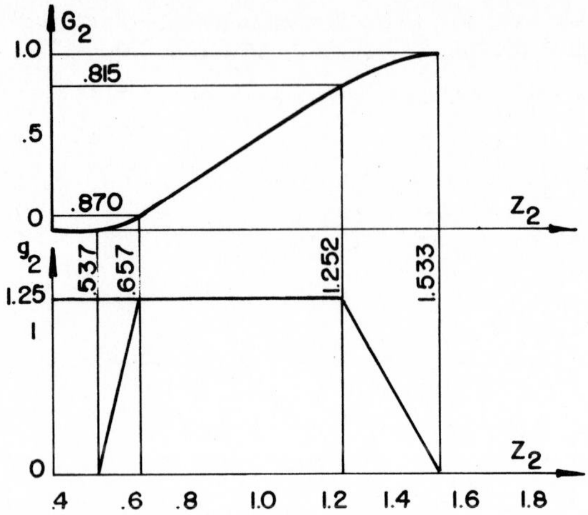

Fig. 85. Distribution function G_2 and density function g_2 for the numerical example given in expressions (IV.6.22) to (IV.6.30).

At this stage, we must raise two points:

1. If $Z_1 = x_1x_2$, $Z_2 = x_3x_4$, $Z_3 = Z_1Z_2$ and $g(Z_3)$ must be calculated, the integration domain becomes more complicated. In this case, the domain consists of 9 "rectangles," as shown in Fig. 86. The integration limits are defined within each "rectangle."

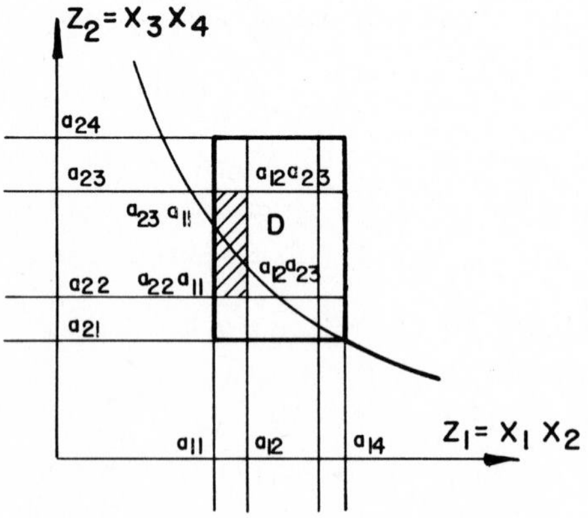

Fig. 86. Example of the integration domains for $Z = x_1x_2x_3x_4$.

2. When the necessity to increase the number of multiplications for seeking the DF arises, the number of rectangles rapidly increases (for example, for eight parameters, the number of "rectangles" reaches 81). The analytical calculation then becomes cumbersome and has to be computerized.

The estimations of the reliability of the calculation methods are presented in Table IV.2 for the procedures of normal and uniform DF.

Table IV.2 Example of the comparison of reliability of AGMA, ISO and Box's methods

Procedure	Method		
	AGMA	ISO	BOX's
I. Normal DF	0.592	0.502	0.536
I. Uniform DF	0.270	0.225	0.245
II. Uniform DF	0.320	0.205	0.250

Table IV.2 should be considered only as an illustration. Since the ISO gear calculation method takes into consideration much more information than the AGMA recommendation, the ISO method should give more reliable results. Of course, it would do so if the initial data were known more accurately. A method which is based on a larger number of parameters is obviously potentially more accurate. On the contrary, a method based on a smaller amount of parameters can never have the possibility of increasing its accuracy, because it is inherently short of information. We have to remember that even relatively accurate initial information can "damage" the calculation which takes into account a considerable number of parameters.

The big advantage of a more developed calculation method is reflected in the feasibility of getting comparative results which facilitate more flexibility for working conditions of a gear set than the less-developed methods permit.

Conclusions

1. The above-described approach permits comparison of different empiric computation methods and estimation of their reliability.
2. This approach permits estimation of the requirements of the accuracy by which the initial parameters have to be defined to get the computation results with the desired accuracy.
3. The number of parameters the considered method includes influences the reliability of the computation: the more parameters, the smaller the reliability.
4. The parameters of the ISO calculation method must be defined by 40-50% higher accuracy to provide the same reliability than the AGMA does.

SELECTED BIBLIOGRAPHY

1. AGMA, Gear Handbook Volume 1, Gear Classification Materials and Measuring Methods for Unassembled Gears. AGMA 380.03, January 1971.

2. Arai, M., and Ishikawa, G., "On the Accuracy of Machine Tool Gears", 1st and 2nd reports, Bulletin Tokyo Institute of Technology, Nos. 75 and 80, 1966.

3. Maruyama, K., and Nakada, T., "On Dynamic Measuring Method of the Rotating Error of the Master Worm-Wheel", Bulletin Tokyo Institute of Technology, 1968.

4. I.I. Murashov, Zubchatye Mechanizmy i Ih Tochnost, Izdatelstvo "Machinostroenie", Moskva, 1967 (In Russian).

5. B.M. Abramov, Kolebanija Prjamozubyh Zubchatyh Koljos, Izdatelstvo Harkovskogo Universiteta. (In Russian).

6. Masao, On the relation between the angular position error and the individual error of the gear, Bulletin of the Tokyo Institute of Technology N95, 1969.

7. Fiacco, A.V. and McCormick, G.P., Nonlinear Programming: Sequential Unconstrained Minimization Techniques. Wiley, New York, London, Sydney, Toronto, 1968.

8. Hadly, G., Nonlinear and Dynamic Programming, Addison-Wesley.

9. Rastrigin, L.A., "Statisticheskie Metody Poiska", Izdatelsvo Nauka, Moskva, 1968 (Statistical Methods of Search, in Russian).

10. Aoki, M. Techniques of Nonlinear Programming, Macmillan, New York.

11. B.Z. Sandler, "The Use of a Random Algorithm for Dynamic Optimization of Mechanisms", Journal of Engineering for Industry, Vol. 99, No. 1, February 1977.

12. Darle W. Dudley, The Evolution of the Gear Art, published by AGMA, Washington, D.C.

13. AGMA 420.04, December 1975.

14. ISO Recommendation R53, Basic Rack of Cylindrical Gears for General Engineering, 1st edition, December 1957.

CHAPTER V

NONLINEAR PROBLEMS

V.1 GENERAL CONSIDERATIONS

This chapter is devoted to nonlinear mechanical problems, for which we will consider three levels of complexity:

1. Nonlinear transformation of kinematic or inertia-free driving motion into driven motion (Fig. 87).
2. Inertial or dynamic nonlinear feedback-free transformation of driving motion into driven motion (Fig. 88).
3. Inertial or dynami linear transformation, taking feedback into account, of driving motion into driven motion (Fig. 89).

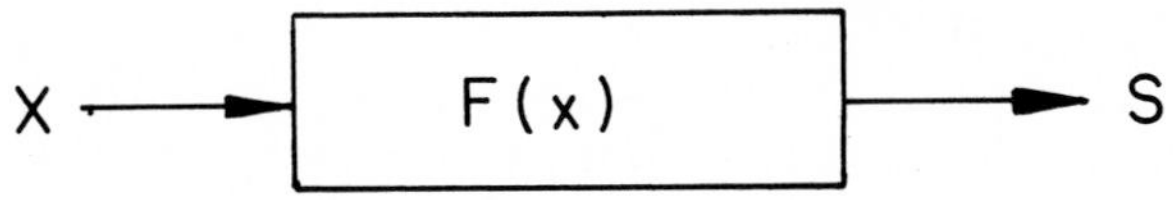

Fig. 87 Nonlinear transformation of kinematic (or inertia-free) driving motion into driven motion.

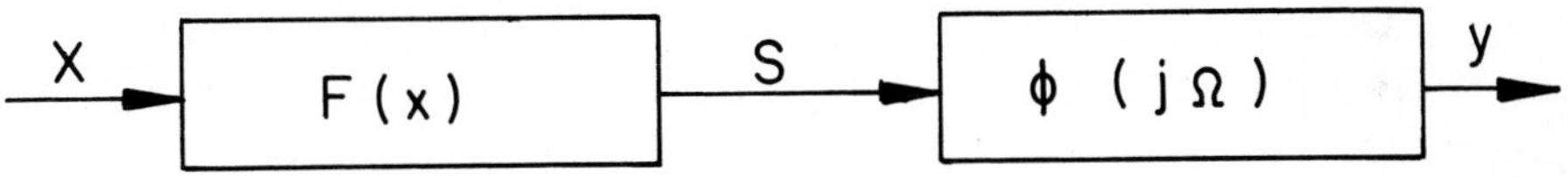

Fig. 88 Inertial or dynamic nonlinear feedback-free transformation of driving motion into driven motion.

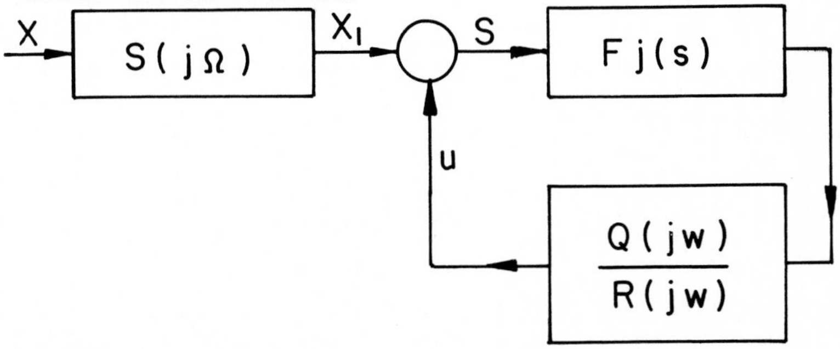

Fig. 89 Inertial or dynamic nonlinear transformation, taking feedback into account, of driving motion into driven motion.

Although we deal here mainly with joint-gap-like nonlinearities which are common in machinery, it should be remembered that the calculations are also applicable to other kinds of linearities.

In this section we describe the general ideas applicable to the solution of such problems, in the order of the complexity levels listed above. We thus begin with the kinematic transformation.

Considering the movement s of a driven link in a mechanical system, we write:

$$
\begin{aligned}
s &= \bar{s} + \mathring{s} \\
V &= \bar{V} + \mathring{V} \qquad \text{(V.1.1)} \\
W &= \bar{W} + \mathring{W}
\end{aligned}
$$

(here we use the same designations as in the previous chapters).

The movement s is assumed to be the result of a nonlinear transformation

$$s = F(x) \qquad \text{(V.1.2)}$$

where x is the driving motion, which is, in turn, represented by the following sum

$$x = \bar{x} + \mathring{x} \qquad \text{(V.1.3)}$$

Since F(x) is a nonlinear function, the superposition principle may not be applied. Thus, the values of $\bar{V}$ and $\bar{W}$ must be calculated as functions of both the variables $\bar{x}$ and $\mathring{x}$. As is obvious, the same conditions hold true with regard to the random components $\mathring{s}$, $\mathring{V}$ and $\mathring{W}$.

Let us now formulate the following problem. For a given nonlinearity $s = F(x)$, the average value $\bar{x}$, the correlation function K_x of the random function $\mathring{x}$ and its distribution law f(x) are known, and the average displacement $\bar{s}$ and the correlation function K_s of the random function $\mathring{s}$ must be found.

The characteristics $\bar{s}$ and K_s can be expressed through the distribution law f(s). However, it has been proved that it is permissible to express the sought characteristics directly through the f(x) - probability density distribution law of the variable x of the nonlinear function $s = F(x)$. Thus:

$$\bar{s} = \int_{-\infty}^{\infty} F(x)f(x)dx \qquad \text{(V.1.4)}$$

and

$$K_s = \int_{-\infty}^{\infty}\int F(x_1)F(x_2)f(x_1,x_2)dx_1dx_2 - \bar{x}_1\bar{x}_2 \qquad \text{(V.1.5)}$$

where the subscripts 1 and 2 distinguish between the values of x for the moments t and t + τ, respectively, and $f(x_1,x_2)$ is the two-dimensional density distribution law of the random function x. We assume this function to be described by a normal distribution law.

Then:

$$f(x) = \frac{1}{\sigma_x\sqrt{2\pi}} \exp[-\frac{(x-\bar{x})^2}{2\sigma_x^2}] \tag{V.1.6}$$

and

$$f(x_1,x_2) = \frac{1}{2\pi\sigma_{x_1}\sigma_{x_2}\sqrt{1-R_x^2}} \exp\{-\frac{1}{2(1-R_x^2)}\left[\frac{\mathring{x}_1^2}{\sigma_{x_1}^2} + \frac{\mathring{x}_2^2}{\sigma_{x_2}^2} - 2R_x\frac{\mathring{x}_1\mathring{x}_2}{\sigma_{x_1}\sigma_{x_2}}\right]\} \tag{V.1.7}$$

where

$$R_x = \frac{K_x}{\sigma_x^2} \tag{V.1.8}$$

For a stationary process $\mathring{x}$ we can simplify:

$$\sigma_{x_1} = \sigma_{x_2} = \sigma_x$$

In practice, the assumptions pertaining to the normality of the distribution law and the stationarity of the random process x (after it has reached a steady state value) are usually valid.

Substituting expression (V.1.7) into equation (V.1.5), we can calculate the correlation function K_s of the movement s of the driven link. We have, however, first to overcome the obstacle that the double integral cannot be expressed as elementary functions. To achieve this aim, we expand the two-dimensional normal distribution into Hermite-Chebyshev polynomials. Then,

$$K_s = \sum_{n=o}^{\infty} R_x^n(t,\tau)a_{1n}a_{2n} - \bar{x}_1\bar{x}_2 \tag{V.1.9}$$

The functions a_{in} are defined from the relationship:

$$a_{in}(\bar{x}_i,\sigma_x) = \frac{1}{\sqrt{2\pi n!}\,\sigma_{x_i}} \int_{-\infty}^{\infty} F(x_i)H_n\left\{\frac{x_i-\bar{x}_i}{\sigma_{x_i}}\right\}\exp[-\frac{1}{2}\left\{\frac{x_i-\bar{x}_i}{\sigma_{x_i}}\right\}^2]dx_i \tag{V.1.10}$$

where $H_n(\xi)$, the symbol of the Hermite-Chebyshev polynomial, is expressed as follows:

$$H_n(\xi) = (-1)^n e^{\xi^2/2} \frac{d}{d\xi^n} (e^{-\xi^2/2}) \tag{B.1.11}$$

The following recurrent relationship is known:

$$H_{n+1}(\xi) = H_n(\xi) - nH_{n-1}(\xi) \qquad (V.1.12)$$

From equation (V.1.11) it is obvious that:

$$H_o(\xi) = 1 \quad \text{and} \quad H_1(\xi) = \xi \qquad (V.1.13)$$

The H_n polynomials are orthogonal with a weight $e^{-\xi^2/2}$ on the straight line $-\infty < \xi < \infty$.

Thus:

$$\int_{-\infty}^{\infty} H_n(\xi)H_m(\xi)e^{-\xi^2/2}d\xi = \begin{cases} \sqrt{2}\ n! & m = n \\ 0 & m \neq n \end{cases}$$

or

$$\frac{1}{\sqrt{2\pi}\ \sigma_{x_i}} \int_{-\infty}^{\infty} H_n\left(\frac{x_i-\bar{x}_i}{\sigma_{x_i}}\right)H_m\left(\frac{x_i-\bar{x}_i}{\sigma_{x_i}}\right)\exp\left[-\frac{(x_i-\bar{x}_i)^2}{2\sigma_{x_i}^2}\right]dx_i = \begin{cases} n! & m = n \\ 0 & m \neq n \end{cases}$$

This means that $H_n((x_i-\bar{x}_i)/\sigma_{x_i})$ is orthogonal with a weight $f(x_i)$ on the straight line $-\infty < x_i < \infty$.

Now equation (V.1.10) can be rewritten in the following manner:

$$a_{in}(\bar{x}_i,\sigma_x) = \frac{1}{\sqrt{n!}} E\left\{F(x_i)H_n\left(\frac{x_i-\bar{x}_i}{\sigma_{x_i}}\right)\right\} \qquad i = 1,2 \qquad (V.1.15)$$

Substituting equations (V.1.12) and (V.1.13) into expression (V.1.15), we obtain:

$$a_{io} = \bar{s}_i \qquad (V.1.16)$$

and

$$a_{i(n+1)} = \frac{x_1}{\sqrt{n+1}} \frac{\partial^n \bar{s}_i}{\partial \bar{x}_i^n} \qquad (V.1.17)$$

The value $\bar{s}_i$ in equation (V.1.17) can be calculated by means of expression (V.1.4).

Since the coefficients a_{in} diminish rapidly (at least faster than 1/n!) only four terms of the series are satisfied, i.e., n = 0,1,2,3.

Obviously, for a stationary consideration, the subscripts i = 1,2 lose their meaning, $\bar{x}_i = 0$, and equation (V.1.9) can be rewritten as follows:

$$K_s = \sum_{n=1}^{\infty} R_x^n(\tau)a_n^2 \qquad (V.1.18)$$

It will be shown further that for the problems that concern us here for $\bar{x} = 0$ and for $\bar{x} \to \infty$, the mean values of the output motion are $\bar{s} = 0$ and $\bar{s} \to \bar{x}$, respectively. Therefore, in equation (V.1.18) the counting of terms begins from n = 1.

Despite the stationarity of the input driving motion x, the output (driven) motion s can be nonstationary because its correlation function K_s depends on t (not only on τ) which follows from the fact that a_n depends on t.

To calculate the variances D_s, D_v and D_w for the driven link from equation (V.1.18), we use the random part of driving movement $\mathring{x}$ and therefore the functions a_n [equation (V.1.19)], keeping in mind the assumption $\bar{x} = 0$.

We thus obtain:

$$D_s = \sum_{n=1}^{\infty} R^n(0)a_n^2 = \sigma_x^2 \sum_{n=1}^{\infty} c_n^2 \qquad (V.1.19)$$

where

$$c_n = \frac{a_n}{\sigma_x}$$

By double differentiation of equation (V.1.18) and inverting the sign (see I.31.5), we obtain $K_v(\tau)$, and by analogy, repeating this procedure once more, we obtain $K_w(\tau)$. Substituting $\tau = 0$ in these expressions, we can calculate the values D_v and D_w. At this point, we have completed the consideration of the first case mentioned at the beginning of this section.

The second case (Fig. 88) comprises a kinematic (inertia-free) transformation followed by a linear inertial (dynamic) transformation. In other words, a movement s acts in the input of the linear dynamic system [characterized by a transformation function $\Phi(j\omega)$], which in turn is a result of a nonlinear kinematic transformation of a movement x. As a result, we obtain a movement y which we calculate as follows:

$$S_y(\omega) = |\Phi(j\omega)|^2 S_s(\omega) \qquad (V.1.20)$$

where S_y and S_s - spectral densities of the movement y and s, respectively. It is clear that the spectrum S_s can be obtained from equation (V.1.18) by applying the treatment given in section I.34. If D_y is needed we use (I.35.2) to obtain:

$$D_y = \int_{-\infty}^{\infty} |\Phi(j\omega)|^2 \; S_s(\omega)d\omega \qquad (V.1.22)$$

$D_{\dot{y}}$ and $D_{\ddot{y}}$ can be found from the following two expressions:

$$D_{\dot{y}} = \int_{-\infty}^{\infty} |\Phi(j\omega)|^2\omega^2 S_s(\omega)d\omega \qquad (V.1.23)$$

and

$$D_{\ddot{y}} = \int_{-\infty}^{\infty} |\Phi(j\omega)|^2\omega^4 S_s(\omega)d\omega \qquad (V.1.24)$$

The third case pertains to a nonlinear differential equation of the following form (Fig. 89):

$$Q(j\omega)s + P(j\omega)y = R(j\omega)x \qquad (V.1.25)$$

where $y = F(s)$.

Here, the equation is composed of two parts - a linear component $Q(j\omega)$ and a nonlinear component $P(j\omega)$. The consideration is made only for the case where the input function x is stationary. To solve this equation we use the method of statistical linearization. In keeping with this method, we must build up an optimal linear approximation for the nonlinear function $F(s)$. Let us assume:

$$y = \bar{h}\bar{s} + \mathring{h}\mathring{s} \qquad (V.1.26)$$

The coefficients $\bar{h}$ and $\mathring{h}$ are constant and are functions of the values of the parameters s and σ_s. Thus:

$$\bar{h} = \bar{h}(\bar{s},\sigma_s) \qquad \text{and} \qquad \mathring{h} = \mathring{h}(\bar{s},\sigma_s) \qquad (V.1.27)$$

When the values $\bar{h}$ and $\mathring{h}$ have been calculated (in accordance with some criterion), they remain constant, and equation (V.1.26) can be said to be linear. This approximation allows us to rewrite expression (V.1.25) separately for the average and random terms of equation (V.1.26) and thus to obtain:

$$Q(j\omega)\bar{s} + P(j\omega)\bar{y} = R(j\omega)\bar{x} \qquad (V.1.28)$$

$$y = \bar{h}\bar{s}$$

$$Q(j\omega)\mathring{s} + P(j\omega)\mathring{y} = R(j\omega)\mathring{x} \qquad (V.1.29)$$

$$\mathring{y} = \mathring{h}\mathring{s}$$

These equations can be formally solved with respect to $\bar{s}$ and $\mathring{s}$:

$$\bar{s} = \bar{\phi}(j\omega,\bar{s},\sigma_s)\bar{x}$$

$$\mathring{s} = \mathring{\phi}(j\omega,\bar{s}\ \sigma_s)\mathring{x} \qquad (V.1.30)$$

where $\bar{\phi}$ and $\overset{\circ}{\phi}$ - transformation functions of the system of equations for the average and random terms, respectively. Equations (V.1.29) and (V.1.30) are linked via the $\bar{s}$ and σ_s values, and they must thus be solved together. It can be seen that equation (V.1.28) has the following solution:

$$\bar{s} = \bar{\ }(0,\bar{s},\sigma_s)\bar{x} = const \tag{V.1.31}$$

Expression (V.1.31) is written on the basis of the stationarity of $x(\bar{x}=const)$. In addition, this fact implies the absence of derivatives, i.e. $j\omega = 0$. Thus:

$$\bar{y} = \frac{R(0)}{P(0)}\bar{x} - \frac{Q(0)}{P(0)}\bar{s} \tag{V.1.32}$$

The straight line (V.1.32) is then put on the graph shown in Fig. 90.

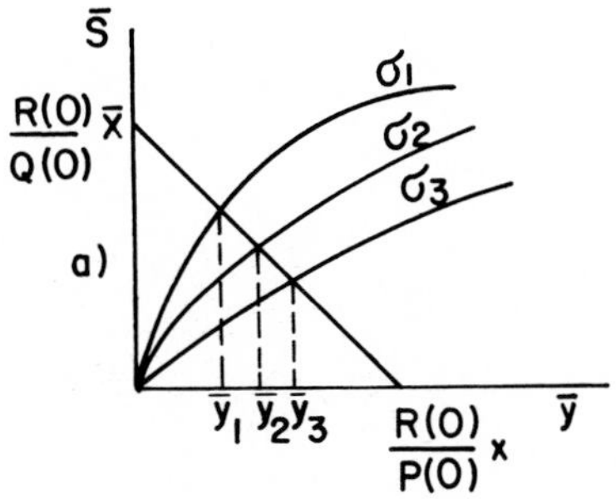

Fig. 90 Graphic interpretation of the seeking of the solution $\bar{s}(\bar{y})$.

On the other hand, the nonlinear function $y = F(s)$ provides us with the means of calculating the dependence $\bar{y}(\bar{s},\sigma_s)$. Here, we use the approach shown in expression (V.1.4).

This approach entails an assumption as to the form of the distribution law $f(s)$. Let us suppose that this law is normal. This assumption is justified for many practical applications and is based on the effect of normalization of a process transformed by a linear operator [in Fig. 89 the motion U coming out of $Q(j\omega)/R(j\omega)$ is more normal than the process y]. Thus:

$$\bar{y} = \frac{1}{\sigma_s\sqrt{2\pi}}\int_{-\infty}^{\infty} F(s)\exp\left[-\frac{(s-\bar{s})^2}{2\sigma_s^2}\right]ds \tag{V.1.33}$$

By solving this integral, we obtain a family of curves for different σ_s value values, as is shown in Fig. 90. The points of intersection between these curves and the straight line give the function:

$$\bar{y} = \bar{y}(\sigma_y) \tag{V.1.34}$$

The next step is to calculate the value of σ_y which is important for the computation of $\bar{y}$.

Let us now consider equation (V.1.29). After choosing as an approximation the criterion of equality of variances on the output of the approximated linear function $\mathring{y} = \mathring{h}\,\mathring{s}$ and the given nonlinear function $y = F(s)$, we obtain:

$$\mathring{h} = \sigma_y/\sigma_s \tag{V.1.35}$$

From equation (V.1.18), we have (assuming s is stationary):

$$K_y = \sum_{n=1}^{\infty} R_s^n(\tau)a_n^2 \tag{V.1.36}$$

where R_s - the normalized correlation function of the movement (or process) s. The a_n functions can be calculated in accordance with equations (V.1.16) and (V.1.17). Thus, we obtain σ_y from equation (V.1.36):

$$\sigma_y^2 = \sum_{n=1}^{\infty} R_s^n(0)a_n^2 \tag{V.1.37}$$

[Note: At this stage we can obtain the definition of $\bar{y}(\sigma_s)$ from equation (V.1.34) if necessary.]

Now, we obtain from expressions (V.1.35) and (V.1.37):

$$\mathring{h} = \frac{\sqrt{\sum_{n=1}^{\infty} R_s^2(0)a_n^2}}{\sigma_s} \tag{V.1.38}$$

By substituting equation (V.1.37) into equation (V.1.29), we obtain this linear equation from which σ_s^2 can be derived:

$$\sigma_s^2 = \int_{-\infty}^{\infty} S_s d\omega = \int_{-\infty}^{\infty} |\Phi(j\omega)|^2 S_x d\omega = \int_{-\infty}^{\infty} \left|\frac{R(j\omega)}{Q(j\omega) + \mathring{h}P(j\omega)}\right|^2 S_x d\omega \tag{V.1.39}$$

This expression is implicit with respect to σ_s because $\mathring{h}$ also depends on σ_s. By solving expression (V.1.39), we define σ_s, and then using equation (V.1.34) we obtain $\bar{s}$.

2. INFLUENCE OF A JOINT GAP ON LINK KINEMATICS

Let us find the probabilistic characteristics of the motion errors of a kinematic pair connected by a joint with a clearance (joint gap). We will consider the two kinds of joint shown in Fig. 91 and 92.

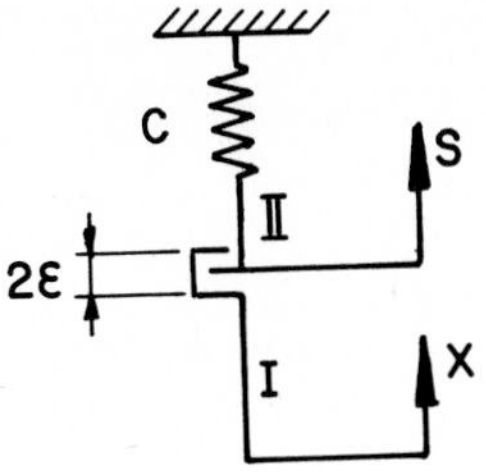

Fig. 91 An "inertia-less" returnable joint-gap.

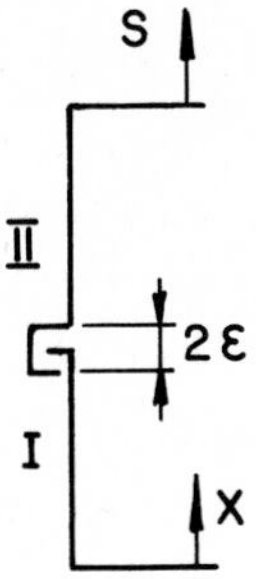

Fig. 92 An example of a conventional joint with a clearance.

The first case (Fig. 91) deals with a joint consisting of a driving link (link I) and a driven link (link II), whose movements are described by x and s, respectively. This joint is "inertia-less," i.e. link II moves only when link I makes contact with it. If contact is not made, link II immediately returns to the equilibrium position where s = 0. The kinematic treatment of this type of joint is meaningless, but the dynamic consideration can be very useful. This type of joint, which illustrates nonlinear stiffness (a spring connected to an oscillating mass by a joint gap), can be described as follows:

$$F(x) = s = \begin{cases} x + \varepsilon; & -\infty < x < -\varepsilon \\ 0 \quad ; & -\varepsilon < x < \varepsilon \\ x - \varepsilon; & \varepsilon < x < \infty \end{cases} \qquad (V.2.1)$$

where 2ε - the value of the gap.

From equation (V.1.4), assuming a normal distribution for x, we obtain:

$$\bar{s} = \frac{1}{\sigma_x\sqrt{2\pi}}\left\{\int_{-\infty}^{-\varepsilon}(x+\varepsilon)\exp\left[-\frac{(x-\bar{x})^2}{2\sigma_x^2}\right]dx + \int_{\varepsilon}^{\infty}(x-\varepsilon)\exp\left[-\frac{(x-\bar{x})^2}{2\sigma_x^2}\right]dx\right\} \qquad (V.2.2)$$

Integration gives:

$$\bar{s} = \frac{\sigma_x}{\sqrt{2\pi}}\left\{\exp\left[-\frac{(\varepsilon-\bar{x})^2}{2\sigma_x^2}\right] - \exp\left[-\frac{(\varepsilon+\bar{x})^2}{2\sigma_x^2}\right]\right\} + (\varepsilon-\bar{x})\,\Phi\left[\frac{\varepsilon-\bar{x}}{\sqrt{2}\sigma_x}\right] - (\varepsilon+\bar{x})\,\Phi\left[\frac{\varepsilon+\bar{x}}{\sqrt{2}\sigma_x}\right] + \bar{x} \qquad (V.2.3)$$

where Φ - Laplace function.

It seems more convenient to denote:

$$Y = \frac{\bar{s}}{\sqrt{2}\sigma_x} ; \qquad \Delta = \frac{\varepsilon}{\sqrt{2}\sigma_x} ; \qquad \xi = \frac{\bar{x}}{\sqrt{2}\sigma_x} \tag{V.2.4}$$

We can then rewrite equation (V.2.3) in the following form:

$$Y = \frac{1}{2\sqrt{\pi}} \left\{ \exp[-(\Delta-\xi)^2] - \exp[-(\Delta+\xi)^2] + \right.$$
$$\left. + \frac{\Delta-\xi}{2} \Phi(\Delta-\xi) - \frac{\Delta+\xi}{2} \Phi(\Delta+\xi) + \xi \right\} \tag{V.2.5}$$

Fig. 93 presents a family of curves $Y(\xi)$ for several values of Δ.

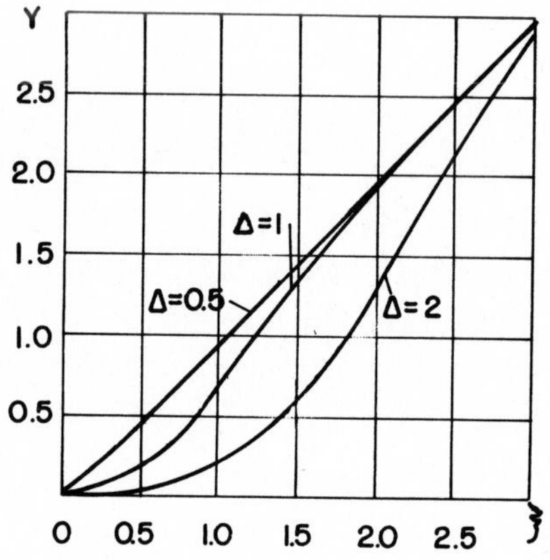

Fig. 93 The ratio $\bar{s}/\bar{y}$ as a function of the gap value.

These graphs indicate that the ratio $\bar{s}/\bar{x}$ tends to 1, but falls below 1 in the range $0 \leq \bar{x} <$ several σ_x. Differentiating equation (V.2.4), we obtain expressions for the average speed and average acceleration of the driven link:

$$\bar{V} = \dot{\bar{x}}\left\{1 - \frac{1}{\sqrt{\pi}} \left[(\Delta+\xi)\exp -(\Delta+\xi)^2\right\} + (\Delta-\xi)\exp\left\{-(\Delta-\xi)^2\right\} - \right.$$
$$\left. - \Phi(\Delta-\xi) - \Phi(\Delta+\xi)\right\} = \dot{\bar{x}}\, A \tag{V.2.6}$$

and

$$\bar{W} = \ddot{\bar{x}}A - \frac{\dot{\bar{x}}^2}{\sqrt{2\pi}\sigma_x} \left\{ \left[1 - 2(\Delta+\xi) - \frac{2}{\sqrt{\pi}}\right]\exp[-(\Delta+\xi)^2] - \right.$$
$$\left. - \left[1 - 2(\Delta-\xi) - \frac{2}{\sqrt{\pi}}\right]\exp[-(\Delta-\xi)^2]\right\} \tag{V.2.7}$$

Analyzing expressions (V.2.6) and (V.2.7), we can draw the following conclusion: The average values of the velocity and the acceleration of the driven link tend towards those of the driving link. The smaller the gap and the bigger σ_x, the stronger this tendency.

We can calculate the correlation function K_s of the motion s from equation (V.1.18). In turn, we can define a_n from equations (V.1.16) and (V.1.17) in the following manner:

$$a_1 = \sigma_x\{1 - \frac{1}{2}[\Phi(\Delta-\xi) + \Phi(\Delta+\xi)]\}$$

$$a_2 = \frac{\sigma_x}{2\sqrt{\pi}}\{\exp[-(\Delta-\xi)^2] - \exp[-(\Delta+\xi)^2]\} \qquad (V.2.8)$$

$$a_3 = \frac{\sigma_x}{\sqrt{6\pi}}\{(\Delta-\xi)\exp[-(\Delta-\xi)^2] + (\Delta+\xi)\exp[-(\Delta+\xi)^2]\}$$

Considering only the centralized value $\overset{o}{x}$ of the input motion x, we substitute $\bar{x} = 0$ into equation (V.2.8). Then, from equation (V.1.19) we obtain:

$$c_1 = 1 - \Phi(\Delta)$$

$$c_2 = 0 \qquad (V.2.9)$$

$$c_3 = \frac{2}{\sqrt{6\pi}}\Delta\exp(-\Delta^2)$$

From expressions (V.2.9) we can now obtain σ_s^2:

$$\sigma_s^2 = \sigma_x^2[1 - \Phi(\Delta) + \frac{2}{\sqrt{6\pi}}\Delta\exp(-\Delta^2)] \qquad (V.2.10)$$

The dependence of σ_s^2/σ_x^2 on Δ is shown in Fig. 94. This graph illustrates the "smooting" effect of this point. The bigger the gap, the smaller σ_s.

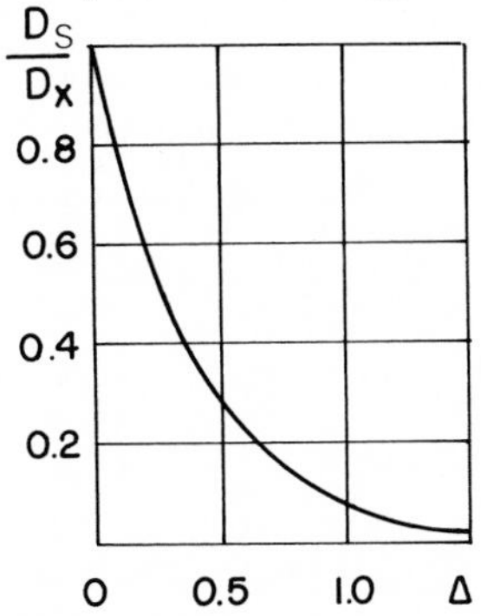

Fig. 94. The ratio of variances of the output and input motions as a function of the gap values (for the case shown in Fig. 91).

Let us now consider the second case shown in Fig. 92. Here, the driven link moves only under the direct pressure of the driving link. When there is no pressure, the driven link cannot move. The nonlinearity describing the motion of the second case can be written as follows:

$$F(x) = s = \begin{cases} x & s - x = 0 \\ 0 & -\varepsilon_1 < s - x < \varepsilon_2 \quad \text{or} \quad \varepsilon_1 + s > x > s - \varepsilon_2 \\ x & s - x = \varepsilon_1 + \varepsilon_2 \end{cases} \tag{V.2.11}$$

Thus, using equation (V.1.4) we obtain:

$$\bar{s} = \int_{-\infty}^{\infty} F(x)f(x)dx - \int_{s-\varepsilon_2}^{s+\varepsilon_1} F(x)f(x)dx \tag{V.2.12}$$

For further calculations we assume $\varepsilon_1 = \varepsilon_2 = \varepsilon$.

As long as we seek an average value, we can substitute for s in the limits of the integral its average $\bar{s}$. Thus, assuming f(x) is normal, we can rewrite equation (V.2.12):

$$0 = \bar{x} - \bar{s} - \frac{\sigma_x}{\sqrt{2\pi}} \{\exp[-(\frac{\bar{s}-\bar{x}-\varepsilon}{\sqrt{2}\,\sigma_x})^2] - \exp[-(\frac{\bar{s}-\bar{x}+\varepsilon}{\sqrt{2}\,\sigma_x})^2]\} - $$
$$- \frac{\bar{x}}{2} [\Phi(\frac{\bar{s}-\bar{x}+\varepsilon}{\sqrt{2}\,\sigma_x}) + (\frac{\bar{x}-\bar{s}+\varepsilon}{\sqrt{2}\,\sigma_x})] \tag{V.2.13}$$

or, using equation (V.2.4) we obtain:

$$0 = \xi - Y - \frac{1}{2\sqrt{\pi}} \{\exp[-(Y-\xi-\Delta)^2] - \exp[-(Y-\xi+\Delta)^2]\} - $$
$$- \frac{\xi}{2} [\Phi(Y-\xi+\Delta) + \Phi(\xi-Y+\Delta)] \tag{V.2.14}$$

Differentiating equations (V.2.13) and (V.2.14), we obtain for the velocities and accelerations, respectively:

$$\dot{\bar{x}} - \dot{\bar{s}} - \frac{1}{\sqrt{\pi}} (\dot{\bar{s}}-\dot{\bar{x}}) \{[Y+2\xi-\Delta]\exp[-(\Delta+Y-\xi)^2] - $$
$$-[\Delta+Y+2\xi]\exp[-(Y-\xi-\Delta)^2]\} - \frac{\dot{\bar{x}}}{\sqrt{2}} [\Phi(\Delta+Y-\xi) + \Phi(\Delta-Y+\xi)] = \tag{V.2.15}$$
$$= \dot{\bar{x}}-\dot{\bar{s}} - \frac{1}{\sqrt{\pi}} (\dot{\bar{s}}-\dot{\bar{x}})A - \frac{\dot{\bar{x}}}{\sqrt{2}} B = 0 ;$$

$$\ddot{x} - \ddot{s} - \frac{1}{\sqrt{\pi}} [(\ddot{s}-\ddot{x})A + \frac{2(\ddot{s}-\ddot{x})^2}{\sqrt{2}\,\sigma_x} \{[\Delta+Y+2\xi][\Delta+Y+\xi]\exp[-(\Delta-Y+\xi)^2] -$$

$$-[\Delta-Y-2\xi][\Delta-Y-\xi]\exp[-(\Delta+y-\xi)^2]\} - \frac{(\dot{s}+2\dot{x})(\dot{x}+\dot{s})}{\sqrt{2}\,\sigma_x} \{\exp[-(\Delta-Y+\xi)^2] - \qquad (V.2.16)$$

$$- \exp[-(\Delta+Y-\xi)^2]\}] - \frac{\ddot{x}}{\sqrt{2}} B + \frac{\dot{x}(\dot{s}-\dot{x})}{2\sqrt{\pi}\,\sigma_x} \{\exp[-(\Delta+Y-\xi)^2] -$$

$$- \exp[-(\Delta-Y+\xi)^2]\} = 0$$

Note that A is used to denote the complicated expression written within the braces in equation (V.2.6) and B as a substitute for $\Phi(\Delta+Y-\xi) + \Phi(\Delta-Y+\xi)$ in equation (V.2.15).

Proceeding to the calculation of D_S, D_V and D_W, we use again the formulas (V.1.16) and (V.1.18). Assuming $\overline{x} = 0$ and calculating a_n functions, we obtain:

$$c_1 = \frac{1 + (2/\sqrt{\pi})\ \Delta\exp(-\Delta^2) - \Phi(\Delta)}{1 + (2/\sqrt{\pi})\ \Delta\exp(-\Delta^2)}$$

$$c_2 = 0 \qquad (V.2.17)$$

$$c_3 = \frac{4\Delta^2 + 6(1-2\Delta^2)c_1 + 3(1-2\Delta^2)c_1^2 + 2(3-2\Delta^2)c_1^3}{1 + (2/\sqrt{\pi})\ \Delta\exp(-\Delta^2)} \cdot \frac{\Delta}{\sqrt{6\pi}} \exp(-\Delta^2)$$

Thus, from equation (V.1.18) we calculate K_s.

The ratio D_s/D_v is shown in Fig. 95. From this figure we can once again draw the following conclusion about the smooting effect of the joint gap: the bigger the gap, the smaller the variance of the driven motion s.

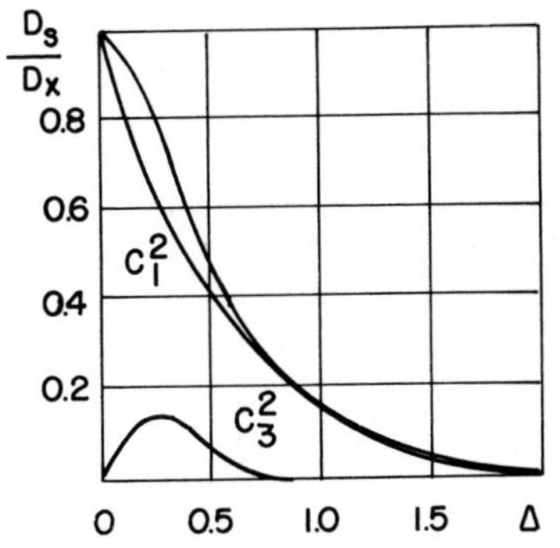

Fig. 95. The ratio of variances of the output and input motions as a function of the gap value (for the case shown in Fig. 92).

To show the effect of this joint on the variances of the velocity and acceleration of the driven link, we have to approximate some form of correlation function R_x. Taking

$$R_x = e^{-\alpha\tau^2} \tag{V.2.18}$$

we obtain for

$$R_{\dot{x}} = 2\alpha e^{-\alpha\tau^2}[1 - 2\alpha\tau^2]$$

and for

$$R_{\ddot{x}} = 4\alpha^2 e^{-\alpha\tau}[3 - 12\alpha^2\tau^2 + 4\alpha^2\tau^4]$$

Correspondingly we obtain:

$$D_{\dot{x}} = 2\alpha\sigma_x^2 \qquad \text{and} \qquad D_{\ddot{x}} = 12\alpha^2\sigma_x^2 \tag{V.2.19}$$

From equations (V.1.18), (V.2.18) and (V.2.19) we obtain:

$$D_{\dot{s}} \simeq 2\alpha\sigma_x^2 \sum_{n=1}^{3} nc_n \tag{V.2.20}$$

and

$$D_{\ddot{s}} \simeq 12\alpha^2\sigma_x^2 \sum_{n=1}^{3} n^2 c_n \tag{V.2.21}$$

The ratio $D_{\dot{s}}/D_{\dot{x}}$ for different Δ (or ε) values is shown in Fig. 96.

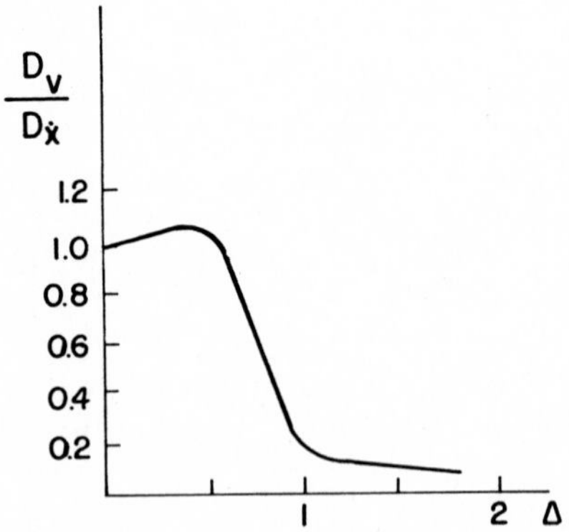

Fig. 96. The ratio of variances of the output and input speeds as a function of the gap value (for the case shown in Fig. 92).

The ratio $D_{\ddot{s}}/D_{\ddot{x}}$ is given as a function of Δ in Fig. 97. The conclusion that can be drawn at this stage is that there are maxima of both these ratios at Δ about 0.5 (Fig. 97). The existence of these maxima is important when accelerations are being considered: increasing the gap (or Δ) further diminishes the effect and for Δ about 2 or more the variances of the velocities and accelerations tend to 0.

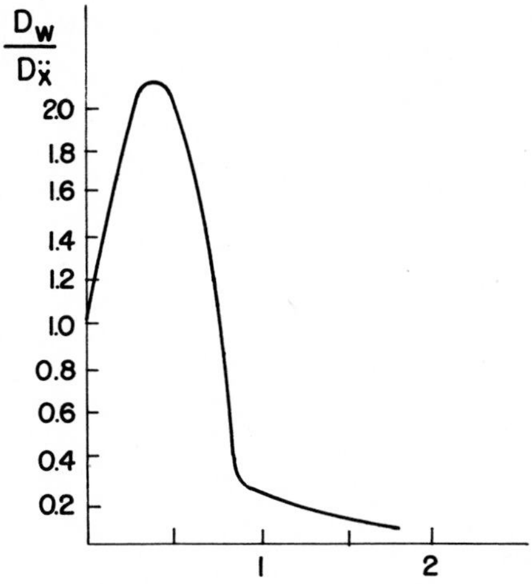

Fig. 97. The ratio of variances of the output and input accelerations as a function of the gap value (for the cases shown in Fig. 93).

Obviously, taking $\varepsilon_1 = 0$ (or $\varepsilon_2 = 0$), we will obtain another form of the formula developed in expression (V.2.14). Substituting $\varepsilon_1 \to \infty$ in the function $s = F(x)$, we get another type of nonlinearity (a relay-type joint) which gives, for instance for $\bar{s}$, the following formula:

$$\xi - Y + \frac{1}{2\sqrt{\pi}} \exp[-(Y-\xi+\Delta)^2] - \frac{\xi}{2}\Phi(Y-\xi+\Delta) + \frac{\xi}{2} = 0 \qquad \text{(V.2.22)}$$

The type of joint gap shown in Fig. 92 has some kinematic applications for mechanisms operating at slow speeds with relatively high friction which prevent inertial movement, for example, the slide cut-off feeders shown in Fig. 98 (a) and (b). In case (a) a reciprocating sliding body is driven by a cosine mechanism with a backlash between the slot and the driving pin. Fig. 98 (b) shows a rotating feeder driven by a spatial cam in which there is a gap between the cam slots and the pins fastened to the rotating disk.

The third case (case c) presented in Fig. 98 comprises an electric commutator driven by a chain which sags thus causing a backlash ε in the sprockets.

This backlash causes a play in the motion s on the commutator contacts. In these cases the smoothing effects described above can be helpful.

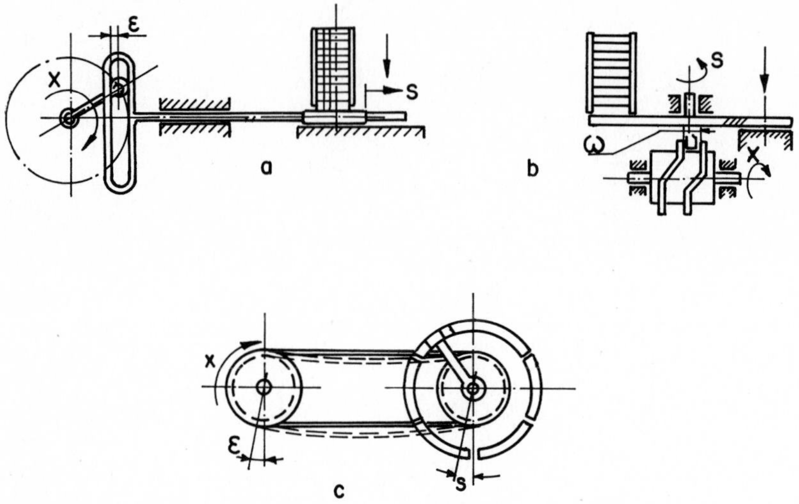

Fig. 98. (a) Reciprocating slide cut-off feeder; (b) rotating slide cut-off feeder; (c) electric commutator.

Example: Let us consider the feeder given in Fig. 98 (b) in which the cam angular velocity $\omega = 10\ \text{sec}^{-1}$; the cam profile errors are described by a correlation function $K_x = 0.001\ e^{-30^2\tau^2}\ \text{mm}^2$ (i.e. $\sigma_x \simeq 0.0316$ mm); and the gap in the joint $\varepsilon = 0.07$ mm. Thus, $\Delta \simeq 0.05$. From Fig. 95 we have $\sigma_s^2/\sigma_x^2 = 0.5$ or $\sigma_s \simeq 0.022$ mm (compared with $\sigma_x \simeq 0.0316$ mm). From Fig. 96 we obtain $\sigma_v^2/\sigma_{\dot{x}}^2 \simeq 1.05$, or knowing from equation (V.2.19) $\sigma_{\dot{x}} \simeq 0.245$ mm/sec we calculate $\sigma_v \simeq 0.251$ mm/sec. By analogy for acceleration we calculate for $\sigma_{\ddot{x}} \simeq 3.286\ \text{mm/sec}^2$, and from Fig. 97 we obtain $\sigma_w^2/\sigma_{\ddot{x}}^2 \simeq 2.1$ and $\sigma_w \simeq 4.76\ \text{mm/sec}^2$.

3. DYNAMICS OF A JOINT GAP (WITHOUT FEEDBACK)

This section is devoted to the second case mentioned at the beginning of section V.1 and illustrated by the layout shown in Fig. 88.

The layout shown in Fig. 88 can be applied to a model such as that shown in Fig. 99 constituting a tiny dynamic system, for instance, consisting of one small mass m fastened to a massive link driven through a joint gap by another massive link. In this case, there is not (or at least this can be easily assumed) any feedback from the mass m to the driving links. Here, the input

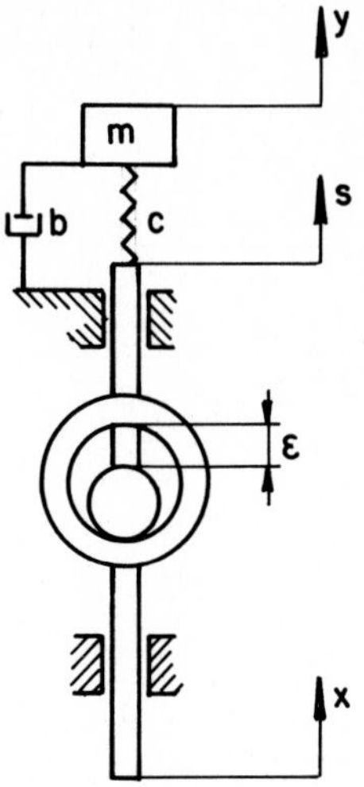

Fig. 99. Model of a dynamic nonlinear feedback-free mechanical system.

motion x and its statistical characteristics are known. We calculate K_s (as is shown in section 2) and then define the spectral density S_s. Thus, if $K_x = \sigma_x^2 e^{-\alpha\tau^2}$ then, as is shown in equation (V.1.17), we obtain for K_s

$$K_s = \sum_{n=1}^{\infty} e^{-n\alpha\tau^2} a_n^2 \simeq \sigma_x^2 \sum_{n=1}^{3} e^{-n\alpha\tau^2} c_n^2 \tag{V.3.1}$$

Remembering expression (V.2.17), we can rewrite equation (V.3.1) as follows:

$$K_s \simeq \sigma_x^2 [e^{-\alpha\tau^2} c_1^2 + e^{-3\alpha\tau^2} c_3^2] \tag{V.3.2}$$

For this correlation function, the spectral density takes the following form (see I.34):

$$S_s = \frac{\sigma_x^2}{2\sqrt{\alpha\pi}} \sum_{i=1}^{n} \frac{1}{\sqrt{n}} \exp(-\omega^2/4\alpha\sqrt{n}) c_n^2 \simeq \frac{\sigma_x^2}{2\sqrt{\alpha\pi}} [\exp(-\omega^2/4\alpha) c_1^2 + \exp[-\omega^2/4\sqrt{3}\alpha) c_3^2] \tag{V.3.3}$$

The differential equation of the dynamic system has the following form:

$$m\ddot{y} + b\dot{y} + cy = cs$$

or (V.3.4)

$$\ddot{y} + \ell\dot{y} + k^2 y = k^2 s$$

Thus:

$$\Phi(j\omega) = \frac{k^2}{k^2-\omega^2 + \ell j\omega} \tag{V.3.5}$$

which gives for the spectral density S_y of the motion y of the excited mass m:

$$S_y \simeq \frac{k^4\sigma_x^2}{|k^2-\omega^2+\ell j\omega|^2\ 2\sqrt{\alpha\pi}}\ [\exp(-\omega^2/4\alpha)c_1^2 + \exp(-\omega^2/4\sqrt{3}\alpha)c_3^2] \tag{V.3.6}$$

Obviously for $\dot{y}$ and $\ddot{y}$, we obtain

$$S_{\dot{y}} \simeq \frac{k^4\sigma_x^2\omega^2}{|k^2-\omega^2+\ell j\omega|^2\ 2\sqrt{\alpha\pi}}\ [\exp(-\omega^2/4\alpha)c_1^2 + \exp(-\omega^2/4\sqrt{3}\alpha)c_3^2] \tag{V.3.7}$$

$$S_{\ddot{y}} \simeq \frac{k^4\sigma_x^2\omega^4}{|k^2-\omega^2+\ell j\omega|^2\ 2\sqrt{\alpha\pi}}\ [\exp(-\omega^2/4\alpha)c_1^2 + \exp(-\omega^2/4\sqrt{3}\alpha)c_3^2] \tag{V.3.8}$$

The variances can then be calculated as follows:

$$\sigma_y^2 = \frac{k^4\sigma_x^2}{2\sqrt{\alpha\pi}} \int_{-\infty}^{\infty} \frac{c_1^2\exp(-\omega^2/4\alpha) + c_3^2\exp(-\omega^2/4\sqrt{3}\alpha)}{|k^2-\omega^2+\ell j\omega|^2}\, d\omega \tag{V.3.9}$$

$$\sigma_{\dot{y}}^2 = \frac{k^4\sigma_x^2}{2\sqrt{\alpha\pi}} \int_{-\infty}^{\infty} \frac{c_1^2\exp(-\omega^2/4\alpha) + c_3^2\exp(-\omega^2/4\sqrt{3}\alpha)}{|k^2-\omega^2+\ell j\omega|^2}\, \omega^2 d\omega \tag{V.3.10}$$

$$\sigma_{\ddot{y}}^2 = \frac{k^4\sigma_x^2}{2\sqrt{\alpha\pi}} \int_{-\infty}^{\infty} \frac{c_1^2\exp(-\omega^2/4\alpha) + c_3^2\exp(-\omega^2/4\sqrt{3}\alpha)}{|k^2-\omega^2+\ell j\omega|^2}\, \omega^4 d\omega \tag{V.3.11}$$

The model discussed above can be illustrated by the following practical example. On a rotating slide cut-off-feeder (Fig. 98b) an electromagnetic relay is mounted. This relay, which belongs to the machine's control system, consists of flat springs with relatively massive contacts on their ends. The non-uniformity of the feeder's disk excites vibrations in the contact and can cause false shortings. The calculation presented above provides us with the possibility of analyzing the situation.

4. DYNAMICS OF A JOINT GAP (WITH FEEDBACK)

Here, we begin the discussion with the model shown in Fig. 100. Let us suppose that the random component of the output motion s of the mass m is

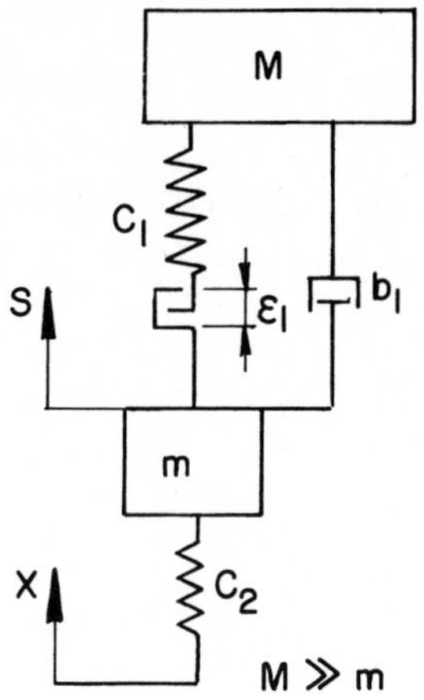

Fig. 100. Model of a dynamic nonlinear system with a clearance.

described by a normal distribution law. (The wider the spectrum of frequencies of the excitement motion x, the stronger the justification for this assumption.) Using this model, we will illustrate the calculation method discussed in section 1 of this chapter. The differential equation describing this model has the following form:

$$\ddot{s} + \ell_1 s + k_2^2 s + y(s) = k_2^2 x \tag{V.4.1}$$

where

$$\ell_1 = \frac{b_1}{m} ; \quad k_1^2 = \frac{c_1}{m} ; \quad k_2^2 = \frac{c_2}{m}$$

(the designations are clear from Fig. 100).

$$y(s) = k_1^2(s \pm \frac{\varepsilon}{2}) = \begin{cases} k_1^2 ; & \varepsilon/2 < s < \infty \\ 0 ; & -\varepsilon/2 \leq s \leq \varepsilon/2 \\ k_1^2 ; & -\infty < s < -\varepsilon/2 \end{cases} \tag{V.4.2}$$

Now, we can rewrite equation (V.4.1) in the form of operators:

$$Q(p)s + P(p)y = R(p)x$$

where

$$Q(p) = p^2 + \ell_1 p + k_1^2$$

$$P(p) = 1 ; \quad R(p) = k_2^2 \tag{V.4.3}$$

Expressions (V.4.3) correspond to expressions (V.1.25). From equation (V.1.26) we have, for the nonlinear function y(s), the linear approximation:

$$y(s) = \bar{h}\bar{s} + \mathring{h}\mathring{s} = \bar{y}(s) + \mathring{y}(s) \tag{V.4.4}$$

The constant coefficients of linearization will be calculated as functions of the parameters $\bar{s}$ and σ_s:

$$h = h(\bar{s},\sigma_s) \quad \text{and} \quad \mathring{h} = \mathring{h}(\bar{s},\sigma_s)$$

In accordance with equations (V.1.28) and (V.1.29), we can rewrite expressions (V.4.3) in the form of two separate equations (linearized equations comply with the superposition principle):

$$\begin{aligned} Q(p)\bar{s} + P(p)\bar{y} &= R(p)\bar{x} \\ \bar{y} &= \bar{h}\bar{s} \end{aligned} \tag{V.4.5}$$

$$\begin{aligned} Q(p)\mathring{s} + P(p)\mathring{y} &= R(p)\mathring{x} \\ \mathring{y} &= \mathring{h}\mathring{s} \end{aligned} \tag{V.4.6}$$

Under the conditions described in equations (V.1.31) and (V.1.32) for the specific case given in expressions (V.4.3), we have:

$$\bar{y} = \frac{R(0)}{P(0)}\bar{x} - \frac{Q(0)}{P(0)}\bar{s} = k_2^2(\bar{x} - \bar{s}) \tag{V.4.7}$$

By means of another approach we can calculate $\bar{y}$ by applying equation (V.1.4) and by assuming normal distribution for the $\mathring{x}$ variable. Thus:

$$\bar{y} = \frac{1}{\sigma_s\sqrt{2\pi}} \int_{-\infty}^{\infty} y(s)\exp[-\frac{(s-\bar{s})^2}{2\sigma_s}]ds$$

which gives:

$$\frac{Y}{k_1^2} = \frac{1}{2\sqrt{\pi}}\{\exp[-(\Delta-\xi)^2] - \exp[-(\Delta+\xi)^2]\} + \frac{\Delta-\xi}{2}\Phi(\Delta-\xi) - \frac{\Delta+\xi}{2}\Phi(\Delta+\xi) + \xi \tag{V.4.8}$$

where:

$$\Delta = \frac{\varepsilon}{2\sqrt{2}\sigma_s}; \quad \xi = \frac{\bar{s}}{\sqrt{2}\sigma_s}; \quad Y = \frac{\bar{y}}{\sqrt{2}\sigma_s}; \quad \Phi(z) = \frac{2}{\sqrt{\pi}}\int_{\infty}^{z} e^{-t^2}dt$$

The dependence between the values of Y/k_1^2 and ξ for different Δ is shown in Fig. 101. (Attention should be paid to the similarity between Fig. 93 and 101: the only difference lies in the scale factor which is a result of the physical differences in the subjects under consideration.)

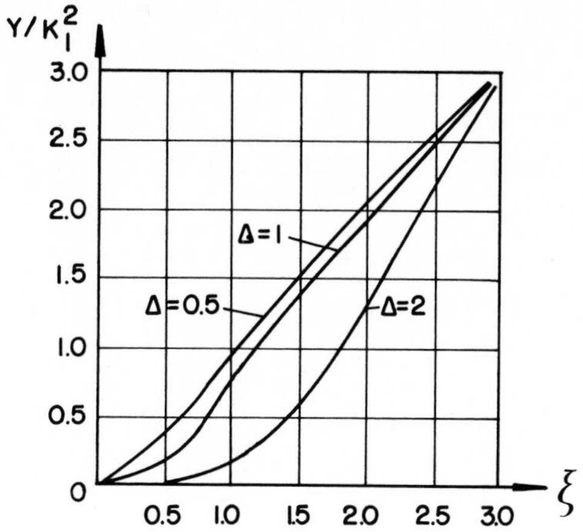

Fig. 101. The value Y as a function of the gap value.

Now, by dividing equation (V.4.7) by $\sqrt{2}\sigma_s$, we obtain:

$$Y = k_2^2(X - \xi) \tag{V.4.9}$$

where

$$X = \bar{x}/\sqrt{2}\sigma_s$$

By solving expressions (V.4.7) and (V.4.9) simultaneously and excluding Y, we obtain for $\bar{s}$ an expression in the form:

$$\bar{s}(\sigma_s, \varepsilon) = \bar{s}(\Delta) \tag{V.4.10}$$

This solution is plotted in Fig. 102. In accordance with Fig. 90, we put the straight lines (V.4.9) on the curves shown in Fig. 101 and thus find the dependence (V.4.10), which is shown in Fig. 103.

Let us now define the variance σ_s^2. For this purpose, we must choose a criterion for the approximation. Here, we take as the criterion the following equality:

$$\mathring{h} = \sigma_y/\sigma_s \tag{V.4.11}$$

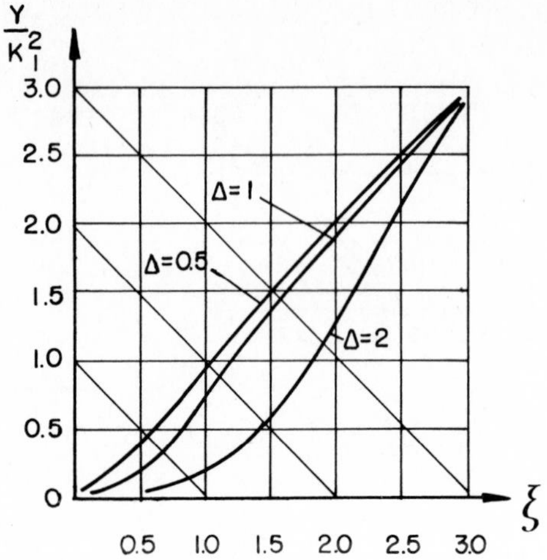

Fig. 102. Graphic solution of $Y(\xi)$.

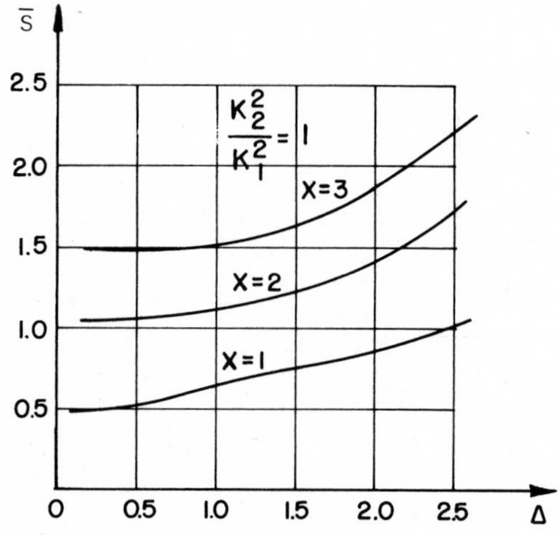

Fig. 103. The dependences $\bar{s}(\Delta)$.

Obviously, expression (V.4.11) holds true for starionary $\overset{\circ}{s}$. We therefore use equations (V.1.37) and (V.2.8) for the condition $\xi = 0$ (or $\bar{s} = 0$ because the centralized value of the motion $\overset{\circ}{s}$ is under consideration). We thus obtain [see equation (V.2.9)]:

$$a_1 = k_{1\,s}^2[1 - \Phi(\Delta)]$$

$$a_2 = 0$$

$$a_3 = k_1^2 \sigma_s \frac{2}{\sqrt{6\pi}} \Delta \exp[-\Delta^2]$$

And finally:

$$\sigma_y = k_1^2 \sigma_s \sqrt{[1 - \Phi(\Delta)]^2 + \frac{2}{3\pi} \Delta^2 \exp[-2\Delta^2]}$$

and

$$\mathring{h} = k_1^2 \sqrt{[1 - \Phi(\Delta)]^2 + \frac{2}{3\pi} \Delta^2 \exp[-2\Delta^2]}$$

This function is presented in Fig. 104.

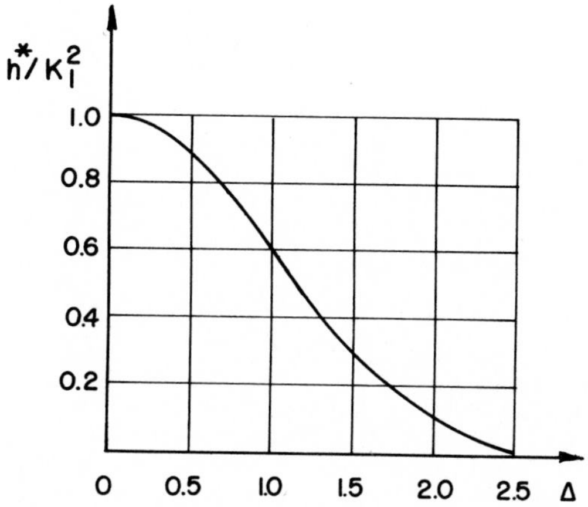

Fig. 104. The linearization coefficient as a function of the gap.

By substituting the linearized approximation $\mathring{h}\mathring{s}$ of y(s) in the differential equation (V.4.1) or (V.4.6), we can express the transform function of the dynamic model under discussion in the form:

$$\Phi(j\omega) = \frac{k_2^4}{|(k_2^2 + \mathring{h} - \omega^2)^2 + \ell^2\omega^2|} \quad \text{(V.4.13)}$$

By knowing the spectral density S_x of the input motion x, we can write from the spectral density S_s of the output motion s the following expression:

$$S_s = \frac{k_2^4 S_x}{|(k_2^2 + \mathring{h} - \omega^2)^2 + \ell^2\omega^2|}$$

and for the variance σ_s we obtain:

$$\sigma_s^2 = \int_{-\infty}^{\infty} \frac{k_2^4 \, S_x \, d\omega}{|(k_2^2 + \mathring{h} - \omega^2)^2 + \ell^2\omega^2|} \tag{V.4.14}$$

The required value σ_s must be calculated from this implicit equation. This value is not only important in its own right, but in addition after being substituted in equation (V.4.10), it gives us the value $\bar{s}$.

Let us now consider another model (shown in Fig. 105), which is described by the following differential equation:

$$\ddot{s} + \ell_o\dot{s} + y_1(s)\cdot s + y_2(s)\cdot s = \ell\dot{x} + y_3(x) \tag{V.4.15}$$

where

$$\ell_o = \frac{b_1 + b_2}{m} \; ; \qquad \ell = \frac{b_2}{m} \; ; \qquad k_1^2 = \frac{c_1}{m} \; ; \qquad k_2^2 = \frac{c_2}{m} \; .$$

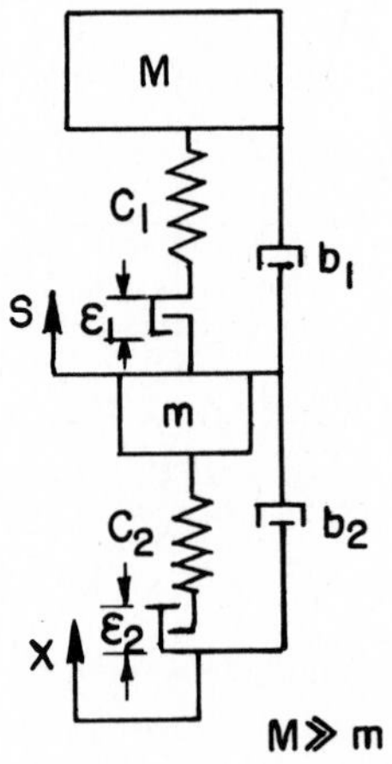

Fig. 105. Model of a dynamic nonlinear system with two clearances.

Let us designate the nonlinear function in the form $y_1(s)$ and $y_2(s)$. Then:

$$y_1 = \begin{cases} k_1^2 \; ; & \varepsilon_1/2 < s < \infty \\ 0 \; ; & -\varepsilon_1/2 < s < \varepsilon_1/2 \\ k_1^2 \; ; & -\infty < s < -\varepsilon_1/2 \end{cases} \qquad y_2 = \begin{cases} k_2^2 \; ; & \varepsilon_2/2 < s < \infty \\ 0 \; ; & -\varepsilon_2/2 < s < \varepsilon_2/2 \\ k_2^2 \; ; & -\infty < s < -\varepsilon_2/2 \end{cases}$$

$$y_3 = \begin{cases} k_2^2 \ ; & \varepsilon_2/2 < x < \infty \\ 0 \ ; & -\varepsilon_2/2 < x < \varepsilon_2/2 \\ k_2^2 \ ; & -\infty < x < -\varepsilon_2/2 \end{cases} \qquad (V.4.16)$$

The linearized functions will then take the following forms:

$$y_1 = \bar{h}_1\bar{s}_1 + \overset{\circ}{h}_1\overset{\circ}{s} \ ; \quad y_2 = \bar{h}_2\bar{s} + \overset{\circ}{h}_2\overset{\circ}{s} \ ; \quad y_3 = \bar{h}_3\bar{x} + h_3\overset{\circ}{x} \ . \qquad (V.4.17)$$

We show here the calculation only for $\overset{\circ}{s}$, the random component of the motion. Using the criterion applied to equation (V.4.11), we obtain:

$$\sigma_{y_1} = \overset{\circ}{h}_1\sigma_s \quad \text{or} \quad \overset{\circ}{h}_1 = \sigma_{y_1}/\sigma_s \qquad (V.4.18)$$

and

$$\sigma_{y_2} = \overset{\circ}{h}_2\sigma_s \quad \text{or} \quad \overset{\circ}{h}_2 = \sigma_{y_2}/\sigma_s$$

Thus, we obtain, remembering (V.4.12):

$$\sigma_{y_1} = \sigma_s k_1^2 \sqrt{[1 - \Phi(\Delta_1)]^2 + \frac{2}{3\pi} \Delta_1^2 \exp[-2\Delta_1^2]}$$

$$\overset{\circ}{h}_1 = k_1^2 \sqrt{[1 - \Phi(\Delta_1)]^2 + \frac{2}{3\pi} \Delta_1^2 \exp[-2\Delta_1^2]} \qquad (V.4.19)$$

where

$$\Delta_1 = \varepsilon_1 / 2\sqrt{2}\, \sigma_s$$

and

$$\sigma_{y_2} = \sigma_s k_2^2 \sqrt{[1 - \Phi(\Delta_2)]^2 + \frac{2}{3\pi} \Delta_2^2 \exp[-2\Delta_2^2]}$$

$$\overset{\circ}{h}_2 = k_2^2 \sqrt{[1 - \Phi(\Delta_2)]^2 + \frac{2}{3\pi} \Delta_2^2 \exp[-2\Delta_2^2]} \qquad (V.4.20)$$

$$\sigma_{y_3} = \sigma_x k_2^2 \sqrt{[1 - \Phi(\Delta_3)]^2 + \frac{2}{3\pi} \Delta_3^2 \exp[-2\Delta_3^2]}$$

$$\overset{\circ}{h}_3 = k_2^2 \sqrt{[1 - \Phi(\Delta_3)]^2 + \frac{2}{3\pi} \Delta_3^2 \exp[-2\Delta_3^2]} \qquad (V.4.21)$$

here

$$\Delta_2 = \varepsilon_2 / 2\sqrt{2}\, \sigma_s \qquad \Delta_3 = \varepsilon_2 / 2\sqrt{2}\, \sigma_x$$

The solution of the differential equation (V.4.15) for the random component given as the value of variance of the output motions, may be expressed as follows:

$$\sigma_s = \int_{-\infty}^{\infty} \frac{|\mathring{h}_3^2 + \ell^2\omega^2| \; S_x d\omega}{|(\mathring{h}_1 + \mathring{h}_2 - \omega^2)^2 + \ell_o^2\omega^2|} \qquad \text{(V.4.22)}$$

The above models discussed are often applicable to real mechanisms widely used in practice, for example, the indexing table shown in Fig. 106.

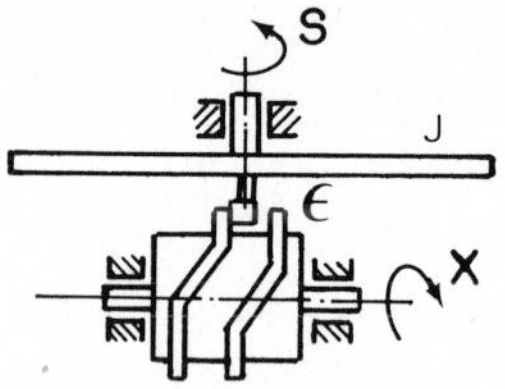

Fig. 106. Layout of the drive of an indexing table as an example of a dynamic system with a clearance.

In this mechanism, a massive disk with a moment of inertia I is driven by a spatial cam provided with a special slot which, in turn, engages sequentially with the pins of the disk. (The difference between this mechanism and that shown in Fig. 98b lies in the fact that the friction in the latter, being much smaller, does not suppress the dynamic effects.) The behavior of the indexing table may be described by means of a nonlinear model because of the gap or backlash ε between the pins and the slot.

Another example of the model under discussion is a gear drive (Fig. 107): because of the gap ε in the engagement of the teeth a nonlinear approach must be used.

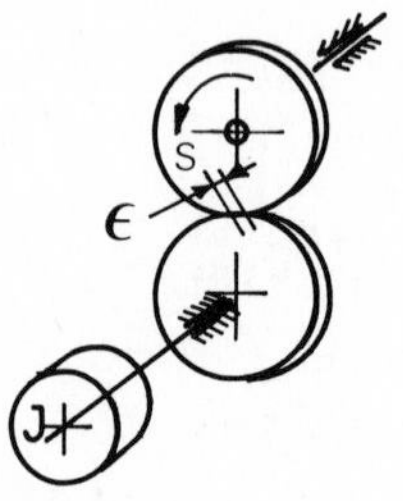

Fig. 107. A gear drive as an example of a dynamic system with a clearance.

5. APPLICATIONS OF STATISTICAL LINEARIZATION

In this section we give a number of examples of the use of statistical linearization in some practical applications: some analyses and synthesis of nonlinear mechanisms are presented.

A. Gear mechanism

It is typical of gear transmissions - even those with constant external loads and ideal constant input velocities - that the velocities of the driven elements are variable because of limited accuracy in the manufacturing and assembling of the mechanisms. In addition, backlashes contribute another complicating factor. The effects which result from these factors may be described in terms of dynamics, especially when the velocities of the gearing elements are high. As a consequence of the inevitable errors which are introduced during gear production and assembly, the dynamic effects are comparable with the static ones, and it is thus necessary to take these errors into consideration. The determination of the real motion of the gear wheel is thus important, because it permits estimation of the kinematic accuracy of the transmission, which influences the quality of many kinds of machine. The complicated dynamic behavior of the gearing mechanism decreases not only its kinematic accuracy but also its strength and durability. It should also be remembered that errors in the pitch of the teeth, gear eccentricity and backlashes promote resonances in the mechanisms.

Most investigators use a deterministic approach (mathematical models) to describe the picture of movement in this kinematic pair. This approach allows us to obtain, in an analytical manner, the form of motion of a particular element under consideration. Such a solution permits the analysis of the influence of the different parameters on the motion at each moment in time. But with this method we run into considerable calculation difficulties.

It seems to us that there are many cases in which the engineer could be satisfied with a lesser amount of information, if it would give him a more direct means of estimating better values for one, two or even more parameters of the gearing mechanisms being designed. In such a case, a statistical approach to the problem can be used.

Let us consider the example of the mechanism shown in Fig. 108. The figure shows a typical transmission in which the motion of an electric motor 1, via a belt 2, drives a gear transmission 3, which transmits the motion to the masses 4. The gear ratio can be defined as:

$$i_1 = \frac{z_o z_2}{z_1 z_3} \tag{V.5.1}$$

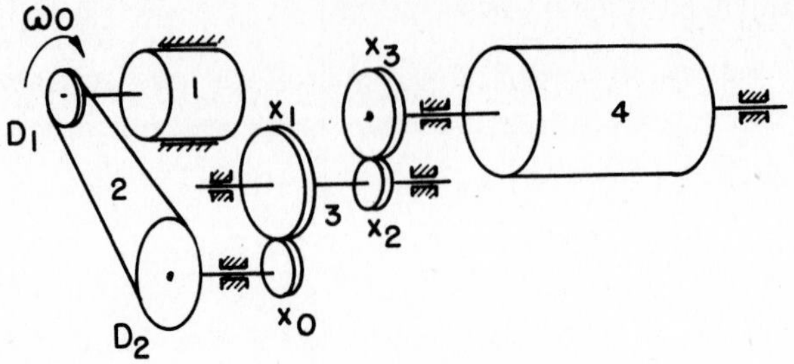

Fig. 108. A gear transmission.

Similarly, the belt transmission has the ratio:

$$i_2 = \frac{D_1}{D_2}$$

where

z_o, z_1, z_2, z_3 - the numbers of the teeth;

D_2, D_1 - the diameters of the pulleys.

To the above-described mechanism, we will apply the dynamic model shown in Fig. 109

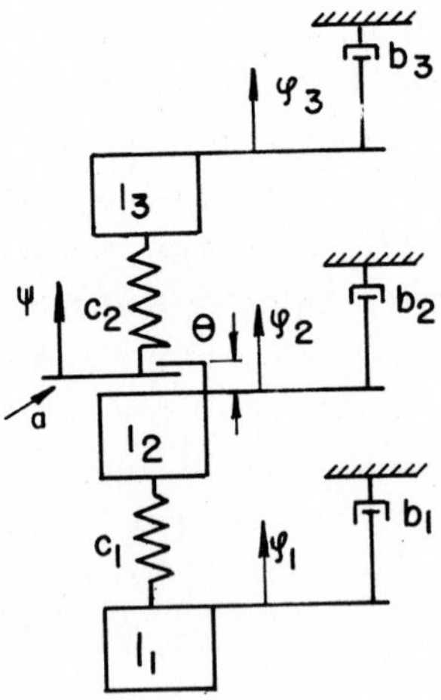

Fig. 109. The lumped dynamic model of the gear transmission shown in Fig. 108.

where

I_1 - moment of inertia of motor's rotor and pulley;

c_1 - stiffness of the belt;

I_2 - moment of inertia of the driven pulley, tooth wheel and shaft;

c_2 - common summary stiffness of the teeth in the gearing;

Θ - summary backlash in the gearing;

I_3 - moment of inertia of the driven masses lumped together with the gear train output shaft.

Let us make the following assumptions:

(1) the moments of inertia of the other wheels are negligible;

(2) the stiffnesses c_1 and c_2 are constant;

(3) the dissipative forces are proportional to the absolute velocities of the moving masses;

(4) the rotation velocity ω_o of the driving motor is constant;

(5) the impact effects can be described by the Kelvin-Voigt impact model.

The stiffness c_2 includes the contact stiffness of the teeth according to the Kelvin-Voigt model, so that c_2 is a composite stiffness made up of the bending, torsion and contact stiffnesses of the mechanism. In this way the impact effect of the mechanism is taken into account.

Now, if we wish to investigate the dynamic behavior of this mechanism, we must take into account the sources of disturbances, i.e. the pitch errors, the eccentricity of the wheel, the profile errors resulting from manufacturing and assembling inaccuracies, and the backlash in the gearing. The input excitement is inserted into the mathematical model at point a (which agrees with the gearing point) as motion $\psi(t)$. The values ω_o, i_1, i_2, I_1 and I_3 are usually obtained during the first stage of the designing, as are the belt cross section and the minimal value of the gearing pitch. We must now seek the other values which permit design of an optimal transmission with a minimal amount of vibration, i.e. I_2, c_2, c_1, z_o, z_1, z_2, z_3, and θ. Obviously, we are not absolutely free in the choice of these values because they are restricted by other construction requirements. Since the real circumstances allow the designer limited freedom, it seems to us that the choice of two optimal parameters is good enough.

For this purpose, we will look for MRSV of the motion errors of the driven mass. According to Fig. 109, this criterion may be expressed as follows:

$$\sigma^2_{\phi_k} \doteq \frac{1}{T}\int_o^T \overset{\circ}{\phi}{}^2_k dt \qquad \text{(V.5.3)}$$

where

k - the number of the mass under consideration;

$\bar{\phi}$ - the mathematical expectation (ME) of the motion;

$\overset{\circ}{\phi}$ - the centralized random value or the random component (RC) of the motion;

T - observation time;

It is obvious that

$$\bar{\phi}_3 = \bar{\phi}_1 \cdot i_1 \cdot i_2 \tag{V.5.4}$$

To improve the dynamic properties of the movement of the mass number k, we need to seek the minimum of $\sigma^2_{\phi_k}$. (It should be remembered that this mathematical model is nonlinear because of the presence of a backlash.) To produce a mechanism with a minimal σ_ϕ value, we have to determine the optimal parameters of the system. In our case these are the stiffnesses of the springs and details, the damping coefficients, the value of the backlash, and the masses of elements. The determination of the optimal parameter combinations can be achieved by application of any of a number of well-known optimization procedures. For a small number of changeable parameters γ_i the following simple method has been perfected. If the following equation system were to be solved, the optimal combination of the parameters Γ_i would be obtained

$$\frac{\partial[\sigma^2_\phi]}{\partial_{\gamma_1}} = 0 \qquad \gamma_1 = \Gamma_1$$

$$. \ . \ . \ . \ . \ . \ . \ . \ . \ . \ . \ . \ .$$

$$\frac{\partial[\sigma^2_\phi]}{\partial_{\gamma_i}} = 0 \qquad \gamma_i = \Gamma_i \tag{V.5.5}$$

$$. \ . \ . \ . \ . \ . \ . \ . \ . \ . \ . \ . \ .$$

$$\frac{\partial[\sigma^2_\phi]}{\gamma_m} = 0 \qquad \gamma_m = \Gamma_m$$

Since in most practical cases the number of changeable parameters γ is limited, the system of m equations is transformed into one or two equations, and the optimization problem thus becomes very simple.

The equation for the motion of the dynamic model shown in Fig. 109 may thus be written as follows:

$$\begin{aligned} I_1\ddot{\phi}_1 + b_1\dot{\phi}_1 - c_1\phi_1 - c_1\phi_2 i_1 &= 0 \\ I_2\ddot{\phi}_2 + b_2\dot{\phi}_2 + c_1\phi_2 - c_1\phi_1/i_1 + i_2 y(\kappa) &= 0 \\ I_3\ddot{\phi}_3 + b_3\dot{\phi}_3 - y(\kappa) &= c_2\psi \\ \phi_2/i_2 - \phi_3 &= \kappa \end{aligned} \tag{V.5.6}$$

where

$$y(\kappa) = \begin{cases} c_2\kappa; & -\infty < \kappa < 0 \\ 0 \;\; ; & 0 \lesssim \kappa \lesssim \theta \\ c_2\kappa; & \theta < \kappa \lesssim \infty \end{cases} \qquad (V.5.7)$$

Using equations (V.1.19) [which is arrived at via expressions (V.1.4), (V.1.17) and (V.1.16)], (V.1.35, and (V.5.7), and remembering equation (V.4.12), we get:

$$\overset{\circ}{h} = \frac{\sigma_y}{\sigma_\kappa} = c_2\sqrt{[1 - \Phi(\Delta)]^2 + \frac{2}{3\pi}\Delta^2 \exp[-2\Delta^2]} \qquad (V.5.8)$$

where

$$\Delta = \frac{\theta}{2\sqrt{2}\,\sigma_\kappa} \qquad \Phi(\Delta) = \frac{2}{\sqrt{\pi}}\int_0^\Delta e^{-x^2}dx \qquad (V.5.9)$$

The following procedure for solving the system (V.5.6) may now be proposed:

(1) write out the dynamic transfer function for each required σ^2 including σ_κ^2;

(2) after solving the implicit integral (V.1.39) with respect to σ_κ find $\overset{\circ}{h}$ by means of (V.5.8) remembering (V.5.9);

(3) substitute $\overset{\circ}{h}$ in the form given in equation (V.1.29) in the other dynamic transfer function to calculate σ_{ϕ_1}, σ_{ϕ_2} and σ_{ϕ_3}; or

(4) use the system (V.5.5) to find the optimal combination of variable parameters γ_i.

Let us now calculate an example for the initial data given in Table I when the amplitude of the gear teeth pitch error α - 0.002 rad;
the eccentricity of the wheels on the shafts e - 0.005 mm;
and the spectral density of the input disturbances ψ is assumed to be harmonic; this assumption is based on the experiments of Arai and Ishikawa (1966) and Maruyama and Nakada (1968) (see Chapter IV).

I_1= 100 kg cm^2	b_1=100 $\frac{kgm^2}{s}$ i_2=0.5 c_1=250 $\frac{nm}{rad}$ θ=0÷0.1 rad z_o=15-50
I_2= 200 kg cm^2	b_2=100 $\frac{kgcm^2}{s}$ i_1=0.333 c_2=5000–1000 $\frac{nm}{rad}$ ω_o=50 1/rad z_1=15-50
I_3=2000 kg cm^2	b_3=100 $\frac{kgm^2}{s}$ z_2=15-50
	z_3=15-50

Table 1. Initial data for the calculated example.

Then, the spectral density depending on the eccentricity of the wheels may be expressed in the following form:

$$S_e = 2e(z_2/z_3)^3 \{\delta[\omega - \frac{\omega_o z_o z_2}{2\pi z_1}] + \delta[\omega - \frac{\omega_o z_o}{2\pi}]$$

where δ - Dirac impulse function.

The spectral density caused by the pitch errors has the form:

$$S\alpha = \frac{(\alpha i_3)^2}{2} \delta[\omega - \frac{\omega_o}{2\pi}] + 2(\alpha \frac{z_2}{z_3})^2 \delta[\omega - \frac{\omega_o z_o}{2\pi z_1}] + \frac{\alpha^2}{2} \delta[\omega - \frac{\omega_o}{2\pi} i_3] \qquad \text{(V.5.10)}$$

The total spectral density S_ψ then becomes:

$$S_\psi = S_e + S_\alpha \qquad \text{(V.5.11)}$$

All the possible teeth combinations providing i_1 with an accuracy of ±10% were found by means of a computer.

The graphs presented in Fig. 110, 111 and 112 show, respectively:

$\sigma^2_{\phi_3}(z_1, z_2, z_3, \theta)$ - for other constant parameters;

$\sigma^2_{\phi_3}(c_2, \theta)$ - for other constant parameters;

$\overset{o}{h}(c_2, \theta)$ - for other constant parameters;

Conclusions

1. The statistical linearization method gives a comparatively easy way of analyzing or synthesizing a mechanical system in such a way as to provide the minimum motion errors, taking into account the influence of the non-linear element (for instance, of a backlash), or obtaining an estimation of its influence.

2. Changing the dimensions of backlashes is one possible way of improving the dynamic properties of gearing mechanisms.

3. Changing the dimensions of the backlashes is one possible way of obtaining an adaptive mechanism, i.e. one whose dynamics can be automatically improved by computer control.

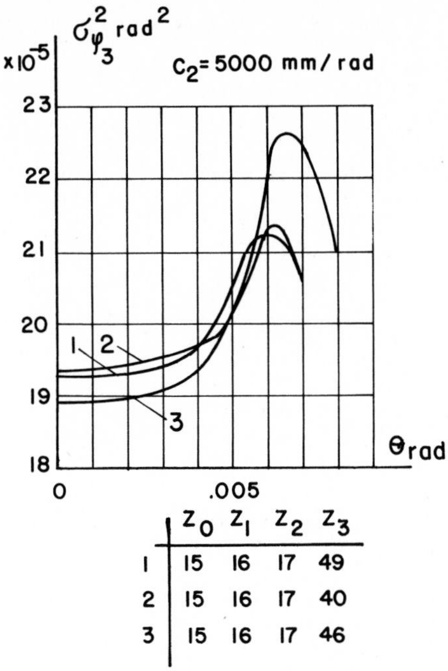

Fig. 110. The variance of the driven shaft's rotation angle errors $\sigma^2_{\phi_2}$ as a function of the gap θ for different combinations of the numbers of teeth in the transmission and the constant lumped stiffness c_2 (for the model shown in Fig. 109).

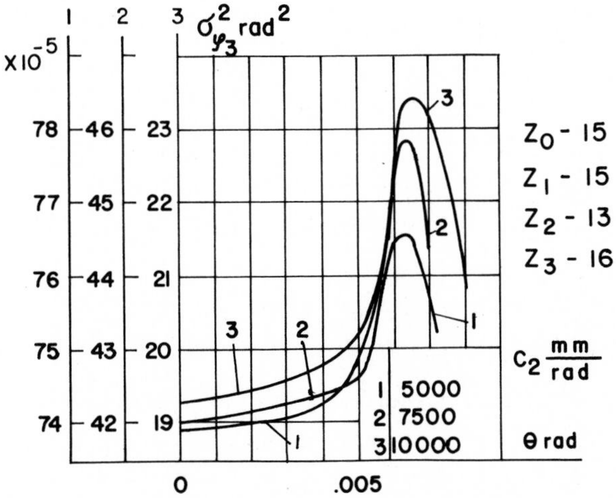

Fig. 111. The variance of the driven shaft's rotation angle errors $\sigma^2_{\phi_2}$ as a function of the gap θ for different lumped stiffnesses c_2 and for a constant combination of the number of teeth (for the model shown in Fig. 109).

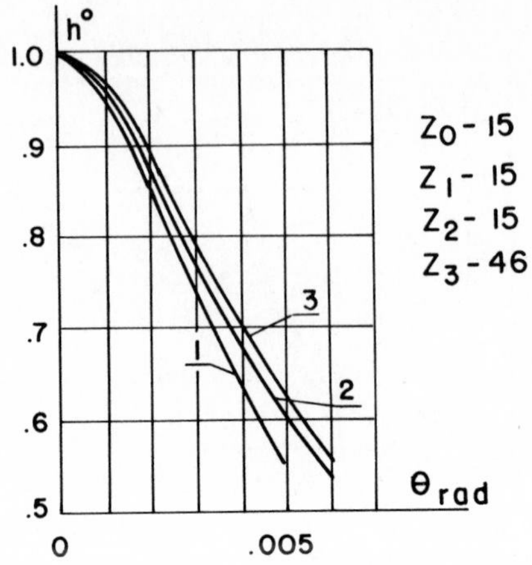

Fig. 112. The linearization coefficient $\overset{o}{h}$ as a function of the gap θ for different lumped stiffnesses c_2 and for a constant combination of the number of teeth (for the model shown in Fig. 109).

B. Cam mechanism

In the model given in Fig. 113, three cases are considered according to the position backlash. The y(s) functions are given as follows:

$$y_o = \begin{cases} c_o ; & \varepsilon_o < \kappa_o < \infty \\ 0 ; & 0 < \kappa_o < \varepsilon_o \\ c_o ; & -\infty < \kappa_o < 0 \end{cases} \qquad x_o - s_2 = \kappa_o \tag{V.5.12}$$

$$y_1 = \begin{cases} c_1 ; & \varepsilon_1 < \kappa_1 < \infty \\ 0 ; & 0 < \kappa_1 < \varepsilon_1 \\ c_1 ; & -\infty < \kappa_1 < 0 \end{cases} \qquad s_1 - s_2 = \kappa_1 \tag{V.5.13}$$

$$y_2 = \begin{cases} c_2 ; & \varepsilon_2 < s_2 < \infty \\ 0 ; & 0 < s_2 < \varepsilon_2 \\ c_2 ; & -\infty < s_2 < 0 \end{cases} \tag{V.5.14}$$

The equations describing the behavior of this model can be written in the following form:

$$\begin{cases} m_1\ddot{\kappa}_1 + b\dot{\kappa}_1 + y_1(\kappa_1) + m_1\ddot{s}_2 = 0 \\ m_2\ddot{s}_2 + b_2\dot{s}_2 + y_2(s_2) - b_1\dot{\kappa}_1 - y_1(\kappa_1) = b_o\dot{\kappa}_o + y_o(\kappa_o) \end{cases} \tag{V.5.15}$$

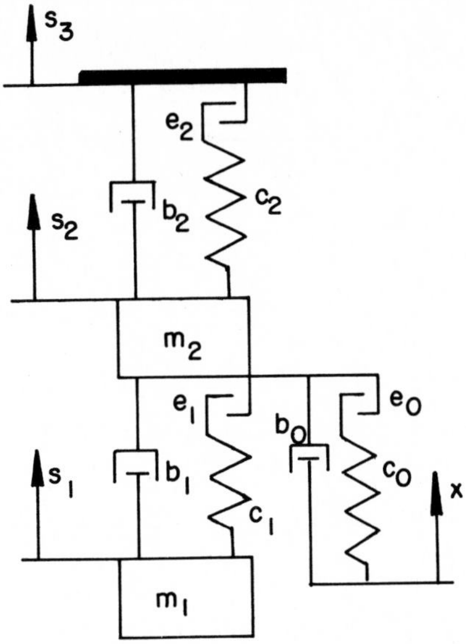

Fig. 113. Dynamic model of a cam mechanism (shown in Fig. 114).

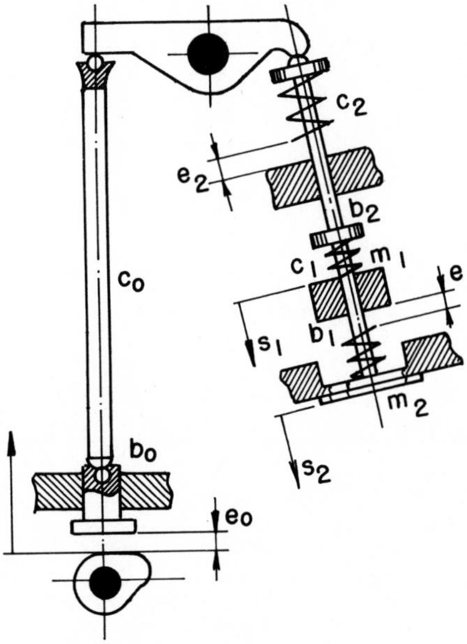

Fig. 114. Cam drive of a value mechanism of an internal combustion engine.

This model is applicable to cam mechanisms in which an added mass is used for dynamic improvement (Fig. 114) and there is a backlash in any one of the three places shown in Fig. 113. Using equations (V.1.35), (V.1.17), (V.1.16) and (V.1.19) for expressions (V.5.4), (V.5.13) and (V.5.14), we get:

$$\overset{\circ}{h} = \sigma_y/\sigma_K = c\sqrt{[1 - \Phi(\Delta)]^2 + \frac{2}{3\pi}\Delta^2\exp[-2\Delta^2]} \qquad \text{(V.5.16)}$$

where y, c, $\overset{\circ}{h}$, Δ and ε have the same index,

Φ - Laplace function,

and

$$\Delta = \frac{\varepsilon}{2\sqrt{2}\,\sigma_s}$$

Figure 115 shows the dependence of $\overset{\circ}{h}$ on ε for a cam mechanism for the three backlash situations mentioned above.

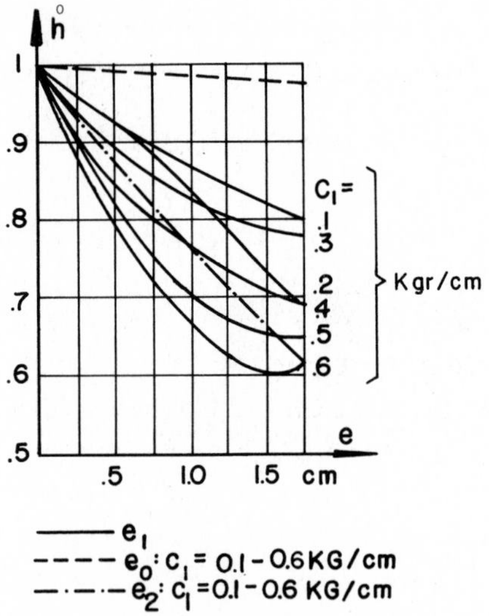

Fig. 115. The linearization coefficient $\overset{\circ}{h}$ as a function of the gap e for different stiffnesses c_1 and different locations of the gaps (e_0, e_1, e_2).

If we wish to design a mechanism with a minimal σ_{s_2} value, we have to find the optimal combination of system parameters γ_i, corresponding to equation (V.5.5). In this case, the parameters are the stiffnesses of the springs and details, the damping coefficients, the value of the backlash, and the masses of elements. For instance, Fig. 116 shows how the choice of the springs can decrease the value of the output σ_{s_2}. Changing the dimensions of the backlashes is one possible way of improving the dynamic properties of a cam mechanism.

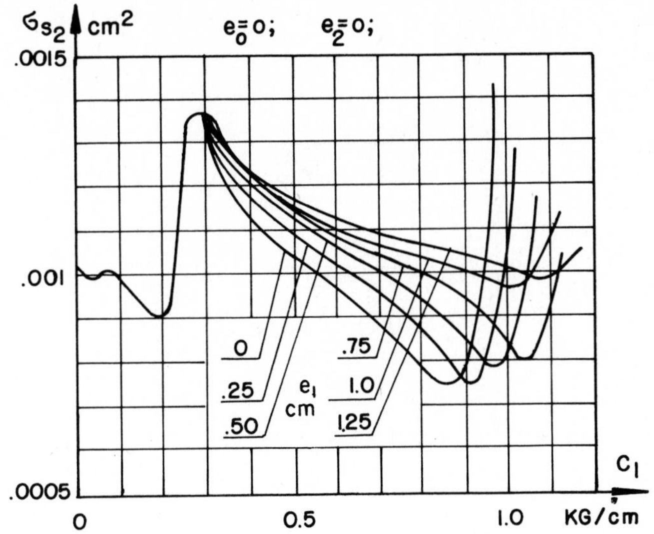

Fig. 116. The RMSV σ_{s_2} as a function of the stiffnesses c_1 for different values of the gap e_1 (while e_o=e_2=0).

C. Electromagnetic relay contacts

Electrothermal corrosion is a result of striking of relay contacts when a circuit is closed, causing damage to the contracts. The example we give here deals with an investigation which attempts to reduce this phenomenon by means of optimization of the mechanical component of the electric relays. The layout of the relay is shown in Fig. 117. When an electric current is passed through the coil 1, frame 2 moves down and brings the moving contacts 3 into contiguity with the immovable contacts 7. Two springs (4 and 6) mounted in frame 2 take part in forming the contact force.

The dynamic model of mechanical system is built on the assumption that the closing process can be divided into two stages: (1) that taking place until the contacts touch (Fig. 118a) and (2) that occurring when the contacts actually touch one another (Fig. 118b).

Fig. 118c shows the dynamic model we have chosen. Such a model has been previously considered by Erk and Finke (1964) and by Lazah. In this model m_1 and m_2 are the massed of the moving contacts 3 and of the frame 4, respectively; c_1 and c_2 are the stiffnesses of the springs 5 and 6, respectively; b_1 and b_2 are the damping coefficients which describe the damping properties of the oscillations during the first stage of motion; (measurements show that m_1, m_2, b_1, b_2, c_1 and c_2 are constant, i.e. in the first stage the system is considered as linear); c_3 is the stiffness of the material of contacts 3 and 7; b_3 is the

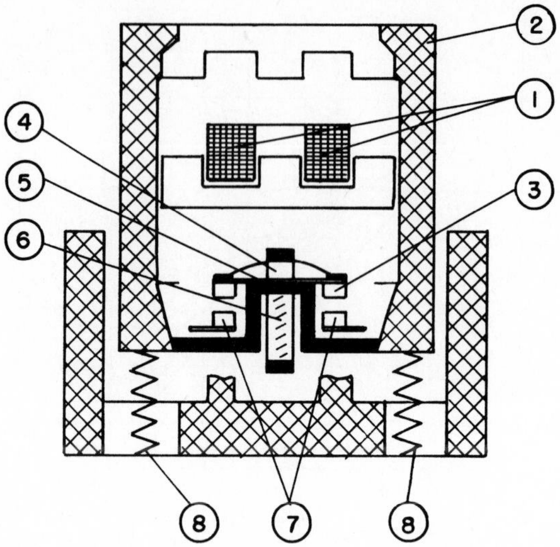

Fig. 117. Layout of the electromagnetic relay under consideration.

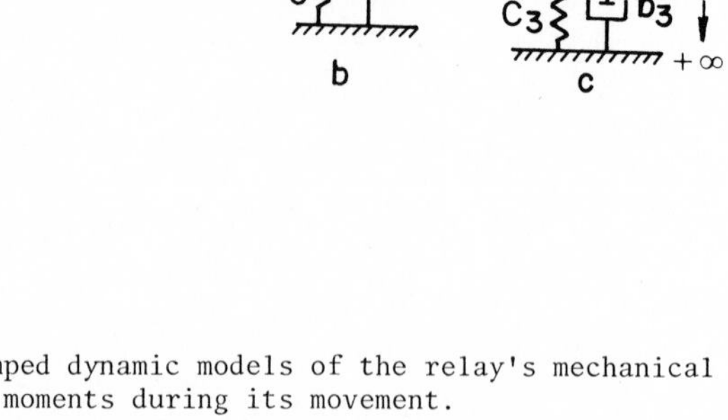

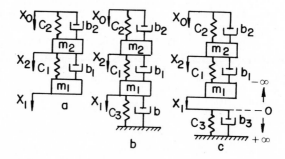

Fig. 118. The lumped dynamic models of the relay's mechanical system at different moments during its movement.

damping parameter in the material of contacts 3 and 7. (The mass of the frame 2 is relatively big and its movement is not affected by other moving masses, i.e. this mass can be excluded from models and equations as can the springs 8.) We can thus see that the dynamic model under consideration refers to a partially linear system.

As experiments indicate that the rebound process has a random character, a statistical approach can be applied in this case. The dynamic system can be described by the following differential equations:

$$\begin{cases} m_2\ddot{x}_2 + c_2x_2 + c_1(x_2 - x_1) + b_2\dot{x}_2 + b_1(\dot{x}_2 - \dot{x}_1) - b_2\dot{x}_o - c_2x_o = 0 \\ m_1\ddot{x}_1 + c_1(x_1 - x_2) + b_1(\dot{x}_1 - \dot{x}_2) + F(x_1,\dot{x}_1) = 0 \end{cases} \qquad \text{(V.5.17)}$$

where

$$F(x_1,\dot{x}_1) = \begin{cases} 0 & -\infty < x_1 < 0 \\ c_3x_1 + b_3\dot{x}_1; & 0 < x_1 < \infty \end{cases} \qquad \text{(V.5.18)}$$

The statistical linearization method will now be used to solve this problem. According to this method, the nonlinear function $y = F(x_1,\dot{x}_1)$ must be replaced by a linear function y_1 of the form:

$$y_1 = h_1x_1 + h_2\dot{x}_1 \qquad \text{(V.5.19)}$$

so that the statistical characteristics (such as the RMSV) of the linearized function y_1 should approximate those of the nonlinear function y which requires the minimum of Δy

$$\Delta y = y - y_1 \qquad \text{(V.5.20)}$$

Let $x_1 = u_1$ and $\dot{x}_1 = u_2$

$$y = F(x_1,\dot{x}_1) = F(u_1,u_2)$$

We can now express the RMSV of Δy in a known form:

$$\sigma^2_{\Delta y} = \int_{-\infty}^{\infty}\int [\Delta y]^2 w(u_1)w(u_2)du_1du_2 \qquad \text{(V.5.21)}$$

where $w(u_1)\cdot w(u_2)$ is the joint distribution law of the probability density. [Since the functions u_1 and u_2 are not correlated, the joint distribution may be expressed as a product of the one-dimensional distributions $w(u_1)$ and $w(u_2)$.]

The conditions for a minimum of the functional (V.5.21) give

$$h_1 = 1/\sigma_1^2 \int_{-\infty} \int F(u_1,u_2)(u_1 - \bar{u}_1)w(u_1)w(u_2)du_1du_2 \tag{V.5.22}$$

and

$$h_2 = 1/\sigma_2^2 \int_{-\infty}^{\infty} \int F(u_1,u_2)(u_2 - \bar{u}_2)w(u_1)w(u_2)du_1du_2 \tag{V.5.23}$$

where σ_1 is the RMSV of the function x_1,
and σ_2 is the RMSV of the function $\dot{x}_1$.

If the spectral density of the input is $S(\omega)$, then

$$\sigma_1^2 = \int_{-\infty}^{\infty} |\Phi(j\omega)|^2 S(\omega)d\omega \tag{V.5.24}$$

and

$$\sigma_2^2 = \int_{-\infty}^{\infty} |\Phi(j\omega)|^2 S(\omega)d\omega \tag{V.5.25}$$

where $\Phi(j\omega)$ is the frequential transfer function (FTF) of the system.

We now have to make an assumption with regard to the form of the distribution laws of u_1 and u_2. Let us take the normal distribution law:

$$w(u_1) = \frac{1}{\sqrt{2\pi}\,\sigma_1} \exp\left[-\frac{(u_1 - \bar{u}_1)^2}{2\sigma_1^2}\right] \tag{V.5.26}$$

$$w(u_2) = \frac{1}{\sqrt{2\pi}\,\sigma_1} \exp\left[-\frac{(u_2 - \bar{u}_2)^2}{2\sigma_2^2}\right] \tag{V.5.27}$$

Because of the lack of dependence between u_1 and u_2 (these functions are not correlated as a function and its derivative), we have to multiply expressions (V.5.26) and (V.5.27) to find the joint distribution law. (At this point we do not need the expansion in Hermite-Chebyshev polynomials.) Then:

$$h_1 = \frac{1}{2\pi\sigma_1^3\sigma_2} \int_{-\infty}^{\infty} \int_{0}^{\infty} (c_3u_1 + b_3u_2)(u_1 - \bar{u}_1)w(u_1)w(u_2)du_1du_2$$

$$h_2 = \frac{1}{2\rho\sigma_1\sigma_2^3} \int_{-\infty}^{\infty} \int_{0}^{\infty} (c_3u_1 + b_3u_2)(u_2 - \bar{u}_2)w(u_1)w(u_2)du_1du_2 \tag{V.5.28}$$

After integration, on the assumption that the process is stationary we obtain:

$$h_1 = c_3\left(\frac{1}{4} + \frac{u_1}{\sqrt{2\pi}\,\sigma_1} + \frac{\bar{u}_1^2}{4\sigma_1^2} \right) + \frac{b_3}{2\pi}\left(\frac{\sigma_2}{\sigma_1} + \frac{\bar{u}_1\sigma_2}{2\sqrt{2\pi}\sigma_1} \right) \qquad \text{(V.5.29}$$

$$h_2 = c_3\left(\frac{1}{2\pi\sigma_2} + \frac{\bar{u}_1}{2\sqrt{2\pi}\,\sigma_2} \right) + \frac{b_3}{4} \qquad \text{(V.5.30)}$$

Knowledge of the linearization coefficients h_1 and h_2 allows the linearized FTF to be written in the following form:

$$\Phi(j\omega) = \frac{(b_o j\omega + c_2)(b_1 j\omega + c_1)}{[c_1+c_2-m_2\omega^2+(b_1+b_2)j\omega]\,[c_1+h_1-m_1\omega^2+(b_1+h_2)j\omega]-(b_1 j\ +c_1)^2} \qquad \text{(V.5.31)}$$

From expressions (V.5.29), (V.5.30) and (V.5.31), we are able to obtain implicit expressions for σ_1^2 and σ_2^2:

$$\sigma_1^2 = \int_{-\infty}^{\infty} |\Phi(j\omega,\sigma_1,\sigma_2)|^2 S_x d\omega \qquad \text{(V.5.32)}$$

$$\sigma_2^2 = \int_{-\infty}^{\infty} |\Phi(j\omega,\sigma_1,\sigma_2)|^2 \omega^2 S_x d\omega \qquad \text{(V.5.33)}$$

For analytical purposes, we will take the excitation function at the input of the system (motion x_o of the frame 2) in the form shown in Fig. 119. Here, the period of one oscillation is greater than the damping time of the contact breaking, so each new period does not have any influence on the previous period.

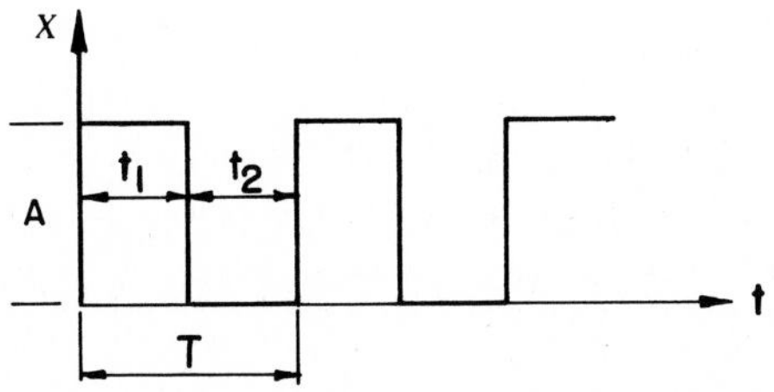

Fig. 119. Proposed shape of the excitation force F for the relay.

These conditions permit this mechanical model to be regarded as stationary. Therefore, we get the spectral density of the input in the form of Fourier series expansion:

$$S = \frac{1}{2} \sum_{n=o}^{\infty} A_n^2 \, \delta(\omega - \frac{2\pi}{T} n) \qquad (V.5.34)$$

where

$$A_n = \begin{cases} \frac{A}{2}; & n=0 \\ 2A/\pi(2n-1); & n=1,2,... \end{cases}$$

A is the stroke of the relay frame (in our case $A \approx 15$ mm), and T is the period (see Fig. 119).

If we assume that at the input the signal has discrete frequencies and if we apply expressions (V.5.32) and (V.5.33), we obtain:

$$\sigma_1^2 = \frac{1}{2} \sum_{n=o}^{\infty} A_n^2 |\Phi(j\omega_1, \sigma_1, \sigma_2)|^2$$

$$(V.5.35)$$

$$\sigma_2^2 = \frac{1}{2} \sum_{n=o}^{\infty} A_n^2 \, \omega_n^2 |\Phi(j\omega_n, \sigma_1, \sigma_2)|^2$$

Because of the rapid reduction of A_n^2 [proportional to $2^2/(2n-1)^2$], a limited number of terms can be taken in these sums.

The optimal contact masses, spring stiffnesses, etc., can be obtain after the equations (V.5.5) have been solved.

The photographs given in Fig. 120 show the dynamic behavior of the contact 3 from Fig. 117, for combinations of mass = m_1 and $3m_1$ and stiffness = c_1 and $3c_1$. The current flowing through the contact changes from 0 to 80 amps.

In this figure, the displacement of the contacts is recorded in the first band; the current flowing through the contacts (load), in the second band; and the rebounds of the armature, in the third band. By analyzing these records, as reach the conclusion that the transient process of contact closing depends essentially on the parameters of the dynamic layout of the mechanical system of the relay. (Of course, other factors, e.g. the electric load which effects the rebound properties of the contacts due to the molten metal micropool.) Choice of the optimal parameters can be aided by the above-described computation technique.

Conclusions

The following conclusions can be drawn from this study:

1. Relay contact closing is usually accompanied by a rebound phenomenon, which is random in character and which decreases gradually.

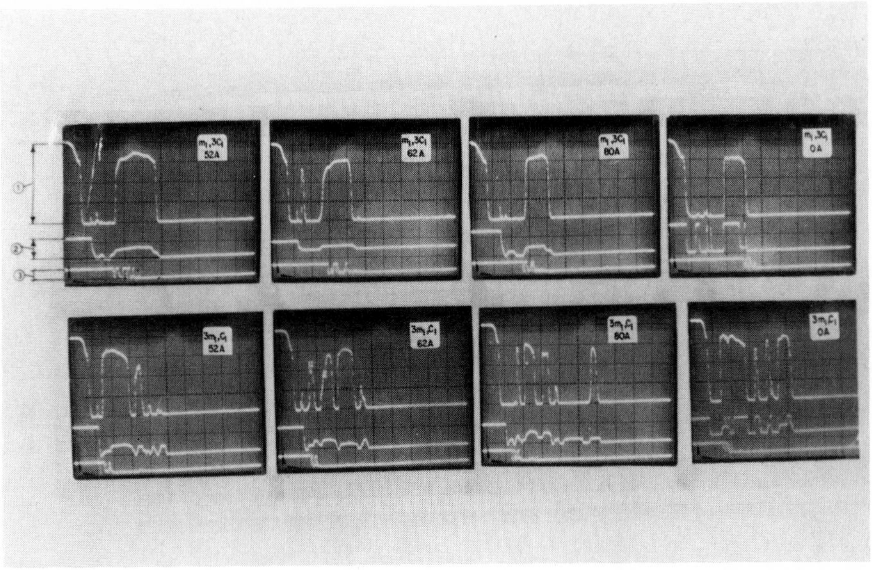

Fig. 120. The behavior of the closing contact in the relay for different values of contact masses and stiffnesses of the spring.

2. Changes in the parameters and structure of the contact mechanical system influence the process of contact closing. Such changes constitute an essential method of improving contact dynamics.
3. An analytical method based on statistical linearization can be used for solving nonlinear equations for two purposes: for a description of the behavior of the contact and for optimization.

6. KINEMATICS OF REBOUND

Ramified kinematic circuits of manufacturing machinery abound in joints. High speeds, which are typical of high-productivity machines, cause impacts, vibrations, fatigue noises and wear-and-tear effects in joint gaps (or backlashes). This situation justifies the consideration of the relative behavior of the elements of a joint. The complexity of the events accompanying the movement of the joint elements and the random character of the factors affecting the action of the joint justify, in turn, the application of a statistical approach.

Several typical examples of joints with which we will deal are presented in Fig. 121. All these kinematic pairs (and some others) can, for the purpose of our considerations be described by the calculation model shown in Fig. 122.

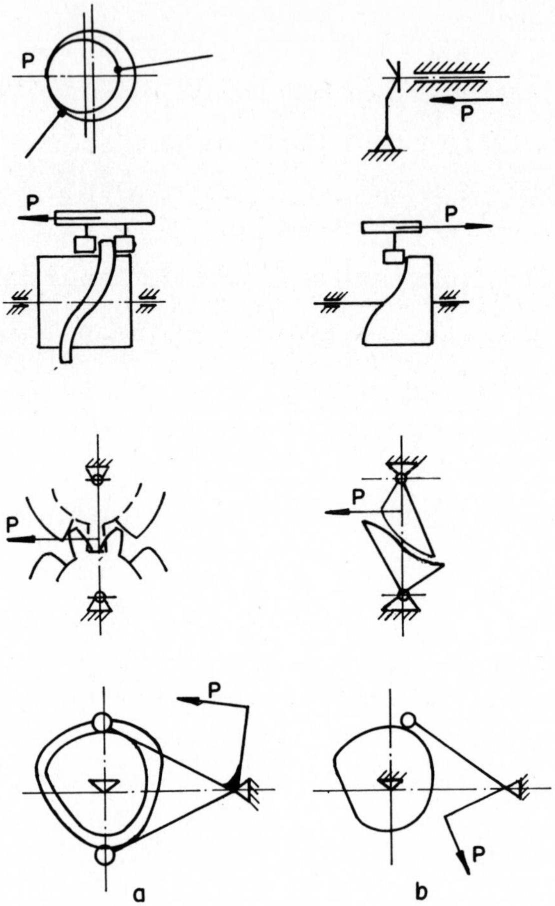

Fig. 121. Typical examples of joints having a backlash or a gap when in action.

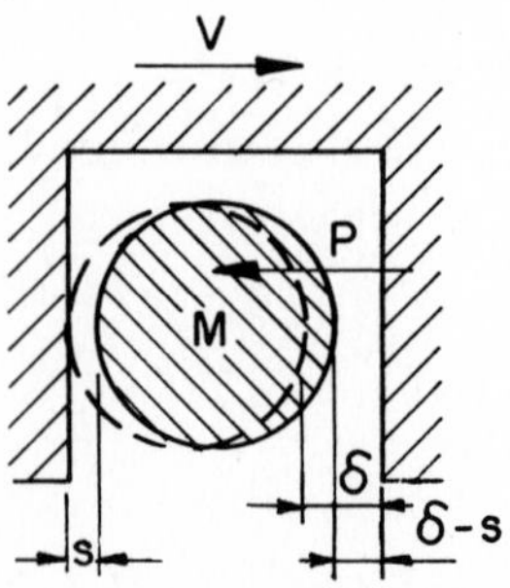

Fig. 122. Kinematic model of the joints presented in Fig. 121.

We will consider the enclosing link as the driver link and the enclosed link as the driven one. Let the velocity of the driven mass M be V, then:

$$V = \bar{V} + \overset{\circ}{V} \qquad \text{(V.6.1)}$$

where $\bar{V}$ - the average value of the velocity;

$\overset{\circ}{V}$ - the random, centralized value of the velocity.

For the steady-state action regime, $\overset{\circ}{V}$ can be assumed to be stationary. Because of the variety and insignificance of the factors causing the random term (for example, pitch errors of the gear wheels, profile errors, wear and tear of the links in the kinematic chain), we can assume normal distribution for this term. Let us assume the correlation function K_V of the random function $\overset{\circ}{V}$ to be given by:

$$K_V = \sigma_V^2 e^{-\alpha\tau^2} \cos\beta\tau \qquad \text{(V.6.2)}$$

where σ_V^2 - variance of the speed;

α and β - constants;

τ - time.

The resultant force P of harmful and useful resistances is applied to the mass M. To define the relative motion between the driven and driving links this force must be compared with the forces of inertia. Here, the acceleration W comes into the picture.

$$W = \bar{W} + \overset{\circ}{W} \qquad \text{(V.6.3)}$$

where

$$\bar{W} = \dot{\bar{V}} \quad \text{and} \quad \overset{\circ}{W} = \dot{\overset{\circ}{V}}$$

From K_V, given by equation (V.6.2), we calculate the correlation function K_W of the random term $\overset{\circ}{W}$, and after substituting $\tau = 0$ we obtain the variance:

$$\sigma_W^2 = \sigma_V^2(2\alpha + \beta^2) \qquad \text{(V.6.4)}$$

The condition of rebound between the driven and driving links may be described by:

$$MW > P$$

or

$$M(\bar{W} + \overset{\circ}{W}) > P$$

or

$$\overset{\circ}{W} > \frac{P - M\bar{W}}{M} = A(t) \tag{V.6.5}$$

where t - time.

When the rebound takes place, a backlash occurs between the links (see Fig. 122). It must be remembered that A(t) depends on the changing force P and the acceleration $\bar{W}$ (both of which are functions of time).

For $\overset{\circ}{W} > A(t)$, the driven and driving links make contact with one another on one side of the gap, and for $\overset{\circ}{W} > A(t)$ this contact passes to the other side of the gap, i.e. at any moment when the random function $\overset{\circ}{W}$ crosses the value of A(t) the links rebound and collide. This brings us to the level crossing problem in random processes (see I.37). The interaction of the function A(t) with a random process $\overset{\circ}{W}(t)$ is shown in Fig. 123. In the time intervals $\tau_1, \tau_2, \ldots, \tau_i, \ldots, \tau_n$ rebounds and collisions take place and the links change their contact surfaces.

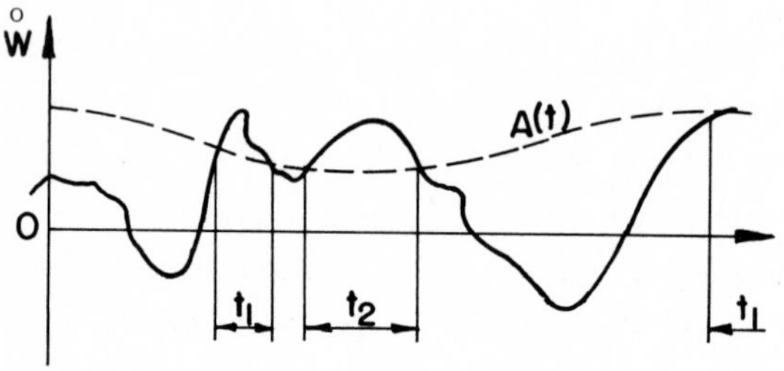

Fig. 123. Interpretation of the level A(t) crossing by a random acceleration $\overset{\circ}{W}$ problem.

We now wish to answer the following questions: What is the share of the sum $\sum_{i=1}^{n} \tau_i$ (for n big enough) relative to the whole duration of the action of the mechanism? What is the value of W for the same period? What is the average value of $\bar{\tau}$? As was explained in I.37, the probability p_τ that $\overset{\circ}{W}$ crosses the value A(t) is given by:

$$p_\tau = p[\overset{\circ}{W} > A(t)] = \int_A^\infty f(W)dW \tag{V.6.6}$$

where $f(\dot{W})$ - distribution function of the random function $\overset{\circ}{W}$.

For normally distributed $\overset{\circ}{W}$, we can rewrite equation (V.6.6) in the following form:

$$p_\tau = \frac{1}{2}\,[1-\Phi\{\frac{A(t)}{\sigma_W \sqrt{2}}\}] \tag{V.6.7}$$

where Φ - Laplace function symbol.

Further, from equation (I.37.16) we can define the average value $\bar{\tau}$:

$$\bar{\tau} = \frac{\int_A^{\infty} f(W)dW}{\int_0^{\infty} f[A(t),u]du} \tag{V.6.8}$$

where $u = \dot{W}$

Which for the normal distribution function f(W) can be simplified to the form:

$$\bar{\tau} = \pi \frac{\sigma_W}{\sigma_u} \exp \frac{[A(t)]^2}{2\sigma_W^2} \{1 - \Phi[\frac{A(t)}{\sigma_W}]\} \tag{V.6.9}$$

where σ_u^2 - variance of $u = \dot{W}$.

This variance must be calculated via the given correlation function K_V. When this correlation function has the form given in equation (V.6.2), we obtain:

$$\sigma_u^2 = \sigma_W^2(12\alpha^2 + 12\alpha\beta^2 + \beta^4) \tag{V.6.10}$$

Thus, substituting equations (V.6.4) and (V.6.10) in expression (V.6.9), we can write:

$$\bar{\tau} = \pi\sqrt{\frac{2\alpha+\beta^2}{12\alpha^2+12\alpha\beta^2+\beta^4}} \exp \frac{[A(t)]^2}{2\sigma_V^2(2\alpha+\beta^2)} \{ 1 - \Phi[\frac{A(t)}{\sigma_V\sqrt{2\alpha+\beta^2}}]\} \tag{V.6.11}$$

In the next step, we can calculate the average number $\bar{n}$ of crossings per unit time of the level A(t) by $\mathring{W}$. From equation (I.37.15) for a stationary process $\mathring{W}$ we obtain:

$$\bar{n} = \int_0^{\infty} u \cdot f[A(t),u]du \tag{V.6.12}$$

For the specific case in which f(W) is the normal distribution function, we substitute equations (V.6.4) and (V.6.10) into equation (V.6.12) to obtain:

$$\bar{n} = \frac{1}{2\pi} \sqrt{\frac{12\alpha^2+12\alpha\beta^2+\beta^4}{2\alpha+\beta^2}} \exp \frac{-[A(t)]^2}{2\sigma_V^2(2\alpha+\beta^2)} \tag{V.6.13}$$

The average value of the gap $\bar{s}$ between the driven and driving links can now be estimated. Knowledge of this gap is essential for the cases shown in the right-hand column of Fig. 121 (mechanisms without kinematic locking of the chain chain). This gap is defined by the obvious expression:

$$\bar{s} = \bar{\gamma} \cdot \bar{\tau} \tag{V.6.14}$$

Comparing $\bar{s}$ with the value of the backlash ε for mechanisms with kinematic locking of the kinematic chain (left-hand column of Fig. 121), we get an idea of the possibility of collision between the links. If we denote the joint distribution density law of the variables V and t by the symbol f_s, we can write:

$$f_s = f_V \cdot f_\tau \tag{V.6.15}$$

Because these variables are independent, the joint distribution law is obtained by nultiplication of its components (see I.24.2). The probability p that the value s will not reach ε (or that the driven link during its rebound will not touch the other side of the gap) is expressed as follows:

$$p_\varepsilon = \frac{1}{2}\, p[s<\varepsilon] = \frac{1}{2}\left\{ \int_{-\infty}^{0} \int_{\varepsilon/V}^{\infty} f_s dV d\tau + \int_{0}^{\infty} \int_{-\infty}^{\varepsilon/V} f_s dV d\tau \right\} \tag{V.6.16}$$

where ε/V - the limit of the variable τ which is derived from the obvious dependence $\tau_{limit} = V_\varepsilon$.

Let us now consider the example of a cam profile which can be described by a normalized correlation function in the form (III.9.14)

$$r = \exp[-29.8\phi^2]$$

By substituting $\phi = \omega t$, we obtain:

$$r = \exp[-29.8\omega^2 t^2]$$

Designating $\alpha = 29.8\omega^2$ for $\omega = 100$ 1/sec, we have $\alpha = 298000$ 1/sec^2. In this case $\beta = 0$. Let us suppose that $A(t) \simeq 10$ m/sec^2 and that this function changes slowly in comparison with the changes in the profile errors, i.e. we can assume this function to be constant for a particular time interval. In addition, let us take the variance of the follower's speed $\sigma_V = 0.01$ m/sec (obviously σ_V is proportional to ω values). Thus, for $\bar{n}$ - the average rebound amount per time unit, we obtain from equation (V.6.13):

$$\bar{n} = \frac{1}{2\pi} \sqrt{6 \cdot 298000}\ \exp\left[-\frac{10^2}{2 \cdot 0.01^2 \cdot 2 \cdot 298000}\right] \simeq 210 \text{ 1/sec}$$

For the average rebound duration $\bar{\tau}$, we obtain from expression (V.6.11):

$$\bar{\tau} = \pi\sqrt{1/(6 \cdot 298000)}\ \exp\left[\frac{10^2}{2 \cdot 0.01^2 \cdot 2 \cdot 298000}\right] \left\{1 - \Phi\left[\frac{10}{0.01\sqrt{2 \cdot 298000}}\right]\right\} \simeq 3.5\ 10^{-4} \text{sec}$$

7. COLLISIONS IN A JOINT GAP

Another consideration of the behavior of the links in a joint gap can be made with the purpose of describing in terms of probability the mutual collisions (impacts) of the links. The layout of the model under discussion in this section is given in Fig. 124. The movement parameters of the driving link are denoted by two primes and those of the driven link, by one prime. Thus, V' and V'' are the velocities of the driven and driving link, respectively. Let us assume:

(1) the velocity of the driven link is constant when this link is not contacting with driving link;

(2) the restitution coefficient of speed R is constant.

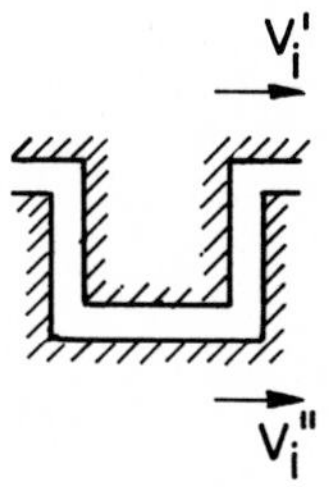

Fig. 124. Collision model for a gap.

We can then describe V' and V'' as the sums of constant average and pure random terms:

$$\bar{V}' = \bar{V}' + \mathring{V}'$$
$$\bar{V}'' = \bar{V}'' + \mathring{V}'' \qquad (V.7.1)$$

At the moment of collision between the two links the relative speed of the impact equals:

$$V' - V''$$

and the rebound speed of the driven link during its free movement in the gap equals:

$$V_n' = V_{n-1}'' + (V'_{n-1} - V_{n-1}'')R \qquad (V.7.2)$$

where the subscripts $n = 0,1,2,...$ denote the ordinal numbers of the rebounds and corresponding speeds.

For the n+1 rebound we have:

$$V'_{n+1} = V_n'' + (V_n' - V_n'')R \qquad (V.7.3)$$

Substituting equation (V.7.2) into equation (V.7.3), we obtain:

$$V'_{n+1} - V'_{n-1}R^2 = V''_n + V''_{n-1}R - V''_n R - V''_{n-1}R^2 \qquad (V.7.4)$$

Remembering that the average values of V' and V" are constant, we obtain from equation (V.7.4):

$$\bar{V}' - \bar{V}' R^2 = \bar{V}'' + \bar{V}''R - \bar{V}''R - \bar{V}''R^2 \qquad (V.7.5)$$

or the identity:

$$\bar{V}' \equiv \bar{V}'' \qquad (V.7.6)$$

To express the ratio of the variances $\sigma^2_{V'}/\sigma^2_{V''}$, we rewrite expression (V.7.5) for random terms in the following form:

$$\sigma^2_{V'}(1 + R^2)^2 = \sigma^2_{V''}(1 + 2R + R^2)^2 \qquad (V.7.7)$$

(Remember that substraction in terms of variance is considered as a sum.) Thus:

$$\frac{\sigma_{V'}}{\sigma_{V''}} = \frac{1 + 2R + R^2}{1 + R^2} \qquad (V.7.8)$$

This expression is shown in graphic form in Fig. 125. A plastic impact of the links (i.e. R = 0) does not change the statistical picture of the behavior of the driven link in the joint gap. On the contrary, an elastic impact leads to a considerable increase of the velocity variance for the driven link.

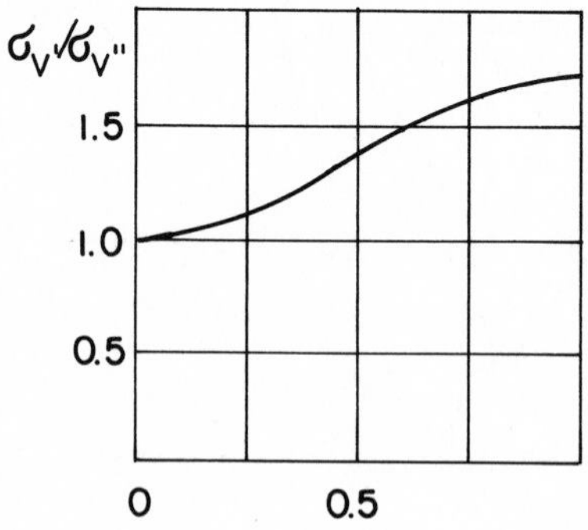

Fig. 125. Ratio of the RMSV of the input and output speeds as a function of the restitution coefficient.

BIBLIOGRAPHY

1. Sevin, E. and Pilkey, W., Optimum Shock and Vibration Isolation. Monograph SVM-6, The Shock and Vibration Information Center, U.S. Government Printing Office, April 1971.

2. Lazah, F.T., 1961, Material and Interface Damping. Shock and Vibration Handbook., ed. C.M. Harris and C.E. Crede, McGraw-Hill, New York.

3. Pervozvansky, A.A., Sluchainie processy v nelineinyh avtomaticheskih sistemah. Fizmatgiz, Moskva, 1962. (Random Processes in non-linear automatic systems - in Russian.)

4. Sandler, B.Z., Suboptimal Dynamic Synthesis of Linearized Mechanical System, an ASME publication on 13th ASME Design Engineering Technical Conference N-Y, October 5-9, 1974.

5. Sandler, B.Z. and Slonim, A., Experimental Investigation of Relay Contact Dynamics. IEEE Transactions on Components, Hybrids, and Manufacturing Technology, Vol. CHMT-3, No. 1, March 1980.

6. Sandler, B.Z., Slonim, A. and Tslaf, A., On the dynamics of a relay's mechanical system. Isr. J. Technol. 14:212-220, 1976.

7. Barkan, P., Study of the contact bounce phenomenon, Trans. IEEE, 86, 231-240, 1967.

8. Erk, A. and H. Finke, Uber die mechanischen Vorgange Während des Prellens einschaltender Kontaktstücke, Electrotech. Z. A86, 129-133, 1965.

CHAPTER VI

MISCELLANEOUS EXAMPLES OF THE PROBABILISTIC APPROACH TO DESIGN PROBLEMS

1. ACCURACY OF MOVEMENT OF A HYDRAULIC PISTON

The investigation of the uniformity of movement of a mass driven by a hydromotor (a piston driven by liquid pressure in a cylinder) is important for applications in which deviations of the velocity are harmful, e.g. the hydrodrive of grinding, lapping, and polishing equipment.

Let us consider the hydromechanism represented schematically in Fig. 126, which consists of a cylinder 1, a piston 2, a piston rod 3 with a driven mass M, and a piping system 4 for pressure supply. We can describe the movement of the mass M by the following differential equation:

$$M\ddot{s} + (\text{sign }\dot{s})\psi\dot{s}^2 = pF - Q \qquad \text{(VI.1.1)}$$

where

s - the displacement of the driven mass;

p - the pressure at the input of the cylinder;

F - the area of the piston;

Q - the useful and detrimental forces;

$\psi = \dfrac{F^3\rho}{2a^2f^2}$ - the coefficient of the hydraulic friction of the liquid flow in the cylinder, where

ρ - density of the liquid;

f - the area of the inlet cross-section;

a - the coefficient of the inlet hydraulic resistance.

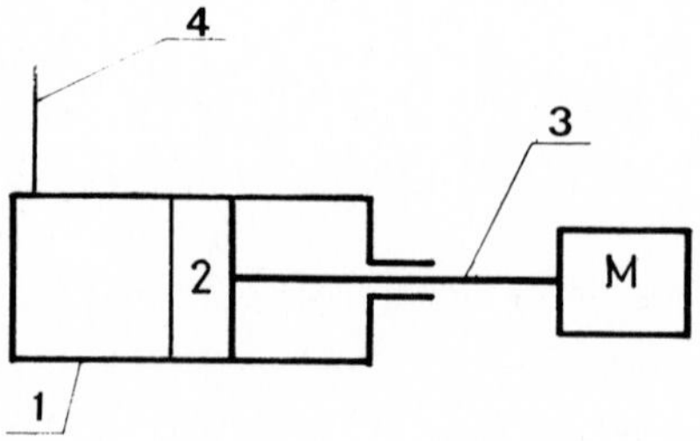

Fig. 126. Layout of the hydromechanism under discussion.

For movement of the piston to the right, the hydraulic friction is directed to the left and thus sign $\dot{s} = 1$.

Denoting

$$m = \frac{2\psi}{M} \qquad \text{and} \qquad A = \frac{pF - Q}{M} \qquad \text{(VI.1.2)}$$

We can rewrite equation (VI.1.1) in the form:

$$\ddot{s} + \frac{m}{2}\dot{s}^2 = A \qquad \text{(VI.1.3)}$$

The excitation A, which causes the movement of the mass M, can be represented as the following sum:

$$A = \bar{A} + \mathring{A}$$

From equation (VI.1.2)

$$\bar{A} = \frac{\bar{p}F - \bar{Q}}{M} \qquad \text{and} \qquad \mathring{A} = \frac{\mathring{p}F - \mathring{Q}}{M} \qquad \text{(VI.1.4)}$$

We now suppose that the desired, constant average value of the pressure $\bar{p}$ is accompanied by a random addition $\mathring{p}$. By analogy, the external resistance force can be represented as the sum of a constant, average value $\bar{Q}$ and a random term $\mathring{Q}$.

Let us now look at the reasons for the appearance of the randomized terms in the excitement. Deviations in the liquid pressure at the input of the cylinder can be explained by variations in the hydraulic resistance, leakages, pulsations of the pressure in the compressors, variable flow rates in the manifold (mostly as a result of the simultaneous action of a number of hydromechanisms and their different paces), temperature changes (which effect the viscosity of the working liquid), and deformation of the pipes. Deviations of the external resistance force may be explained by a number of factors. For instance, the friction between the guides and the moving parts is not strictly constant and the processing forces the mechanism is required to execute, also vary at random since they depend on the variable dimensions and material properties of the blank. All these factors are in practical terms, independent of one another, each of them taken separately being not significant. Thus, the right-hand side of the differential equation (VI.1.1) is approximately normally distributed.

On the other hand, we have good reason to assume that the realizations of the acting forces of the pressure and external forces are stationary after the transient processes have been completed. (The transient processes are considered to be over when, for instance, the compressors have finished accelerating, the manifold has been filled up, all mechanisms are in action, etc.)

Variations of the forces cause random variation of the motion $\mathring{s}$ of the mass. Consequently, the velocity of this motion will have deviations $\mathring{V}$ from strict uniformity and acceleration $\mathring{W}$ will occur. What we are seeking in this section are some statistical characteristics of $\mathring{s}$, $\mathring{V}$ and $\mathring{W}$. To make the discussion more specific we assume that the spectral density of the force random deviations S_A can be measured and approximated by the expression:

$$S_A(\omega) = \frac{\sigma_A^2}{2\sqrt{\alpha\pi}} \exp[-\omega^2/4\alpha] \tag{VI.1.5}$$

for which the correlation function has the form:

$$K_A(s) = \sigma_A^2 \exp[-\alpha s^2] \tag{VI.1.6}$$

where ω - has the dimension 1/s.

From equation (VI.1.2), the value σ_A can be defined as follows:

$$\sigma_A^2 = \frac{F^2\sigma_p^2 + \sigma_Q^2}{m^2} \tag{VI.1.7}$$

where

σ_p^2 - the variance of the pressure fluctuations;

σ_Q^2 - the variance of the external force fluctuations.

(Note: the spectral density $S_A(\omega)$ can be expressed as the sum of separate spectral densities S_p and S_Q of the pressure and external forces, respectively.)

After substituting $y = \mathring{s}^2$ in expression (VI.1.3), we can rewrite the equation in the following form:

$$\frac{dy}{ds} + my = 2\bar{A} + 2\mathring{A} \tag{VI.1.8}$$

(Note: if $\dot{s}^2 = y$, then $dy/ds = 2\dot{s}\ddot{s}$, which gives $\ddot{s} = dydt/2dsdt = dy/2ds$.)

Equation (VI.1.8) is linear with respect to y, and thus in accordance with the superposition principle the solution must be expressed as the following sum:

$$y = y_o + \bar{y} + \mathring{y} \tag{VI.1.9}$$

where

y_o - the solution of the homogeneous equation;

$\bar{y}$ - the partial solution for A in the right-hand side of the equation;

$\mathring{y}$ - the random solution.

The first two terms of equation (VI.1.9) can be found in trivial ways. We thus concentrate here on seeking the solution for the random term $\overset{\circ}{y}$. Because of the random nature of the term, we will consider that we have found the solution when some of probabilistic characteristics are known. As was shown previously in equation (I.35.1), the spectral density S_y of the auxilliary variable y in the equation (VI.1.8) under discussion has the following form:

$$S_y(\omega) = \frac{4S_A(\omega)}{|j\omega + m|^2} \qquad \text{(VI.1.10)}$$

Using the reversed Fourier transformation for the correlation function K_y of the variable $\overset{\circ}{y}$ and equation (VI.1.5) we obtain:

$$K_y(s) = \frac{2\sigma_A^2}{\sqrt{\alpha\pi}} \int_{-\infty}^{\infty} \frac{\exp[j\omega s - \omega^2/4\alpha]}{|j\omega + m|^2} d\omega \qquad \text{(VI.1.11)}$$

To find the variance σ_y^2 of the variable $\overset{\circ}{y}$ we have to substitute s = 0 in equation (VI.1.11), which brings us to the following expression:

$$\sigma_y^2 = K_y(0) = \frac{2\sigma_A^2}{\sqrt{\alpha\pi}} \int_{-\infty}^{\infty} \frac{\exp[-\omega^2/4\alpha]}{|j\omega + m|^2} d\omega \qquad \text{(VI.1.12)}$$

Let us consider again the auxilliary variable y. In accordance with the definition:

$$y = \dot{s}^2 \qquad \text{or} \qquad y = V^2 \qquad \text{(VI.1.13)}$$

Thus, from equation (I.16.2) we can write:

$$\sigma_y^2 = 4\bar{V}^2\sigma_V^2 + 2\sigma_V^4 \qquad \text{(VI.1.14)}$$

Solving this quadratic equation with respect to σ_V^2, we obtain:

$$\sigma_V^2 = -\bar{V}^2 \pm \sqrt{\bar{V}^4 + \sigma_y^2/2} \qquad \text{(VI.1.15)}$$

Substituting equation (VI.1.12) into equation (VI.1.15), we obtain:

$$\sigma_V^2 = -\bar{V}^2 \pm \sqrt{\bar{V}^4 + \frac{\sigma_A}{\sqrt{\alpha\pi}} \int_{-\infty}^{\infty} \frac{\exp[-\omega^2/4\alpha]}{|j\omega + m|^2} d\omega}$$

Let us now pass over to the calculations of the acceleration errors. The derivative of the auxilliary function y is expressed in the form:

$$\dot{y} = 2\dot{s}\ddot{s} = 2VW \qquad \text{(VI.1.16)}$$

and

$$W = \frac{\dot{y}}{2V} \tag{VI.1.17}$$

From expression (I.18.2) we obtain for equation (VI.1.17):

$$\sigma_W^2 = \frac{\bar{V}^2\sigma_{\dot{y}}^2 + \bar{\dot{y}}\sigma_V^2}{4\bar{V}^2} \tag{VI.1.18}$$

where, obviously, $\bar{\dot{y}}$ - the average or mean value of $\dot{y}$;

$\sigma_{\dot{y}}^2$ - the variance of the variable $\dot{y}$.

Hydromechanisms are used mostly under conditions in which the mean value of the velocity $\bar{V}$ is constant. Thus, from equation (VI.1.13):

$$\bar{\dot{y}} = 2\dot{\bar{V}} = 0 \tag{VI.1.19}$$

Then, expression (VI.1.18) must be rewritten as follows:

$$\sigma_W^2 = \frac{\sigma_{\dot{y}}^2}{4\bar{V}^2} \tag{VI.1.20}$$

Now from equation (VI.1.10) we obtain:

$$S_{\dot{y}} = \frac{4\omega^2 S_A(\omega)}{|j\omega + m|^2} \tag{VI.1.21}$$

Remembering equation (VI.1.5), we can write for $\sigma_{\dot{y}}^2$:

$$\sigma_{\dot{y}}^2 = \frac{2\sigma_A^2}{\sqrt{\alpha\pi}} \int_{-\infty}^{\infty} \frac{\omega^2 \exp[-\omega^2/4\alpha]}{|j\omega + m|^2}\, d\omega \tag{VI.1.22}$$

And substituting equation (VI.1.22) into equation (VI.1.20), we obtain finally:

$$\sigma_W^2 = \frac{\sigma_A^2}{2\bar{V}^2\sqrt{\alpha\pi}} \int_{-\infty}^{\infty} \frac{\omega^2 \exp[-\omega^2/4\alpha]}{|j\omega + m|^2}\, d\omega \tag{VI.1.23}$$

Let us now try to define the errors of the operation time of the piston in the hydromechanism under consideration. For this purpose, we will rewrite equation (VI.1.3) in the following form:

$$\dot{V} + \frac{m}{2} V^2 = A \tag{VI.1.24}$$

Expression (VI.1.24) can be rearranged:

$$\frac{dV}{A - \frac{m}{2} V^2} = dt \tag{VI.1.25}$$

Integrating (VI.1.25) we obtain:

$$t = \frac{1}{mA} \ln \frac{1 + V\sqrt{m/2A}}{1 - V\sqrt{m/2A}} + C \tag{VI.1.26}$$

Where C - the constant of integration.

The initial conditions are that when $t = 0$, $V = 0$: thus $C = 0$, and we can finally write:

$$\frac{1 + V\sqrt{m/2A}}{1 - V\sqrt{m/2A}} = e^{\beta t} \tag{VI.1.27}$$

where

$$\beta = \sqrt{2Am} \tag{VI.1.28}$$

From equation (VI.1.27), we obtain:

$$V = \sqrt{\frac{m}{2A}} \text{ th } \frac{\beta t}{2} \tag{VI.1.29}$$

(For $\beta t = 5$ the value of V is about 99.5% that of $\sqrt{m/2A}$.)

Integrating equation (VI.1.29) once more, we obtain for the displacement at time t the following expression:

$$s(t) = \int_0^t \sqrt{m/2A} \text{ th } \frac{\beta t}{2} dt = \frac{2}{\beta} \sqrt{m/2A} \ln \text{ch } \frac{\beta t}{2} \tag{VI.1.30}$$

And, for time t_s reduced to reach the displacement s, we obtain from equation (VI.1.30):

$$t_s = \frac{2}{\beta} \text{ Arch } \exp\left[\frac{\beta s}{2} \sqrt{m/2A} \right] \tag{VI.1.31}$$

The only practical way of finding the variance σ_t of this t_s value application of the expression (I.13.7), as explained in Section 13 of Chapter 5. For this purpose, we must substitute back into equation (VI.1.31) the expressions for m, A and β [given by equations (VI.1.2) and (VI.1.28)]. Thus:

$$t_s = \frac{2}{\sqrt{(pF-Q)/\psi}} \text{ Arch}[s\psi/M] \tag{VI.1.32}$$

Assuming s, M, F, ψ to be determined (not random values, while p and Q are random variables with variances σ_p, σ_Q, we can write an equation corresponding to expression (I.13.7) as follows:

$$\sigma_t^2 \simeq \frac{\psi[F^2\sigma_p^2 + \sigma_Q^2]}{[pF - Q]^3} \{\mathrm{Arch}\ \exp[s\psi/M]\}^2 \qquad \text{(VI.1.33)}$$

2. PNEUMATIC MECHANISMS

Pneumatic devices are widely used because of their relative simplicity, reliability, and ease of control. The drawbacks of this type of mechanism result mainly from the high sensitivity of the parameters dependent on the air which serves as the working agent. These parameters - especially pressure - change during the work because of variable aerodynamic friction in the pipes, valves and other accessories; the fact that numerous pieces of equipment receive a supply of compressed air from a single source; and changes in air temperature along the pipeline. As a result the air pressure at the input of a pneumomechanism will fluctuate in a random fashion.

In general the dynamics of a pneumomechanism are described by asystem of differential equations which depict the movement of the pneumatically driven mass and the changes of the air parameters in the working volume. The work of a pneumomechanism differs from that of a hydraulic mechanism in the nature of outflow of the air through the orifices and the process of filling up of the cylinder volume. Let us consider the mechanism the layout of which is given in Fig. 127. Let us suppose the processes of outflow and filling up are adiabatic and the pressure p_r in the receiver 1 is constant. From thermodynamics we know that the rate of flow of the air through the pipeline is described by a formula:

$$G = \alpha F_p p_r \sqrt{\frac{2g}{RT_r} \cdot \frac{k}{k-1} [\beta^{2/k} - \beta^{(k+1)/k}]} \qquad \text{(VI.2.1)}$$

where

α - coefficient of aerodynamic resistance;

F_p - cross-sectional area of the pipe 2 (m^2);

p_r - air pressure in the receiver 1;

T_r - absolute temperature of the air in the receiver;

R - gas constant;

$\beta = p/p_r$ - ratio of the pressure in cylinder 3 to that receiver, where

k - adiabatic exponent (k = 1.41).

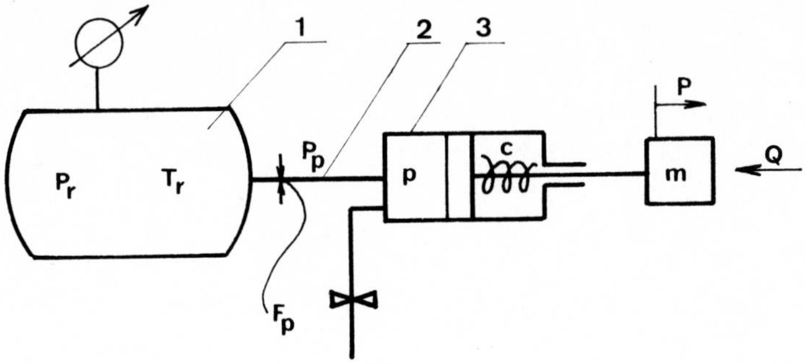

Fig. 127. Layout of the pneumomechanism under consideration.

At this stage, we must distinguish between supercritical and subcritical regimes. If we denote p_{cr} as the critical pressure, then:

$$\beta_{cr} = \frac{p_{cr}}{p_r} = [2/(k+1)]^{k/(k-1)} \qquad \text{(for air } \beta_{cr} \simeq 0.528) \tag{VI.2.2}$$

for the supercritical regime

$$p_r > \frac{p}{\beta_{cr}} \tag{VI.2.3}$$

and for the subcritical regime

$$p_r < \frac{p}{\beta_{cr}} \tag{VI.2.4}$$

where p - pressure in the cylinder.

For the supercritical regime, the pressure p_1 in the cylinder input orifice is constant, i.e.

$$p_1 = \beta_{cr} p_{cr} = 0.528 p_r > p \tag{VI.2.5}$$

Substituting p_1 from equation (VI.2.5) into equation (VI.2.1), we obtain for supercritical flow rate G_{cr}

$$G_{cr} = \alpha F_p p_r [2/(k+1)]^{1/(k-1)} \sqrt{\frac{2g}{RT_r} \cdot \frac{k}{k+1}} \tag{VI.2.6}$$

Under standard conditions (T_r = 293°K) we have:

$$G_{cr} \simeq 0.023\, \alpha F_p p_r \tag{VI.2.7}$$

Now let us find the time required to fill the cylinder from the initial value of the pressure p_o to the final value p_1 ($p_1 < 0.528\, p_r$) while the air temperature remains constant. For the cylinder volume V_c we have:

$$pV_c = G_c RT \tag{VI.2.8}$$

where G_c - instantaneous value of the air weight;

T - the air temperature.

During an elementary time period dt, the pressure will change over a value dp, and the amount of air by $G_{cr}dt$. Thus:

$$(p + dp)V_c = RT(G_c + G_{cr}dt) \tag{VI.2.9}$$

Subtracting equation (VI.2.8) from equation (VI.2.9), we obtain:

$$dt = \frac{V_c}{RT}\frac{dp}{G_{cr}} \tag{VI.2.10}$$

By integration we obtain:

$$t_1 = \frac{V_c}{RT}\frac{p_1 - p_o}{G_{cr}} \tag{VI.2.11}$$

By substituting equation (VI.2.7) into expression (VI.2.11), we finally reach:

$$t_1 = \frac{V_c}{0.67T}\frac{p_1 - p_o}{\alpha F_p p_r} \tag{VI.2.12}$$

For a subcritical regime, $p_1 = p > \beta_{cr} p_{cr} = 0.528\ p_r$.

Now, in equation (VI.2.1) the value of β varies from the initial value 0.528. In this case, we must substitute in the differential equation (VI.2.10) G_{cr}, which is not constant and is defined by expression (VI.2.1). Thus:

$$dt = \frac{V_c}{RT\alpha F_p p_r} \frac{\sqrt{\frac{RT}{2g}\frac{k-1}{k}}}{\sqrt{\beta^{2/k} - \beta^{(k+1)/k}}} \tag{VI.2.13}$$

Since

$$p = \beta p_r \qquad dp = p_r d\beta$$

therefore:

$$dt = \frac{0.022\ V_c}{\alpha F_p T} \sqrt{T_r}\ \beta^{-1/k}\ [1 - \beta^{(k-1)/k}]^{-1/2}\ d\beta \tag{VI.2.14}$$

To integrate this equation, we introduce an auxilliary function:

$$\lambda^2 = 1 - \beta^{(k-1)/k} \tag{VI.2.15}$$

which gives

$$2\lambda d\lambda = -\frac{k-1}{k}\beta^{-1/k}\ d\beta \tag{VI.2.16}$$

After substituting equations (VI.2.15) and (VI.2.16) in expression (VI.2.14), we obtain:

$$dt = - \frac{0.022V_c}{\alpha F_p T} \sqrt{T_r} \frac{2k}{k-1} d\lambda \qquad \text{(VI.2.17)}$$

The limits of integration are determined by the initial value of β_o and the critical value of β_{cr}. Thus:

$$t_2 = \frac{0.154\ V_c}{\alpha F_p T} \sqrt{T_r}\ (0.41 - \sqrt{1 - \beta_o^{0.29}})\sec \qquad \text{(VI.2.18)}$$

In the general case, the time t^* required to a pressure sufficient to move the piston and overcome the load and the forces of resistance may be written in the form:

$$t^* = t_1 + t_2$$

The variance σ_*^2 of this time is a sum of variances σ_1^2 and σ_2^2 which corresponding to the values t_1 and t_2, respectively:

$$\sigma_*^2 = \sigma_1^2 + \sigma_2^2 \qquad \text{(VI.2.19)}$$

To calculate σ_1^2 and σ_2^2, we use the approximation (I.13.7).

For the supercritical regime assuming V_c = const, F_p = const, and α - const (determined) and knowing T, p_r, p_1 and p_o to be random variable, we obtain:

$$\sigma_1^2 = [V_c/0.67\alpha F_p]^2 \{(\partial t_1/\partial p_1)^2\sigma_{p_1}^2 + (\partial t_1/\partial p_o)^2\sigma_{p_o}^2 + (\partial t_1/\partial T)^2\sigma_T^2 + (\partial t_1/\partial p_r)^2\sigma_{p_r}^2\} =$$

$$= [V_c/0.67\alpha F_p]^2 \{(1/F_p p_r)^2\sigma_{p_1}^2 + (\frac{p_1 - p_o}{T^2 F_p p_r})^2\sigma_T^2 + (\frac{p_1 - p_o}{T F_p p_r^2})^2\sigma_{p_r}^2 + (\frac{1}{F_p P_r})^2\sigma_{p_o}^2 \qquad \text{(VI.2.20)}$$

For the subcritical regime assuming V_c = const, F_p = const, and α = const (determined) and knowing T, T_r, and β_o to be random variables, we arrive at:

$$\sigma_2^2 = [0.154V_c/\alpha F_p]^2 \{(\partial t_2/\partial T)^2\sigma_T^2 + (\partial t_2/\partial T_r)^2\sigma_{T_r}^2 + (\partial t_2/\partial \beta_o)^2\sigma_{\beta_o}^2 =$$

$$= [0.154V_c/\alpha F_p]^2 \{[\sqrt{T_r}/T^2(0.41 - \sqrt{1 - \beta_o^{0.29}})]^2\sigma_T^2 + \qquad \text{(VI.2.21)}$$

$$+ [\frac{0.41 - \sqrt{1 - \beta_o^{0.29}}}{T\sqrt{T_r}}]^2\sigma_{T_r}^2 + [\frac{\sqrt{T_r}\ \beta_o^{-0.71}}{T\sqrt{1 - \beta_o^{0.29}}}]^2\sigma_{\beta_o}^2\}$$

Obviously, expressions (VI.2.20) and (VI.2.21) can be simplified for specific cases which are possible when, for instance, the thermodynamic process can be completed under conditions of pure supercritical fill up of the cylinder (or pure subcritical). Simplification can also be achieved when some of the other parameters can be defined as determined (not random).

To calculate the movement of the piston, we must deduce the differential equation for its displacement. This requires some intermediate steps. The thermodynamic equation for the air in the volume of the cylinder has the following form:

$$p_c V_c = G_c RT \tag{VI.2.22}$$

(the subscript c indicates values belonging to the cylinder volume).

For the volume V_c, we can substitute the obvious expression:

$$V_c = F_c s$$

where s - the displacement of the piston;

F_c - the cylinder's cross-sectional area.

After differentiating equation (VI.2.22), we obtain:

$$p_c dV_c + V_c dp_c = RTdG_c = RTGdt \tag{VI.2.23}$$

or

$$p_c \frac{ds}{dt} + s\frac{dp_c}{dt} = \frac{d(sp_c)}{dt} = \frac{RT}{F_c} G$$

For the supercritical airflow regime, the piston moves such that G_{cr} = const [see expression (VI.2.7)]. Thus after integration of equation (VI.2.23), we obtain:

$$sp_c = s_o p_o + \frac{RT}{F_c} G_{cr} t \tag{VI.2.24}$$

(This expression is written for the initial conditions: when $t = t_o = 0$, then $s = s_o$ and $p = p_o$).

For the layout shown in Fig. 127 (where 3-cylinder, 4-piston, 5-spring with stiffness c), the differential equation of the movement of the piston 4 may be written as:

$$m\frac{dV_c}{dt} - \eta p_c F_c + cs = Q \tag{VI.2.25}$$

where

Q - the load, which includes the useful and harmful forces.

Now, by expressing p_c in terms of equation (VI.2.24) and substituting it into equation (VI.2.25), we obtain:

$$m \frac{d^2 s}{dt^2} - \eta \frac{s_o}{s} p_o F_o - \eta \frac{RTG_{cr}}{s} t + cs = Q \qquad \text{(VI.2.26)}$$

This equation is essentially nonlinear. For the subcritical regime of the air flow we have to substitute for the value of G from expression (VI.2.1) for this regime. We will consider here the situation in which the pressure p_c in the cylinder can be taken as constant during the movement of the piston. For such a simplified case, when the process can be assumed to be subcritical for most of the period of the piston's movement (which is the case for mechanisms with relatively long cylinders, low resistance of the manifold, and a relatively high load), we can approximate the description of the piston's movement by a linear differential equation. For instance, the mechanism shown in Fig. 127 can be described by an equation which follows from expression (VI.2.25):

$$m\ddot{s} + cs = Q + p \qquad \text{(VI.2.27)}$$

or

$$\ddot{s} + k^2 s = A$$

where

$$k^2 = \frac{c}{m}; \qquad A = \frac{Q + p}{m}; \qquad p = \eta p_c F_c$$

Assuming that the term A can be represented as the sum of a determined avera average value $\bar{A}$ and a random item $\mathring{A}$, we can again seek the probabilistic characteristics of the random part of the solution $\mathring{s}$. (The determined solution is obtained in a trivial way.)

To describe the random excitation $\mathring{A}$ we have to measure the frequential picture of the random items of the forces p and Q. For example, let us consider the case in which the load can be taken as strictly constant and the air pressure changes at random, as is shown in Fig. 128. In this Figure, we can see 10 realizations of a random process measured in a workshop by means of a pressure transducer over a period of ten days between 9 am and 11 am. The correlation function of this random process, which is shown in Fig. 129, may be approximated by the expression:

$$K_p = \sigma_p^2 e^{-\alpha t^2} \cos\beta t = 0.065\, e^{-0.009t^2} \cos 0.157t \qquad \text{(VI.2.28)}$$

where α and β - constant coefficients;

σ_p^2 - variance of pressure.

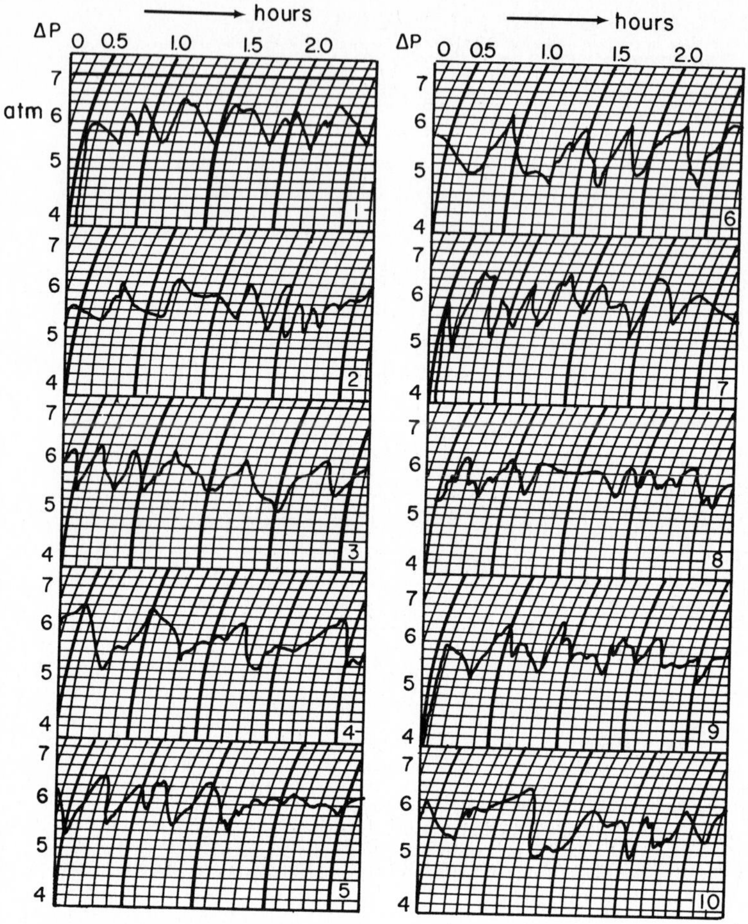

Fig. 128. An example of the air pressure changes measured in some workshop over a period of five days. Each line corresponds to one day, and each shift comprised three hours.

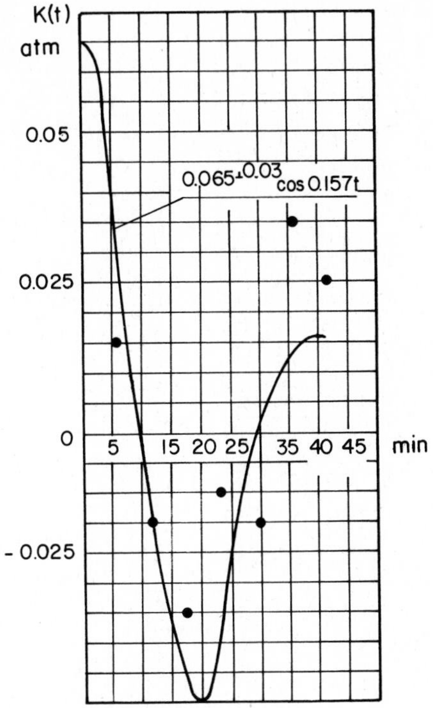

Fig. 129. Correlation function of the randomly changing air pressure (see Fig. 128).

Obviously, for K_p the correlation function of the driving force we have an expression of the same form, in which:

$$\sigma_p^2 = \eta^2 F_c^2 \sigma_p^2$$

Then, for the spectral density S_p of the moving force p (on the basis of (I.34) we obtain:

$$S_p = \frac{\sigma_p^2}{4\sqrt{\alpha\pi}} \left\{ \exp[-(\beta-\omega)^2/4\alpha] + \exp[-(\beta-\omega)^2/4\alpha] \right\} \tag{VI.2.29}$$

The transfer function $(j\omega)$ corresponding to equation (VI.2.27) has the following form:

$$\Phi(j\omega) = \frac{1}{|k^2 - \omega^2|^2} \tag{VI.2.30}$$

Thus, for the spectral densities of the random terms of the displacement s, the speed V, and the acceleration W of the driven mass we obtain, respectively:

$$S_s(\omega) = \frac{S_p}{|k^2 - \omega^2|^2}$$

$$S_v(\omega) = \frac{\omega^2 S_p}{|k^2 - \omega^2|^2}$$

$$S_w(\omega) = \frac{\omega^4 S_p}{|k^2 - \omega^2|^2}$$

The variances of the displacement σ_s^2, speed σ_v^2, and acceleration σ_w^2 can thus be expressed as:

$$\sigma_s^2 = \frac{\sigma_p^2 F^2 \eta^2}{4\sqrt{\alpha\pi}} \int_{-\infty}^{\infty} \frac{\exp[-(\beta-\omega)^2/4\alpha] + \exp[-(\beta+\omega)^2/4\alpha]}{|k^2 - \omega^2|^2} d\omega$$

$$\sigma_v^2 = \frac{\sigma_p^2 F^2 \eta^2}{4\sqrt{\alpha\pi}} \int_{-\infty}^{\infty} \frac{\omega^2(\exp[-(\beta-\omega)^2/4\alpha] + \exp[-(\beta+\omega)^2/4\alpha])}{|k^2 - \omega^2|^2} d\omega \qquad \text{(VI.2.31)}$$

$$\sigma_w^2 = \frac{\sigma_p^2 F^2 \eta^2}{4\sqrt{\alpha\pi}} \int_{-\infty}^{\infty} \frac{\omega^4(\exp[-(\beta-\omega)^2/4\alpha] + \exp[-(\beta+\omega)^2/4\alpha])}{|k^2 - \omega^2|^2} d\omega$$

Substituting numerical values for α, β and σ_p^2 which describe the excitation caused by the random term of pressure [see (VI.2.28)], and the numerical values for the piston area F and for k^2 the term which describes the inertial mass and stiffness of the spring, we obtain the variances describing the dynamic accuracy of the piston's movement.

3. BELT TRANSMISSION

The belt drive - a friction transmission with flexible links - has a number of advantages over other forms of transmission, such as gear transmissions. These advantages include simplicity, smoothness, absence of noise, possibility of covering big gaps between shafts without additional links, and the possibility of high power transmission with a minimum of links. However, the slip which accompanies the process of power transmission by any belt drive constitutes a serious disadvantage and a major limitation on its use in many cases. Any mechanism in which a strict speed ratio has to be guaranteed cannot be based on a belt drive. It is commonly accepted that the slip accounts for about 0.01-0.02 of the nominal ratio. In a working transmission the slip may be regarded as a random function because it is influenced by random factors, such as the friction between the belt and the pulley, and the variable tension of the sides of the belt. Thus, the question that follows naturally is: what are the probabilistic characteristics of the slip parameters, the knowledge of which may aid the designer in reaching a decision in some specific cases?

The layout shown in Fig. 130 illustrates the process of power transmission by a belt drive. The pulley on the right-hand side is the driving pulley and that on the left-hand side, the driven one. As is known from belt drive theory, the belt wrap angle α around the pulley is divided in two parts:

α' - the slippage angle, the angle at which the slip between the belt and the pulley occurs;

α'' - the angle at which there is no slip between the belt and the pulley.

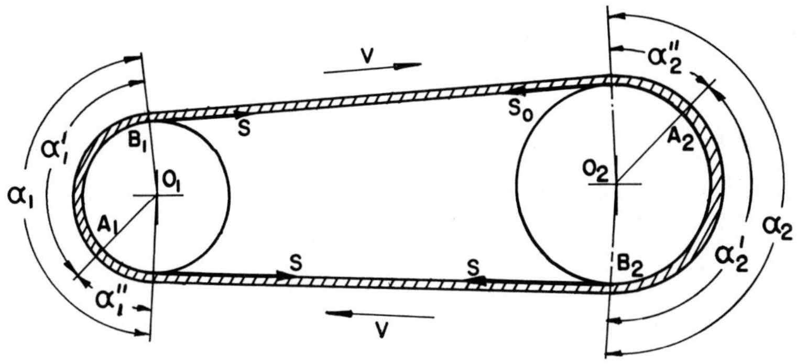

Fig. 130. Layout of a belt drive showing the changes in the stresses in the belt due to the power transmission in the drive.

For a normally acting transmission, the inequality $\alpha' < \alpha$ holds good. (At the moment at which $\alpha' \geqslant \alpha$, the torque cannot be transmitted, the slip becomes significant, and the belt jumps off the pulley, thus disconnecting the shafts if special precautions are not employed.) The slippage angle is expressed by the equation (based on Euler's law):

$$\alpha' = \frac{1}{\xi} \ln S/S_o \tag{VI.3.1}$$

where ξ - the friction coefficients;

S and S_o - the forces of tensions in the slack and tight sides of the belt.

The slip of a flexible link such as a belt is explained by its relatively high elasticity. The relationship between the elongation of the belt and the angle α' is defined by:

$$\varepsilon = \frac{S_o}{AE} (e^{\xi\alpha} - 1) \tag{VI.3.2}$$

where

A - the area of the cross-section of the belt or any other flexible link;

E - modulus of elasticity;

Or from equation (VI.3.1) we obtain:

$$\varepsilon = (S - S_o)/AE$$

In the remainder of this discussion, we will use the subscript 1 for the driving elements and the subscript 2 for the driven ones. In Fig. 130 the direction of slip in the limits of the angle α_1' is opposite to that of the rotation of the pulley, and the deformation of the belt decreases from a maximum at point A_1 (where the deformation corresponds to tension S) to a minimum at point B_1 (where the deformation corresponds to tension S_o). Within this limits of the angle (the driven pulley), the direction of the slip is the same as that of the pulley's rotation. The deformation of the belt decreases from a minimum at point A_2 (where the deformation corresponds to tension S_o) to a maximum at point B_2 (where it again corresponds to tension S). The speed of the elastic slip ν is given by:

$$\nu = V\varepsilon$$

where V - the peripheral speed of the pulleys.

Since we have to take into consideration the slip on each of the two pulleys, we have:

$$\nu = 2\varepsilon = 2\,\frac{S - S_o}{EA} = \frac{2Q}{EA} \qquad \text{(VI.3.3)}$$

where $Q = S - S_o$.

An important conclusion can be derived from this expression: for $\alpha' < \alpha$ the value ν does not depend on the friction coefficient.

Since we have now introduced a random element into our calculations, we are no longer following the classic treatment. Since Q is a random variable, the value of ν will change at random, and we must thus seek its probabilistic characteristics. Since:

$$Q = \bar{Q} + \mathring{Q} \qquad \text{(VI.3.4)}$$

then

$$\nu = \bar{\nu} + \mathring{\nu} \qquad \text{(VI.3.5)}$$

The characteristics of expression (VI.3.4) can be measured or defined, i.e. the distribution law f(Q) is known. From chapter I, section 23, we can define the distribution law $f(\nu)$ of the slip in the following form for the general case:

$$f(\nu) = f(\nu AE/2)(AE/2) \tag{VI.3.6}$$

In a specific case, for instance for a normal function f(Q) with variance σ_Q^2 of the force Q and average $\bar{Q}$, we obtain:

$$f(\nu) = \frac{AE}{2\sigma_Q\sqrt{2\pi}} \exp[- \frac{(2\bar{Q}/EA - 2\nu EA)^2}{2\sigma_Q^2}] \tag{VI.3.7}$$

Obviously, we can also obtain a normal distribution for the slip, i.e. the RMSV σ_ν for the slip ν can be expressed as:

$$\sigma_\nu = \frac{2\sigma_Q}{AE} \tag{VI.3.8}$$

and for the average slip as:

$$\bar{\nu} = \frac{2\bar{Q}}{EA} \tag{VI.3.9}$$

when the slip becomes significant, i.e. $\alpha'' \geq \alpha$, then the equations for σ_ν and $\bar{\nu}$ obviously take a different form. In this case, ν is the sum of the slip ν' on the first pulley and the slip ν'' on the second pulley, such that

$$\nu = \nu' + \nu'' \tag{VI.3.19}$$

wherein

$$\nu' = \frac{S_o}{EA}(e^{\xi\alpha_1} - 1) \tag{VI.3.11}$$

and

$$\nu'' = \frac{S_o}{EA}(e^{\xi\alpha_2} - 1) \tag{VI.3.12}$$

Thus, the slip is a function of the two variables S_o and ξ. The two-dimensional distribution function f(ν) of the slip has the form

$$f(\nu) = p\{(S_o,\xi)\} \subset D = \iint_D f(S_o,\xi)dS_o d\xi$$

where

p - probability symbol;

D - integration domain;

$f(S_o,\xi)$ - two-dimensional distribution law of the variables S_o and ξ.

Because S_o and ξ are independent, the distribution law can be expressed as a product (see I.21) of $f(S_o)$ and $f(\xi)$ - the distributions of the tension S_o and the friction coefficient ξ, respectively:

$$f(S_o,\xi) = f(S_o)\cdot f(\xi) \tag{VI.3.13}$$

The integration domain is represented graphically in Fig. 131. This domain is defined by the limits of the variables S_o and ξ. These limits are:

$$\frac{EV\nu_o}{e^{\xi\alpha}-1} \leqslant S_o \leqslant \frac{AE\nu}{e^{\xi\alpha}-1} \tag{VI.3.14}$$

$$\xi_1 \leqslant \xi < \xi_2 \tag{VI.3.15}$$

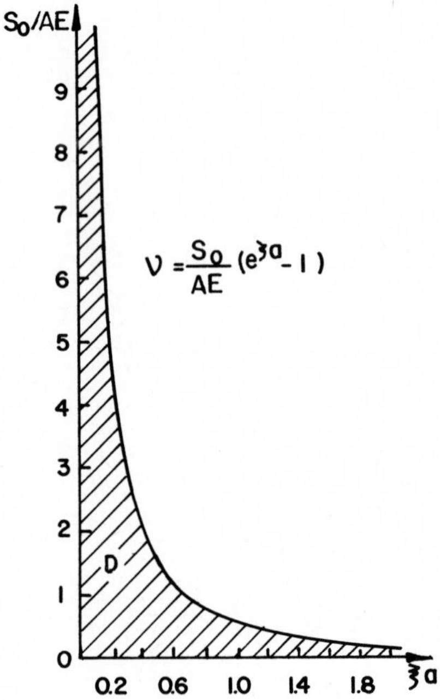

Fig. 131. An example of a possible existance domain for the tension and friction coefficient (which yield a two-dimensional random variable).

In some cases, the left boundary may equal 0 (i.e. $\nu_o = 0$ and $\xi_1 = 0$). For instance for uniform $f(S) = f_s = \text{const}$ and $f(\xi) = f_\xi = \text{const}$, we obtain for $F(\nu)$:

$$F(\nu) = \int_{\xi_1}^{\xi_2} \int_{AE\nu_o/(e^{\xi\alpha}-1)}^{AE\nu/(e^{\xi\alpha}-1)} f(S_o)\cdot f(\xi)dS_o d\xi = \tag{VI.3.16}$$

$$= AE(\nu-\nu_o)f_s\cdot f\xi\{ \frac{\ln[(e^{\xi 2\alpha}-1)/(e^{\xi 1\alpha}-1)]}{\alpha} - \xi_2+\xi_1 \} = B(\nu-\nu_o)$$

Differentiating expression (VI.3.16), we obtain for the distribution law $f(\nu)$ the following expression:

$$f(\nu) = B = \text{const} \tag{VI.3.17}$$

This means that in this case the slip is described by a uniform distribution law.

From equation (VI.3.17) we obtain for the slip variance σ_ν^2

$$\sigma_\nu^2 = \frac{B^2}{12} \tag{VI.3.18}$$

substituting the values α_1 and α_2 for α in expression (VI.3.16), we obtain:

$$\sigma_\nu^2 = \sigma_{\nu'}^2 + \sigma_{\nu''}^2 = \frac{B_1^2 + B_2^2}{12} \tag{VI.3.19}$$

where B_1 and B_2 correspond to α_1 and α_2, respectively.

The average value for the slip $\bar{\nu}$ may be approximated as follows:

$$\bar{\nu} \simeq \frac{\bar{S}_o}{EA} (e^{\bar{\xi}\alpha} - 1) \tag{VI.3.20}$$

And then we have for the slip:

$$\nu = \bar{\nu} \pm 3\sigma_\nu \tag{VI.3.21}$$

Since the elasticity of the belt attentiates the errors or roughnesses of the motion, let us now define quantitatively the effects of smoothening of the motion caused by the belt. We will consider the two different models represented in Fig. 132 and 133. In the first model, pulley 1, which is driven by a pair of gear wheels, rotates with a speed ω which is made up of a constant term $\bar{\omega}$ and a random term $\overset{\circ}{\omega}$. Thus:

$$\omega = \bar{\omega} + \overset{\circ}{\omega} = \dot{\bar{\theta}} + \dot{\overset{\circ}{\theta}}$$

The speed ω is transformed by the belt drive to the speed $\dot{\psi}$ of pulley 11, which drives the mass J_1. Taking into consideration that the stiffness of the belt c and the damping coefficient b_1 are constant, we can write the movement equation for the mass J_1 as follows:

$$J_1\ddot{\psi} + b_1\dot{\psi} + c\psi = c\theta \tag{VI.3.22}$$

In the second model - that shown in Fig. 133 - the driving pulley 1, with moment of inertia J_2, rotates with speed $\dot{\phi}$ due to the belt drive. Pulley 1 drives pulley 11 with a speed $\dot{\psi}$, which via a pair of gear wheels z_1 and z_2, drives the mass J_1. By analogy with the first model, the gear wheels introduce some random disturbance or excitation x which is shown in Fig. 134 in the form

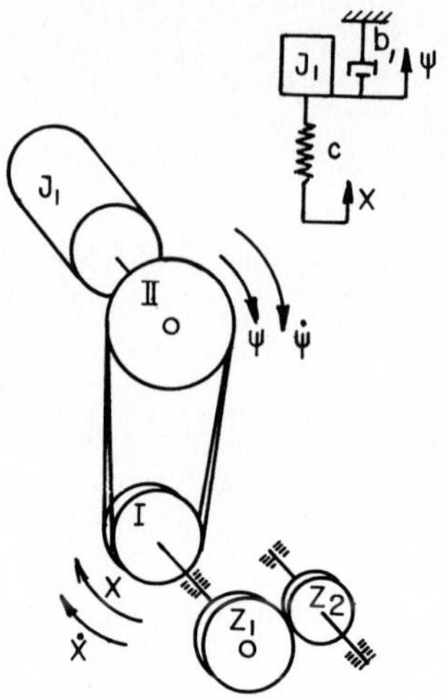

Fig. 132. Layout and dynamic model of a single-mass belt drive.

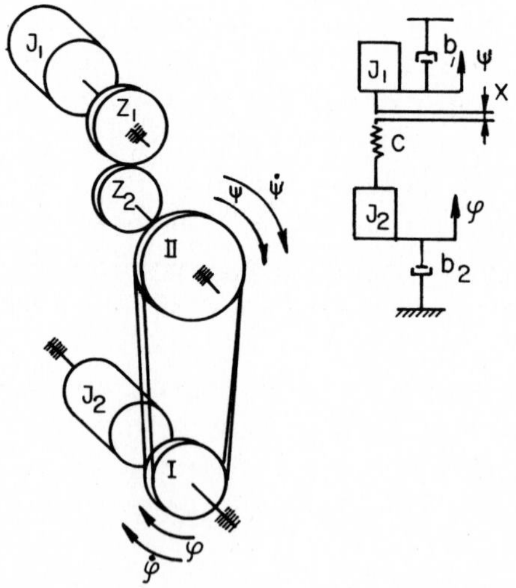

Fig. 133. Layout and dynamic model of a two-mass belt drive.

of a gap. The motion of the masses J_1 and J_2 may be described by the following equations:

$$\begin{cases} J_2\ddot{\phi} + b_2\dot{\phi} + c(\psi-\phi) = cx \\ J_1\ddot{\psi} + b_1\dot{\psi} - c(\psi-\phi) = -cx \end{cases} \qquad \text{(VI.3.23)}$$

Denoting $b_1/J_1 = 2n_1$; $c/J_1 = k_1^2$; $b_2/J_2 = 2n_2$; $c/J_2 = k_2^2$

we can rewrite equations (VI.3.22) and (VI.3.23)as, respectively:

$$\ddot{\psi} + 2n_1\dot{\psi} + k_1^2\psi = k_1^2\theta \qquad \text{(VI.3.24)}$$

and

$$\begin{cases} \ddot{\phi} + 2n_2\dot{\phi} + k_1^2(\psi-\phi) = k_1^2 x \\ \ddot{\psi} + 2n_1\dot{\psi} - k_2^2(\psi-\phi) = -k_2^2 x \end{cases} \qquad \text{(VI.3.25)}$$

The constant parts of the excitation $\bar{x}$ and θ do not influence the dynamics of the system. The random terms $\mathring{x}$ and $\mathring{\theta}$ cause random motions $\mathring{\psi}$ and $\mathring{\phi}$. The linearity of the equations permits the application of the superposition principle which means that for each term of x and θ we find a separate solution.

The solution to equation (VI.3.24) can then be obtained in the form:

$$S_\psi = \frac{k_1^4}{|k_1^2 - \omega^2 + 2n_1 j\omega|^2} S_\theta \qquad \text{(VI.3.26)}$$

where S_ψ, S_θ,S_ϕ and S_x - the spectral densities of the input and output motions, respectively.

Obviously, the angular speed can be expressed as follows:

$$S_{\dot{\psi}} = \frac{k_1^4\omega^2}{|k_1^2 - \omega^2 + 2n_1 j\omega|^2} S_\theta \qquad \text{(VI.3.27)}$$

And for the variance σ_ψ^2, we obtain

$$\sigma_\psi^2 = \int_o^\infty \frac{k_1^4 S_\theta}{|k_1^2 - \omega^2 + 2n_1 j\omega|^2} d\omega \qquad \text{(VI.3.28)}$$

For the second model, the equation system (VI.3.25) given for the transfer functions the following expressions for the calculation of ψ and ϕ, respectively:

$$\Phi_{\psi}(j\omega) = \frac{k_2^2(k_1^2+\omega^2-2n_1j\omega) - k_1^2k_2^2}{[2n_2j\omega-\omega^2-k_1^2][2n_1j\omega-\omega^2-k_2^2] - k_1^2k_2^2} \tag{VI.3.29}$$

$$\Phi_{\psi}(j\omega) = \frac{k_1^2(2n_1j\omega-\omega^2-k_2^2) + k_1^2k_2^2}{[2n_2j\omega-\omega^2-k_1^2][2n_1j\omega-\omega^2-k_2^2] - k_1^2k_2^2} \tag{VI.3.30}$$

Obviously, for the variances σ_{ψ}^2 and σ_{ψ}^2 we obtain, for a given spectral density $S_x(\omega)$:

$$\sigma_{\psi}^2 = \int_0^{\infty} |\Phi_{\psi}(j\omega)|^2 S_x(\omega)d\omega \tag{VI.3.31}$$

$$\sigma_{\psi}^2 = \int_0^{\infty} |\Phi_{\psi}(j\omega)|^2 S_x(\omega)d\omega \tag{VI.3.32}$$

Analyzing the expressions obtained, we see that the natural frequencies k_1 and k_2 significantly effect the outcome of the calculations, i.e. the values of the variances σ_{ψ}^2 and σ_{ϕ}^2. This fact gives us a powerful tool for optimizing the dynamics of a belt transmission. Obviously, the same effect will occur in geared belts and elastic couplings.

4. THRUST BEARINGS

As a result of their limited although high accuracy, thrust rolling bearings, such as shaft and turret supports, are major sources of vibration. Thus bearings, being vibration exciters, cause noise and decrease the quality of mechanisms.

Comprehensive studies on radial roller and ball bearings as sources of noise have already been carried out by Tallian and Gustafsson [1,2] *inter alia*. Our study differs from previous works in the following main aspects:

(1) Thrust bearings are the subject of the study.

(2) Remembering that the shape deflections of the tracks, balls or rollers are random, we have applied a statistical approach to the description of this phenomenon.

(3) Since the location of the contact points between the balls and the tracks (denoted "ball passing" in [1] and [2]) is a random process, we have tried to describe it in terms of probability.

(4) Since bearings never operate as isolated elements, there is no point in calculating the dynamics of a single separate bearing. We have thus considered the bearing as a vibration exciter at the input of the dynamic mechanical system to which it belongs.

It seems to us that by knowing the theoretical statistical description of the excitation spectrum that the shaft receives from the bearing, we will be able to estimate the dynamics and the noise of the shaft and thus decrease the negative effects caused by the vibration. In addition, knowledge of the excitation spectrum will enable us to make an acoustic diagnosis of the sources of error. We will thus try to build a statistical model of the errors of thrust bearings.

Let us consider two possibilities:

Case 1 (Fig. 134) consists of a shaft, supported by two roller bearings (or ball bearings) and one thrust ball bearing. In this model the upper ring of the thrust bearing is always exactly horizontal, i.e. perpendicular to the shaft axis (because of the roller bearings).

Case 2 (Fig. 135) differs from Case 1 only in the fact that the upper ring is free to incline in accordance with the errors of the bearing elements. This is the more realistic case.

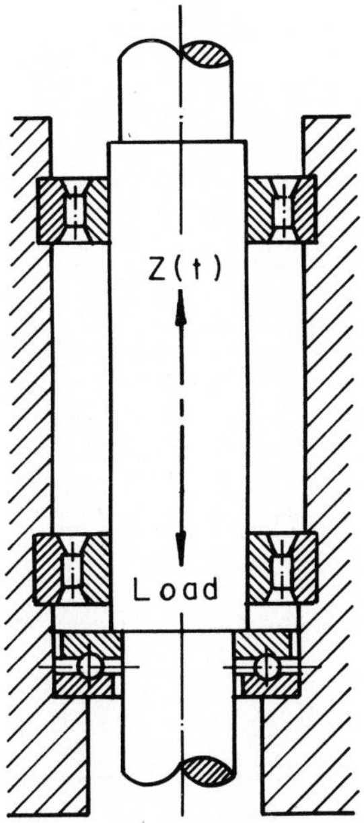

Fig. 134. Layout of thrust-bearing support with a horizontal upper ring.

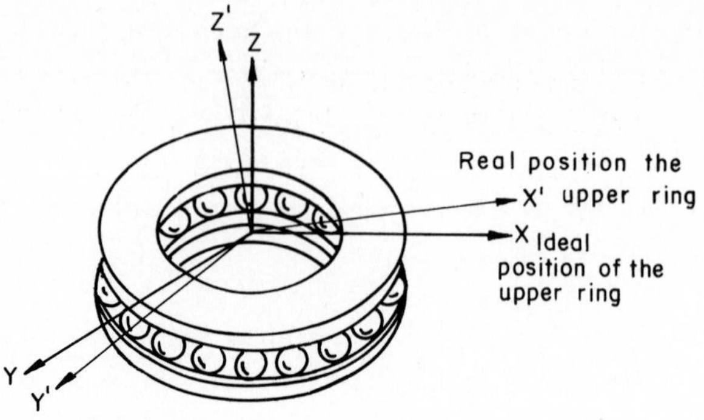

Fig. 135. Layout of a thrust-bearing with a free inclined upper ring.

The following general assumptions are made for both cases:

(1) the lower ring is fixed;

(2) the excitation described by $z(t)$ results from errors in the lower groove, the upper groove and the rolling elements, and is directed along the z axis;

(3) the excitation function $z(t)$ will be known when its spectral density S_z is known.

Case 1

Let us begin the discussion with the first case. The layout of the structure of the error $z(\phi)$ is shown in Fig. 136. The lower and upper grooves are described by the random functions $z_1(\phi)$ and $z_2(\phi)$, respectively, and the diameter of the balls, by $D + d$, where d is also a random function. (D represents the average diameter of the ball.) At any moment, both grooves are in contact with one of the balls, and there are some moments during bearing rotation when the contact passes from one ball to another. This mode of bearing behavior allows us to define $z(\phi)$ as:

$$z(\phi) = z_1(\phi) + z_2(\phi) + d(\phi) + x(\phi) \tag{VI.4.1}$$

where the errors z_1, z_2 and d can be measured for any of the bearing components. In addition to the layout given in Fig. 136 we consider separately z_3 which is the error caused by the eccentricity of the bearing rings as a result of the accuracy limitations arising during processing and assembly. The term $x(\phi)$ is included in equation (VI.4.1) to describe the jump-over from ball to ball, i.e. "ball passing". The spectral densities or correlation functions or each of the above-mentioned random functions, together with the distribution law, give the statistical description of these functions.

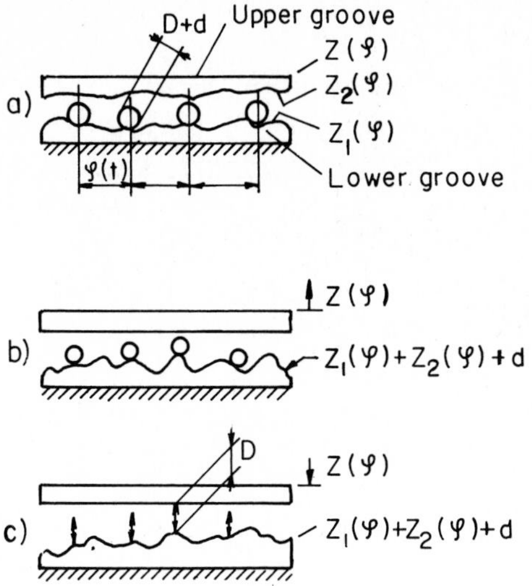

Fig. 136. Three stages of the formation of kinematic excitation in a thrust bearing. A proposed approach.

Obviously, instead of the variable ϕ, we can substitute its dependence on time. For instance, in the case of uniform rotation,

$$\phi = \frac{\omega}{2} t \tag{VI.4.2}$$

where ω = speed of angular rotation.

The division by 2 in equation (VI.4.2) is necessary because the rolling elements move with half the rotational velocity of the shaft. Thus, instead of random functions $z(\phi)$ we can deal with random functions $z(t)$. Fig. 136b shows a simplified, but statistically equivalent, model of the bearing. Because of the linear nature of the values of $z(t)$, we can assume that the lower groove includes all the above-mentioned errors, i.e. that by applying equation (VI.4.2) we obtain:

$$Z(t) = z_1(t) + z_2(t) + d(t) \tag{VI.4.3}$$

Then

$$K_Z(\tau) = K_{z_1}(\tau) + K_{z_2}(\tau) + K_d(\tau)$$

$$S_Z(\omega) = S_{z_1}(\omega) + S_{z_2}(\omega) + S_d(\omega) \tag{VI.4.4}$$

where S is the spectral density, K the correlation function, ω the frequency, and τ the time. The expression (VI.4.4) is valid because the random components of equation (VI.4.3) are independent. Let us remember that the correlation function of a sum of random variables equals the sum of correlation functions. [The function $x(\phi)$ or $x(t)$ will be added later in equation (VI.4.7).]

Taking into consideration the fact that the values of z_1, z_2 and d are small in comparison with the diameter of the balls, we can reduce the layout to that shown in Fig. 136c. Here, instead of balls one can imagine "sticks" with an average height D. In this case, the form of the function $z(t)$ can be predicted, as is shown in Fig. 137. Points "a" are the jump-over points ("ball passing"). The average value of the period $\bar{T}$ can be estimated as

$$\bar{T} = \frac{1}{n} \sum_{i=1}^{n} T_i \tag{VI.4.5}$$

and, correspondingly, the average frequency of this phenomenon $\bar{\nu}$ is

$$\bar{\nu} = 1/\bar{T} \tag{VI.4.6}$$

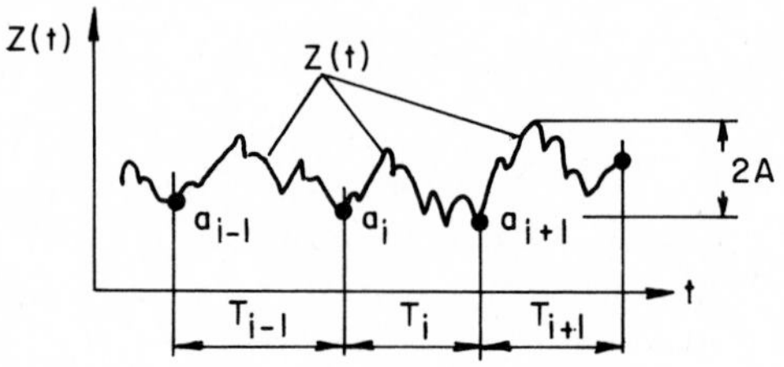

Fig. 137. Example of the kinematic excitation of the upper ring caused by the irregularities of the elements of a thrust bearing.

During the time intervals T_i, the upper ring moves according to the random process $Z(t)$. The spectral density S_Z may be assumed to have the form

$$S_Z = S_z + S_x \tag{VI.4.7}$$

It follows from equation VI.4.4 that the value of S_Z can be calculated by measuring its components. We must now seek the definition of $S_x(\omega)$, as is described below.

Let us calculate the probability of the situation in which rolling element number i - k is moved away from the upper ring (or groove) by a distance $\Delta < \Delta_k$, which can be reduced to 0 when rolling element number i touches this ring (or groove). From this moment, the upper ring moves in accordance with $z_1(t)$, as shown in Fig. 138.

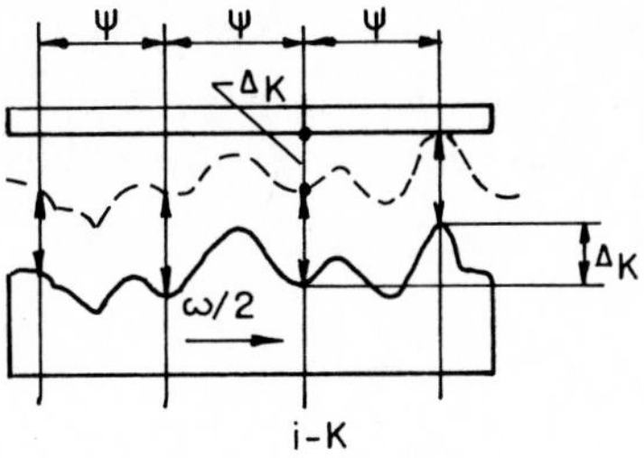

Fig. 138. Model of the touching and "pass-over" process in the thrust bearing.

Note 1

$$\Delta_k(t) = z_i - z_{i-k} \geq 0 \tag{VI.4.8}$$

It is assumed that the random function z(t) is normally distributed.

Note 2

Since a linear combination of normally distributed values is also normal, the distribution law f(Δ) of the random value Δ has the form

$$f(\Delta) = \frac{1}{\sigma_\Delta\sqrt{2\pi}} \exp[(\Delta-\bar{\Delta})^2/2\sigma_\Delta^2] \tag{VI.4.9}$$

For the general case, the distribution law will have the form $f(\Delta,\bar{\Delta},\sigma_\Delta)$ where $\bar{\Delta}$, the mathematical expectation of the Δ_k value, is given by

$$\bar{\Delta}_k = \bar{\Delta}_i - \bar{\Delta}_{i-k} = 0 \tag{VI.4.10}$$

Since $\Delta_1 = \Delta_{i-k}$, and σ_Δ the root-mean-square value of Δ_k is given by

$$\Delta_k = \Delta_i - \Delta_{i-k} = 0 \tag{VI.4.11}$$

where $\sigma_z = \sigma z_i = \sigma t_{i-k}$ and r_k is the correlation coefficient describing the ties between section i and i-k of the z function, then the probability $p(0 < \Delta < \Delta_k)$ can be expressed as follows:

$$p(0 < \Delta < \Delta_k) = \frac{1}{2\sigma_z\sqrt{\pi(1+r_k)}} \int_{-\infty}^{\Delta_k} \exp[-\Delta^2/4\ {}_z^2(1+r_k)]d\Delta$$

To estimate the average value $\bar{\nu}$ of the number of rolling-element "touches" per unit of time, we have to solve a classic "level-crossing" problem in stationary random process analysis (See I.37), which gives:

$$\bar{\nu}_k = \frac{\sigma_{\dot{\Delta}}}{2\pi\sigma_\Delta} \exp[-(a-\bar{\Delta})^2/2\sigma_\Delta^2] \qquad \text{(VI.4.12)}$$

For the general case of the distribution law, we get (see I.37)

$$\bar{\nu} = \int_0^\infty \dot{\Delta} f(a,\dot{\Delta}) d\dot{\Delta}$$

where a is the level under consideration.

In our case $a = 0$, $\Delta = 0$ so that

$$\bar{\nu}_k = \sigma_{\dot{\Delta}}/2\pi\sigma_\Delta \qquad \text{(VI.4.13)}$$

where $\sigma_{\dot{\Delta}}$ is the RMSV of the time derivative of the function $\Delta(t)$. For calculation of $\sigma_{\dot{\Delta}}$ we have to know the autocorrelation function $K_\Delta(\tau)$ of the random process $\Delta(t)$. Then:

$$\sigma_{\dot{\Delta}}^2 = - \frac{d^2 K_\Delta(\tau)}{d\tau^2} \quad \text{for } \tau = 0 \qquad \text{(VI.4.14)}$$

In addition, the value of $K_\Delta(\tau)$ can be expressed when the autocorrelation function $K_z(\tau)$ of the grooves is known. From equation (VI.4.8) we obtain:

$$K_\Delta(\tau) = 2[K_z(\tau) + K_{z_i z_{i-k}}(\tau)] \qquad \text{(VI.4.15)}$$

where $K_{z_i z_{i-k}}(\tau)$ are the joint correlation functions for sections i and i-k of the $Z(\tau)$ function.

In accordance with Fig. 137 we can calculate $\bar{T}$ from equations (VI.4.6) and (VI.4.13). The analytical form of the spectral density S_x may be expressed as follows:

$$S_x = \frac{\bar{A}^2}{2} \delta(\nu) \qquad \text{(VI.4.16)}$$

where δ - the Dirac impulse function.

$\bar{A}$ - the average deviation of the random function Z.

Note:

The rigorous definition of $\bar{A}$ is

$$p(|Z - \bar{Z}| < \bar{A}) = 0.5$$

which means that in 50% of the cases the deviation of Z will be bigger than $\bar{A}$ and in the other 50%, smaller. Thus, $\bar{A}$ can be considered as the average deviation of A from its mean value. This concept is widely applied in artillery.

To estimate the value $\bar{A}$, we will proceed as follows. Let us determine $\sigma_{Z'}$ the RMSV of the random function Z(t) between points a_i. Considering the joint distribution law of Z(t) and $Z(t + \bar{T}/2) = Z'$ (during half the period that the most considerable deviations occur), we have

$$f[Z(t),Z(t+\bar{T}/2)] = \frac{1}{\sigma_Z\sqrt{1-r_T^2}\,\sqrt{2\pi}} \exp[-\frac{1}{2(1-r_T^2)\sigma_Z^2}\{Z - r_T\frac{\sigma_Z}{\sigma_Z'}Z'\}] \quad (VI.4.17)$$

where

$$r_T = K(\bar{T}/2)/\sigma_Z \quad \text{and} \quad \sigma_{Z'} = \sigma_Z\sqrt{1 - r_T^2} \quad (VI.4.18)$$

Now, for the normally distributed Z, where $\bar{A} = 0.675\ \sigma_{Z'}$ which is the so-called average deviation, we get:

$$\bar{A} = 0.675\ \sigma_Z\sqrt{1-r_T} \quad (VI.4.19)$$

If ε is the eccentricity of the rings of the bearings, then the spectral density of the errors of thus originating may be expressed in the following manner:

$$S_{Z_3}(\omega) = \frac{\varepsilon^2}{2}\delta(\omega)$$

Case 2

The geometry of the second case is represented in Fig. 139. Three points A, B and C determine the location of the upper ring in terms of three random coordinates Z_A, Z_B and Z_C. As in the previous case, these coordinates are estimated statistically. For the second case we can draw the following three conclusions.

(1) At any moment the upper ring is supported by three rolling elements. This is the reason that the average number of "touches" ν_3 ("ball passings") per unit of time has to be three times larger than that in the previous case. From equation (VI.4.13) we obtain:

$$\bar{\nu}_3 = 3\sigma_{\dot{\Delta}}/2\pi\sigma_\Delta \quad (VI.4.20)$$

(2) It is natural to assume that the average locations of the points A, B and C (Fig. 139) create an equilateral triangle (a=b=c). The deviations of the locations of these points (the apices of the triangle) appear to be divisible by the pitch of the rolling elements. The frequency $\bar{\nu}_k$ of the appearance of a deviation at a distance which equals "k" pitches from the apices is given by equation (VI.4.13).

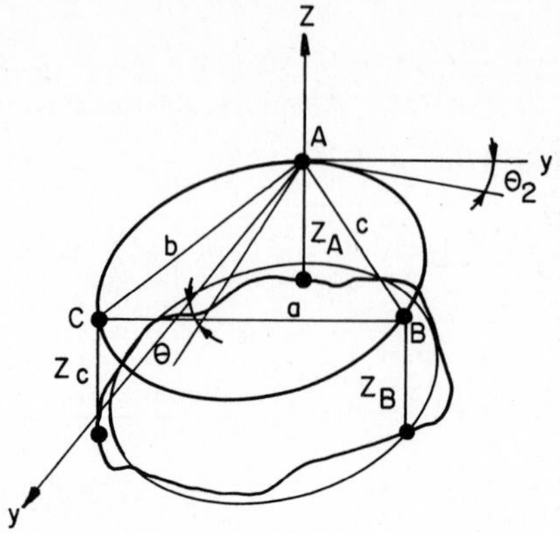

Fig. 139. Geometrical layout of the free-inclined upper ring in a thrust bearing.

(3) To estimate the maximal values of the average deviations of the inclination angles θ_1 and θ_2, we make use of triangle ABC (Fig. 139). Obviously, when $Z_A = \bar{A}$ and $Z_B = Z_C = -\bar{A}$, the average value $\bar{\theta}_1$ will be maximal. Thus, we obtain θ_1 as a ratio between the difference in the levels $Z_A - Z_B$ and the altitude of the triangle

$$\bar{\theta}_1 = 4\bar{A}/3R \tag{VI.4.21}$$

The maximal average value of $\bar{\theta}_2$ will occur when $Z_B = -\bar{A}$ and $Z_C = \bar{A}$ and can be expressed as a ratio between the difference in the levels Z_B and Z_C and the side CB of the triangle. Thus,

$$\bar{\theta}_2 = 2\bar{A}/\sqrt{3R} \tag{VI.4.22}$$

where, from equation (VI.4.18) it is known that

$$\bar{A} = 0.675\ (1 - r_T)\sigma_Z \tag{VI.4.23}$$

Example

As an example, we will determine the spectral density of the kinematic excitement caused by an SKF 51109 thrust bearing. The grooves of the rings 1 and 2 were measured by means of Taylor-Hobson rotary Talysurf 4, the errors being ignored (Fig. 140). The correlation function and its approximation are shown in Fig. 141.

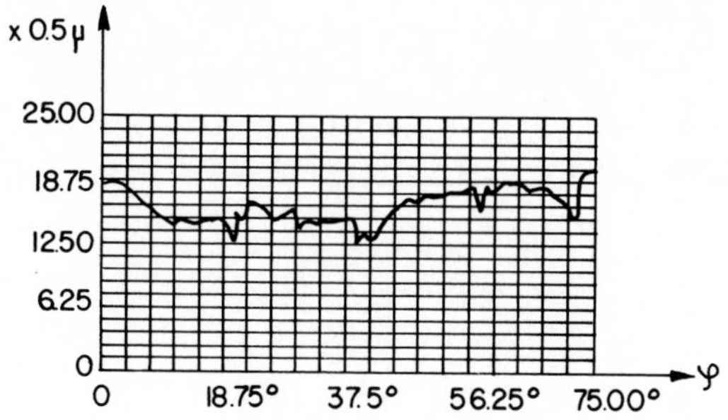

Fig. 140. A section of the groove irregularities measured on a ring of a thrust bearing of the SKF 51109 type.

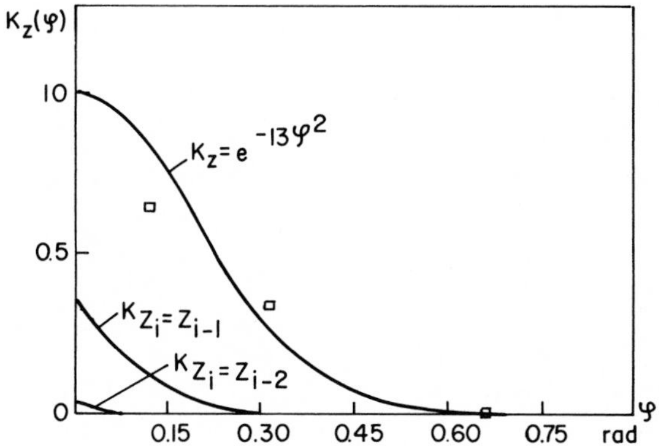

Fig. 141. Approximate correlation functions of the irregularities shown in Fig. 140.

From equation (VI.4.4), we can write

$$S_Z(\omega) = \frac{1}{\pi}\int_0^{\infty} [K_{z_1}(\tau) + K_{z_2}(\tau)]\cos\omega\tau d\tau \tag{VI.4.24}$$

Since measurements had shown that

$$K_Z(\tau) = K_{z_1}(\tau) = K_{z_2}(\tau) = \sigma_Z^2 e^{-13\omega^2\tau^2} \tag{VI.4.25}$$

where $\sigma_Z = 0.6$ μm.

Equation (VI.4.24) may be written as [see I.34]:

$$S_Z(\omega) = \frac{\sigma_Z^2}{4\omega\sqrt{13\pi}} \exp[-\omega^2/52\omega^2] \simeq 0.0285/\omega \ \mu m \qquad \text{(VI.4.26)}$$

To calculate the value of $\bar{\nu}$ according to equation (VI.4.12), we have to obtain the value of $K_\Delta(\tau)$ from equation (VI.4.15). As follows from the definition of a joint correlation, we have

$$K_{z_i z_{i-k}}(\tau) = K_Z(\tau+\theta_k) \qquad \text{(VI.4.27)}$$

where $\theta = k\psi/\omega$, $\psi = 2\pi/n$ (in our case $\psi = 0.285$ rad), and n is the number of balls in the bearing under consideration (in our example n = 22). Figure 141 shows that the value of $K_{z_i z_{i-k}}(\tau)$ is about 1% that of $K_Z(\tau)$ so that we can use for calculations an expression based on equation (VI.4.15) in the following form:

$$K_\Delta(\tau) \simeq 2[K_Z(\tau) + K_Z(\tau+\psi/\omega)] \qquad \text{(VI.4.28)}$$

From equations (VI.4.25) and (VI.4.14), we obtain for $\sigma_{\dot{\Delta}}^2$:

$$\sigma_{\dot{\Delta}}^2 = 67.7 \ \sigma_Z^2\omega^2$$

From expressions (IV.4.11, (IV.4.13) and (IV.4.16), we obtain the calculated spectral density (Fig. 142). As noted earlier, it is sufficient to consider only the case when k = 1. Then, for $\omega = 100$ 1/s, $r_K \simeq 0.348$ and $\sigma_{\dot{\Delta}} \simeq 494$ µm/sec, we obtain $\sigma_\Delta \simeq 0.98$ µm, $\nu_1 \simeq 80$ 1/s $\simeq 500$ rad/s, $\bar{\nu}_3 = 240$ 1/s $\simeq 1500$ rad/s, $\bar{T} \simeq 0.04$ s, from equations (VI.4.11, (VI.4.13), (VI.4.20) and (VI.4.6), respectively. From equation (VI.4.25), in accordance with equation (VI.4.16), we get:

$$r_{\bar{T}/2} \simeq 0.594$$

Then

$$\sigma_Z' = 0.6\sqrt{1 - 0.594^2} \simeq 0.48 \ \mu m$$

From equation (VI.4.18), $\bar{A} = 0.324$ µm, and from equation (VI.4.19) $S_X \simeq 0.52\ \delta\times(1500)$ µm^2.

Conclusions

(1) The theoretical statistical model of kinematic excitation caused by a thrust rolling bearing can be built in the form of the spectral density of the excitation.

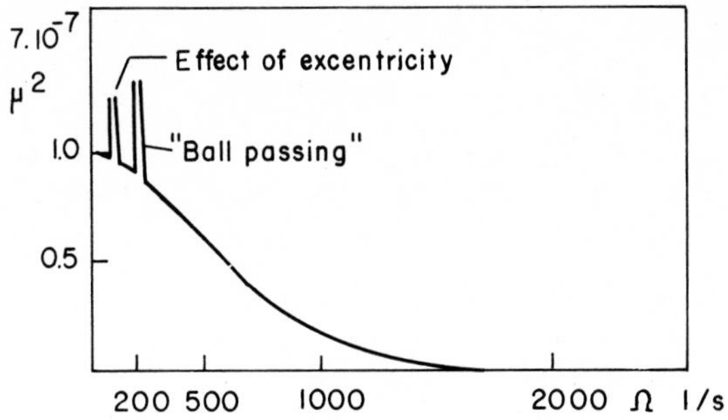

Fig. 142. Calculated spectral density of the kinematic excitations corresponding to the measured bearing.

(2) A significant portion of the kinematic excitation caused by the thrust bearing is due to the passing from one rolling element to another.

BIBLIOGRAPHY

1. Tallian, T.E. and O.G. Gustafsson, 1965. Progress in roller bearing vibration research and control. ASLE Trans., 8 (3).
2. Tallian, T.E. and O.G. Gustafsson. Dec. 6, 1963. Final Report on the Study of the Vibration Characteristics of Bearings, Research Laboratory SKF Industries, Inc., Engineering & Research Center, King of Prussia, PA.

5. ROLLING SUPPORTS (INCLUDING STATISTICAL SIMULATION FOR THE GENERAL CASE)

Let us consider the following model, which consists of a trace 1, upon which two rolling bodies 2 are located, and plane surface 3, which is supported by the rolling bodies. The trace, the rollers and the upper surface have random deviations as is shown in Fig. 143a. Using the idea applied in the previous section and illustrated in Fig. 136, we transform the model into the layout shown in Fig. 143b. Here, the random errors z_3 of the upper surface 3 and the error z_2 of the rollers are lumped to the trace 1. Thus, the correlation function K(x) of the transformed trace includes the errors of the whole system and can be described as follows:

$$K(x) = K_1(x) + K_2(x) + K_3(x) \qquad \text{(VI.5.1)}$$

where

$K_1(x)$ - the correlation function of the errors on the trace;
$K_2(x)$ - the correlation function of the errors of the rollers;
$K_3(x)$ - the correlation function of the errors of the upper surface.

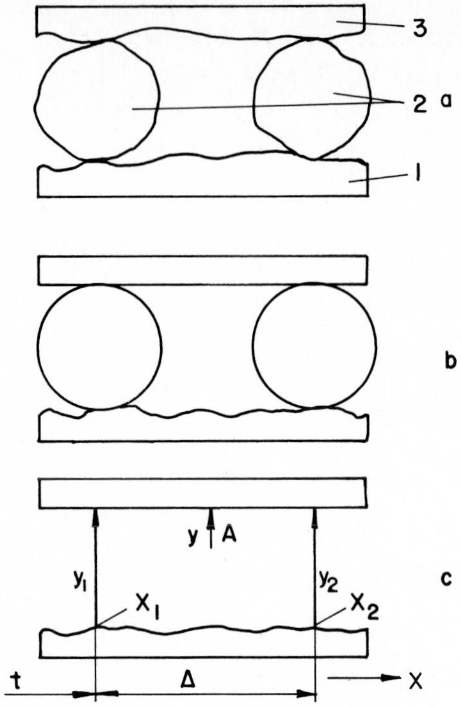

Fig. 143. Three stages of the formation of kinematic excitation in a rolling support.

The correlation function K(x) may be expressed as the sum of the correlation functions K_1, K_2 and K_3 since these functions are independent of one another.

In the next step, we replace the rollers by two "sticks" and obtain the layout given in Fig. 143c.

We now define the problem as follows: What is the motion of a point A located midway between the sticks on the upper surface when the trace 1 moves with some speed V? Expression (VI.5.1) can be rewritten in the following form:

$$K(t,\tau) = K_1(t,\tau) + K_2(t,\tau) + K_3(t,\tau)$$

where $\tau = x/V$, and t - time.

At any moment, the sticks support the upper surface at points with coordinates x_1 and x_2, and obviously the coordinate y of point A is given by:

$$y = (y_1 + y_2)/2 \qquad \text{(VI.5.2)}$$

where $y_1 = y(x_1)$ and $y_2 = y(x_2)$

and $x_1 = x(t)$ and $x_2 = x(t+\Delta)$.

If the distance between the two sticks is $\Delta \cdot V$, we define the variance from expression (VI.5.2), by the following formula (see I.14):

$$\sigma_A^2 = \frac{\sigma_y^2}{2} + \frac{K(\Delta)}{2} \qquad \text{(VI.5.3)}$$

where

σ_y^2 - the lumped variance of the trace which can be calculated as the sum of variances of the trace σ_1^2, the rollers σ_2^2 and the upper surface σ_3^2; thus: $\sigma_y^2 = \sigma_1^2 + \sigma_2^2 + \sigma_3^2$.

$K(\Delta)$ - the value of the correlation function $K(x)$ for $x = \Delta \cdot V$.

When Δ is very large, the value of the correlation function $K(x)$ tends to 0, and from equation (VI.5.3) we obtain for the variance of the random function $y(t)$:

$$\sigma_A^2 \simeq \frac{\sigma_y^2}{2} \qquad \text{(VI.5.4)}$$

To define the correlation function $K(t,\tau)$ of the random movement $y(t)$ of point A, we must write the following expression (see I.28):

$$K_A(t,\tau) = E\{\overset{\circ}{y}(t)\overset{\circ}{y}(t+\tau)\} \qquad \text{(VI.5.5)}$$

where τ - is a time interval and the argument of this correlation function.

Substituting equation (VI.5.2) into equation (VI.5.5), we obtain:

$$K_A(\tau) = \frac{1}{4} E\{[x(t) + x(t+\tau)][x(t+\tau) + x(t+\tau+\Delta)]\} =$$

$$= \frac{1}{4} E\{x(t)x(t+\tau) + x(t)x(t+\tau+\Delta) + x(t+\Delta)x(t+\tau) + x(t+\Delta)x(t+\Delta+\tau)\} \qquad \text{(VI.5.6)}$$

For a stationary process, we rewrite expression (VI.5.6) in the following form:

$$K_A(\tau) = \frac{1}{4} [2K_y(\tau) + K_y(\tau+\Delta) + K_y(\tau-\Delta)] \qquad \text{(VI.5.7)}$$

where K_y - is the correlation function of the given random surface.

We will now consider a model describing a radial ball (or roller) bearing (Fig. 144). The Figure shows an arc 1 of a radius ρ on which two rolling bodies II supporting an arc III are placed. The angular distance between the rollers is constant and equals ψ. We will discuss the situation in which the outer arc is pressed against the inner arc by a force P constantly directed towards the center.

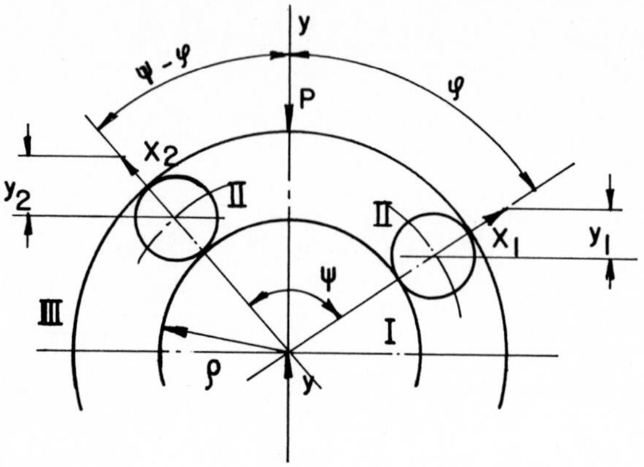

Fig. 144. Geometry of the formation of kinematic excitation in a radial ball or roller bearing

As in the above-described case, assuming that the arcs and rollers have random irregularities on their surfaces, we can ask how the position of the center of the outer arc will change as the inner arc rotates. We need to take into consideration the changes in the angles ϕ and $\psi - \phi$, as can be seen from Fig. 144.

The centers of the rollers are described by the coordinates x_1 and x_2. Correspondingly, their projections y_1 and y_2 on the y axis are:

$$y_1 = x_1\cos(\psi - \phi)$$
$$y_2 = x_2\cos\phi \qquad \text{(VI.5.8)}$$

In this case, from equation (VI.5.2) we obtain for y:

$$y = (y_1 + y_2)/2$$

and for the variance σ_y^2 we have:

$$\sigma_y^2 = \frac{\sigma_{y_1}^2 + \sigma_{y_2}^2}{4} + \frac{K(\psi)}{2} \qquad \text{(VI.5.9)}$$

Now, from expression (VI.5.8) we can write:

$$\sigma_{y_1}^2 = \sigma_x^2\cos^2(\psi-\phi)$$

and (VI.5.10)

$$\sigma_{y_2}^2 = \sigma_x^2\cos^2\phi$$

For $K(\psi)$, according to the definition of a correlation function (see I.28-I.29) we obtain:

$$K(\psi) = E\{x_1\cos(\psi-\phi)\cdot x_2\cos\phi\} =$$
$$= \cos(\psi-\phi)\cdot\cos\phi\cdot E\{x_1\cdot x_2\} = \quad \text{(VI.5.11)}$$
$$= \cos(\psi-\phi)\cdot\cos\phi\cdot K(\Delta) = \cos(\psi-\phi)\cdot\cos\phi\cdot\sigma_x^2\cdot R(\Delta)$$

where $\Delta = \psi\rho$

Expression (VI.5.9) can now be rewritten as:

$$\sigma_y^2 = \frac{\sigma_x^2}{2}\left\{ \frac{\cos^2(\psi-\phi) + \cos^2\phi}{2} + R(\Delta)\cos(\psi-\phi)\cdot\cos\phi \right\} \quad \text{(VI.5.12)}$$

For the specific cases in which $\phi = 0$ and $\phi = \frac{1}{2}\psi$, we obtain for σ_y^2 the expressions (VI.5.13) and (VI.5.14), respectively:

$$\sigma_y^2 = \frac{\sigma_x^2}{2}\left[\frac{\cos^2\psi+1}{2} + R(\Delta)\cdot\cos\psi\right] \quad \text{(VI.5.13)}$$

$$\sigma_y^2 = \frac{\sigma_x^2}{2}\cos^2\frac{\psi}{2}\cdot[1 + R(\Delta)] \quad \text{(VI.5.14)}$$

Let us now discuss the more general case of an arbitrary number of "sticks." (Here, we omit the consideration of the initial situation in which the rolling elements and errors of the traces and pass directly to the final model, as was done in the previous cases.) In the model under consideration (Fig. 145), N sticks 1 of identical heights are located at distances Δ from one another and are guided by constant guides 2. The sticks support a straight line 3 which rests in position C. The mass center (m.c.) of this line determines its direction of rotation (or the direction of the angle θ). By moving the randomly changing function $y(x)$ with a horizontal speed V, we cause the vertical movement y_i of the sticks and, as a result, the movement y_x of the point m.c. The latter movement is the subject of our discussion. The correlation function and the density distribution of the random function $y(x)$ are known, and the correlation function and the density distribution of the motion y_c are to be sought.

Since an analytical solution to such general problem would be too complicated, we propose the use of computer-aided statistical simulation. The algorithm we intend to use may be explained as follows. The straight line is lowered from position *a* (Fig. 145) until it touches the highest stick (the maximal value of y_1 is y_{max}) and thus reaches position *b*. The line then begins to rotate in the direction dictated by the location of its m.c. relative to the

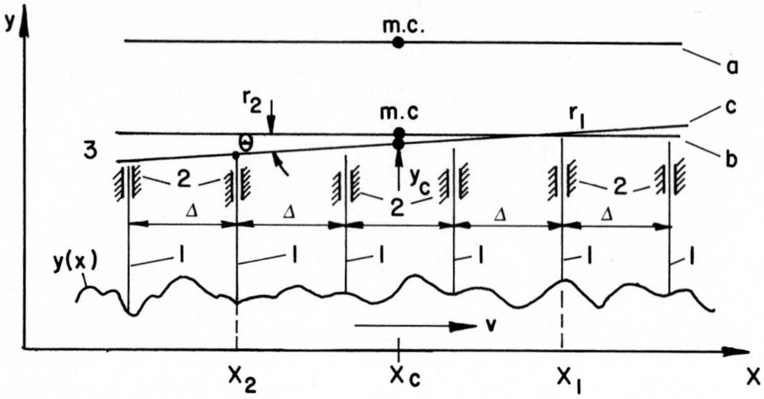

Fig. 145. Layout of a lumped kinematic model in which the rolling elements are replaced by "sticks."

touching point r_1. If the point r_1 is situated to the right of the m.c., the line rotates anticlockwise and vice versa. As a result of its rotation, the line touches the top of eack stick until the minimal value of the angle θ is reached. At this moment, the line rests on two points r_1 and r_2. It must then be checked whether the m.c. is located between these two points. If this condition is satisfied, the values of θ_{min} and y_c are stored. If the condition is not met, the algorithm considers the point r_2 as the initial point of contact and repeats the above-described procedure until the requirement with regard with the point m.c. has been satisfied. When the data for y_c and θ_{min} have been stored, the surface y(x) is moved in the direction of the speed V for one step Δx, and the calculations are reiterated. Obviously, Δx has to be small in comparison with the distance Δ and the length of the waves of the surface. The flowchart of this algorithm is given in Fig. 146. The chart may be explained as follows

A - the highest stick (stick 1) is chosen;

B - the relative location of the m.c. of the straight line is checked;

C - if the point m.c. is to the right of stick 1, the second highest stick (stick 2) is sought between the highest stick and the last stick;

D - if the point m.c. falls to the left of stick 1, stick 2 is sought between the highest stick and the first stick;

E - the minimal inclination angle of the straight line resting on two sticks (the highest and the second highest) is sought;

F,G - whether the m.c. is located between these two sticks is checked;

H - if the results of checking in F,G are positive, the angle θ_{min} and the coordinate y_c of the m.c. of the line are stored and printed.

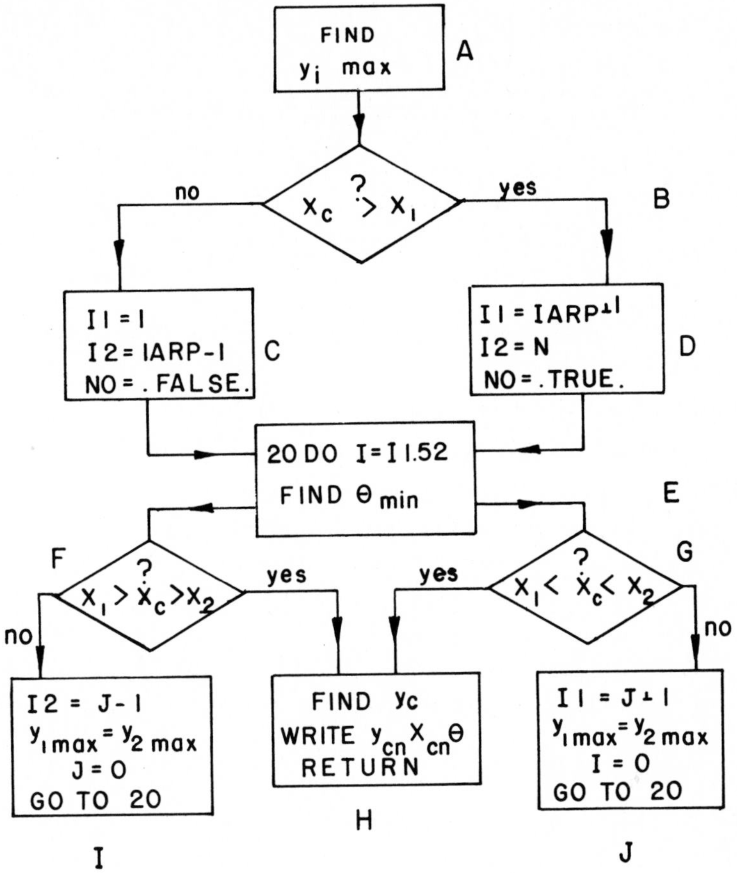

Fig. 146. Flowchart of the simulation algorithm for the studying of the behavior of the upper surface.

I,J - if the result of checking in F,G are negative, then stick 2 is called stick 1, and the procedure is repeated to find a new stick 2.

As has been mentioned, this calculation is reiterated for each step Δx, and the stored data y_c and θ_{min} are processed statistically. In Fig. 147 an example of a random surface $y(x)$ is shown, and above it, the random process $y_c(x)$ for the case in which the straight line is supported by 10 sticks. (The shift of the beginning of the differentiated process in comparison with the given function $y(x)$ is explained by the location of the m.c. along the x axis.)

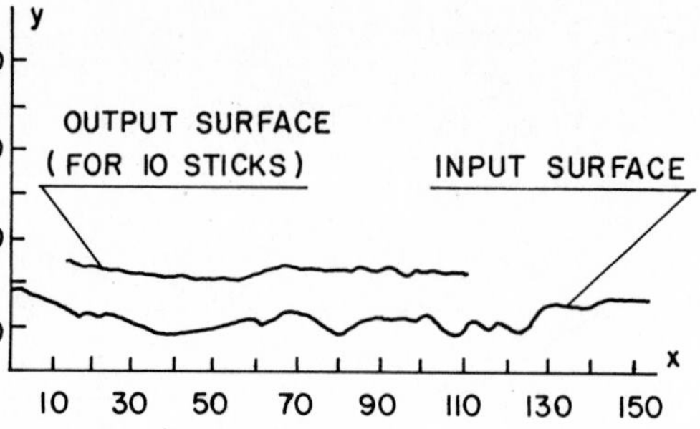

Fig. 147. Section of a measured random surface which is used for the purpose of simulation.

The correlation function of the y(x) random surface is shown in Fig. 148 and is marked by the sign "0" (zero "sticks"). The correlation functions calculated for 4, 6, 8 and 10 sticks for certain constant distances Δ between them are also shown in Fig. 148 and are marked 4, 6, 8 and 10, respectively.

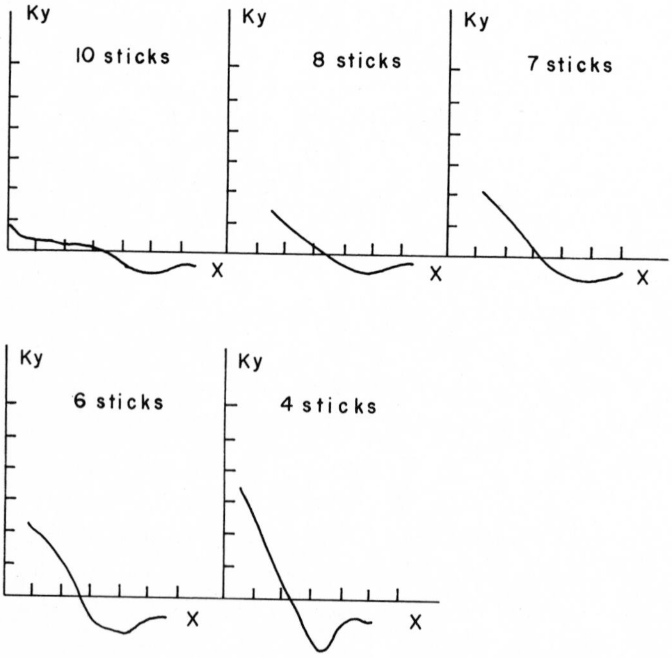

Fig. 148. Calculated correlation functions for different numbers of supporting "sticks."

The dependence between the values of the variances σ_y^2 and the number of sticks N supporting the straight line is shown in Fig. 149. This dependence is described by a hyperbola-type curve. It can be seen that the smoothing effect becomes more efficient as N, the number of "sticks" (or any other kind of supports), is increased, up to a maximum of about 6. The larger the number N, the smaller the variances σ_y^2 of the random function y_c.

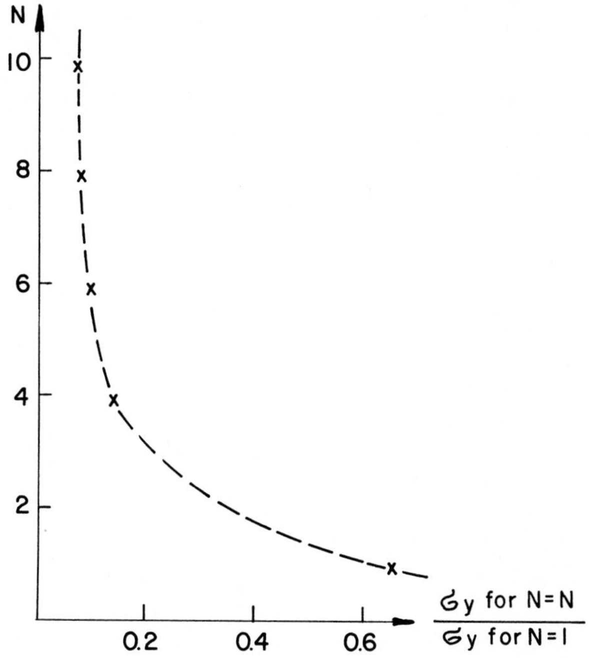

Fig. 149. Dependence between the number of "sticks" and the variance σ_y^2 of the movement of the mass center of the upper surface.

The frequential contents of the y_c random functions thus obtained can be estimated by calculating the spectral density of y_c. For instance, the correlation functions presented in Fig. 148 show that there is a certain shift in the direction of higher frequencies (this follows from the fact that the correlation functions 4, 6, 8 and 10 have steeper slopes). Analytically, this fact can be qualitatively proved by applying equation (VI.5.7). If we express the y(x) process as a function of time by means of substituting x = Vt (the motion is assumed to be uniform), we obtain:

$$y(x) = Y(t)$$

Now let us assume the normalized correlation function of this process to have the following form (in accordance with the curve 0 shown in Fig. 148):

$$R_Y(\tau) = e^{-\alpha|\tau|}\cos\beta\tau \tag{VI.5.15}$$

The normalized spectral density $S_y(\omega)$ is thus given by:

$$S_Y(\omega) = \frac{\alpha}{\pi}\frac{\omega^2+\alpha^2+\beta^2}{(\omega^2-\beta^2-\alpha^2)^2+4\alpha^2\omega^2} \tag{VI.5.16}$$

Now, substituting equation (VI.5.15) into expression (VI.5.17) (the straight line always lies on two sticks), we obtain the following expression for the correlation function R_{Y_c} of the process $Y_c(t)$ (the movement of the m.c. of the supported line):

$$R_{Y_c}(\tau) = \frac{1}{2}e^{-\alpha|\tau|}\cos\beta\tau + \frac{1}{4}e^{-\alpha|\tau+\Delta|}\cos\beta(\tau+\Delta) + \frac{1}{4}e^{-\alpha|\tau-\Delta|}\cos\beta(\tau-\Delta) \tag{VI.5.17}$$

which, in terms of Fourier transforms, gives the following formula for the spectral density S_{Y_c}:

$$S_{Y_c}(\omega) = \frac{\alpha}{\pi}\frac{\omega^2+\alpha^2+\beta^2}{(\omega^2-\beta^2-\alpha^2)^2+4\alpha^2\omega^2}\left[\frac{1}{2}+\frac{1}{4}\cos\beta\Delta(e^{-\alpha|\Delta|}+e^{\alpha|\Delta|})\right] + \frac{\omega\sin\beta\Delta}{2\pi}(e^{-\alpha|\Delta|}+e^{\alpha|\Delta|})\frac{\alpha^2+\omega^2-\beta^2}{(\omega^2+\beta^2+\alpha^2)^2-4\beta^2\omega^2} \tag{VI.5.18}$$

The second term, which is proportional to ω, indicates the shift of the spectral contents of the Y_c process in the direction of higher frequencies.

6. SYNTHESIS OF MECHANICAL SYSTEMS (PRINCIPLE OF VARIATION)

We have already considered some synthesis problems for special applications, for example, for cam mechanisms (chapter III) and for gear transmissions (chapter IV). In this section we will discuss in brief the use of the calculus of variations in dynamic accuracy problems of mechanisms. This approach offers an additional tool to the designer of automatic manufacturing machines when a certain level of accuracy is required. Let us look at Fig. 150 in which:

X_o - the ideal, prescribed motion law;
X - the motion law executed in reality;
x - the deviation of the motion law;

$$X = X_o + x \tag{VI.6.1}$$

x_d - the calculated dynamic component of the deviation of the motion law;
x_s - the random component of the deviation of the motion law.

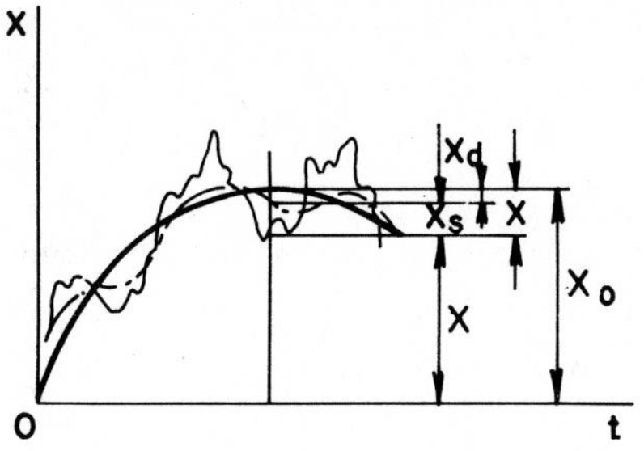

Fig. 150. General case describing the movement of a machine part.

In some engineering problems x_d may be a useful component, and in such a case it is included in the prescribed motion law (or it may be the only component of the motion law). The deviation is then described only by the random component. Vibrofeeders and other vibrotools are examples of such a situation. Usually, however, in machine building both components of the deviation are harmful and means must be undertaken to minimize or eliminate their occurence.

In the following discussion we will denote the input and output values by subscripts 1 and 2, respectively. As the criterion of accuracy of the motion law, we will take (see I.27):

$$D_X^2 = \frac{1}{T}\int_0^T X^2(t)dt \qquad \text{(VI.6.2)}$$

For cyclic mechanisms

$$\frac{1}{T}\int_0^T x(t)dt = 0 \qquad \text{(VI.6.3)}$$

where T - time interval which is much larger than the time of a cycle of the mechanism.

Thus, from equations (VI.6.1) and (VI.6.3) it follows that:

$$D_X = D_{X_o} + D_x \qquad \text{(VI.6.4)}$$

where

$$D_{X_o} = \frac{1}{T}\int_0^T X_o^2(t)dt$$

$$D_x = \frac{1}{T}\int_0^T x^2(t)dt$$

Further discussion is devoted to the consideration of the possibility of synthesizing mechanisms which, other conditions being equal, provide the minimal value of D_x on the output of the mechanism. When the system under consideration is sufficiently close to being linear, the following expression may be applied:

$$D_{x_2} = \frac{1}{\pi}\int_0^\infty |\Phi(j\omega)|^2 S_{x_1}(\omega)d\omega = \frac{1}{\pi}\int_0^\infty F d\omega \qquad \text{(VI.6.5)}$$

where, as in previous cases:

$\Phi(j\omega)$ - the transfer function;

$S(\omega)$ - spectral density of the excitation;

ω - frequency.

The relationship (VI.6.5) is a functional for which the following natural variational problems can be formulated:

1. Let a transfer function $\Phi(j\omega)$ be given: this function provides for a motion X_{02} on the output when a motion X_{01} is provided on the input. We now ask what will be the transfer function $\Phi_o(j\omega)$ which for an input $X_1 = X_{01} + x$ will provide the minimal value for x_2, i.e. a minimum for D_{x_2} (Fig. 151).

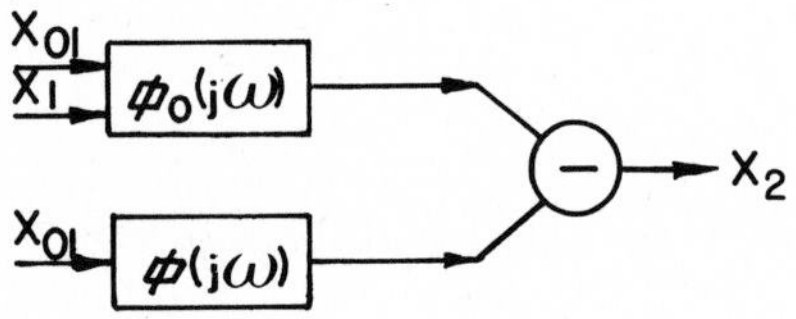

Fig. 151. Structural layout of a dynamic system.

The following situations are examples of this problem. In these examples, and in many others, we must seek an improved transfer function for the minimization of x_2.

(a) In a certain machine, a vibrofeeder is installed on a vibrating frame whose vibrations are described by a spectrum S_{x_1}. The vibrofeeder is built to carry out X_{02} when the excitement is X_{01}.

(b) A cam mechanism, which must carry out a motion X_{02}, but because of the profile deviations x_1, the mechanism carries out motion $X_2 = X_{02} + x_2$.

(c) A mechanical measuring device which is installed on a moving vehicle whose vibrations y_1, caused by the random deviations of the road's surface, disturb to extract the useful signal X_{02} of the measurements.

The layout given in Fig. 151 indicates that the value x_2 may be expressed in the form:

$$x_2 = \Phi(j\omega)X_{01} - \Phi_o(j\omega)X_{01} - \Phi_o(j\omega)x_1 \tag{VI.6.6}$$

or

$$x_2 = [\Phi(j\omega) - \Phi_o(j\omega)]X_{01} - \Phi_o(j\omega)x_1$$

Thus,

$$S_{x_2} = |\Phi(j\omega) - \Phi_o(j\omega)|^2 S_{X_{01}} - |\Phi_o(j\omega)|^2 S_{x_1} \tag{VI.6.7}$$

and

$$D_{x_2} = \frac{1}{\pi}\int_o^\infty \{|\Phi(j\omega) - \Phi_o(j\omega)|^2 S_{X_{01}} + |\Phi_o(j\omega)|^2 S_{x_1}\}\, d\omega = \frac{1}{\pi}\int_o^\infty F d\omega \tag{VI.6.8}$$

To find the transfer function $\Phi_o(j\omega)$ minimizing the value D_{x_2} we must solve the following equation (which is a particular case of Euler's equation):

$$\frac{\partial \Phi}{\partial \Phi_o} = 0 \tag{VI.6.9}$$

This brings us to a solution in the form:

$$\Phi_o(j\omega) = \frac{S_{X_{01}}}{S_{X_{01}} + S_{x_1}} \Phi(j\omega) \tag{VI.6.10}$$

Substituting expression (VI.6.10) into equation (VI.6.8), we obtain:

$$D_{x_2} = \frac{1}{\pi}\int_o^\infty |\Phi(j\omega)|^2 \frac{S_{X_{01}} S_{x_1}}{S_{X_{01}} + S_{x_1}} d\omega \tag{VI.6.11}$$

As an example, let us consider a simple oscillator consisting of a mass m and a rod with stiffness c (Fig. 152) located on a platform. The mass m is driven via the rod by some mechanism. Let us assume that the oscillator is designed to transmit a motion X_{01} which is described by a constant spectral density $S_{X_{01}} = A$ in the range of frequencies $\omega_2 - \omega_1$. In this case, the transfer function of the oscillator has the form:

$$\Phi(j\omega) = \frac{c}{c - \omega^2 m} \tag{VI.6.12}$$

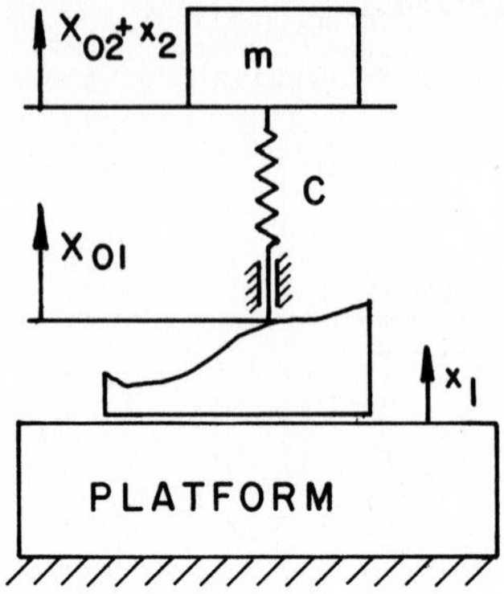

Fig. 152. Layout of a mechanical system in which the disturbance x_1 must be reduced.

As a result of the excitement characterized by the spectrum $S_{X_{01}} = A$, the oscillator generates a motion X_{02} whose spectrum has the following form:

$$S_{X_{02}} = \left| \frac{c}{c - \omega^2 m} \right|^2 A \tag{VI.6.12}$$

The platform introduces into this dynamic system a disturbance x_1 which we describe by its spectral density $S_{X_1} = B$ for a certain range of frequencies. Thus, instead of the desired motion X_{02} we obtain X_2 which differs from the desired movement by x_2. By changing the mechanical system in such a way as to confer on it a transfer function $\Phi_o(j\omega)$ in accordance with equation (VI.6.10), we can obtain the minimal value for x_2. For the case with which we are dealing the function Φ_o has the following form:

$$\Phi_o(j\omega) = \frac{cA}{(A + B)(c - \omega^2 m)} \tag{VI.6.13}$$

Let us analyze this expression and investigate the changes that must be made to the structure of the oscillator to provide the above-shown transfer function $\Phi_o(j\omega)$. Expression (VI.6.13) can be rewritten as follows:

$$\Phi_o(j\omega) = \frac{cA}{Ac + Bc - (A + B)\omega^2 m} \tag{VI.6.14}$$

Let us denote:

$$Ac = c_1; \quad Bc = c_2; \quad m(A+B) = m_1$$

The transfer function $\Phi_o(j\omega)$ corresponds to the model shown in Fig. 153, in which m_1 is the new mass and c_1 and c_2 are the new stiffnesses. Obviously, an additional spring has been introduced. In this model the motion x_2 has the smallest possible value.

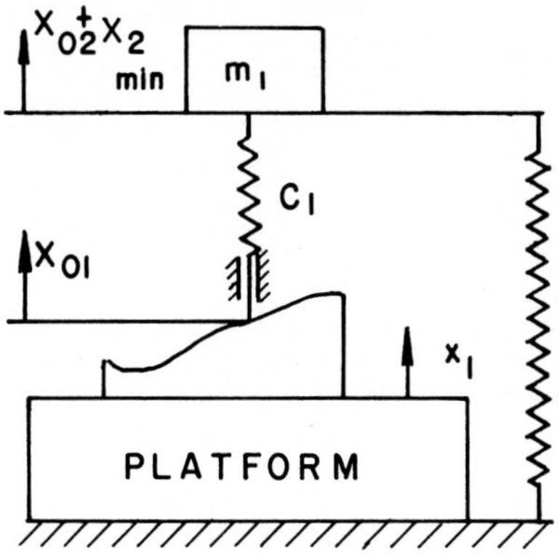

Fig. 153. The optimized system (corresponding to Fig. 152) in which the influence of the disturbance x_2 has been minimized.

Note: In accordance with expression (VI.6.10) the transfer function $\Phi_o(j\omega)$ generally includes poles located in the right and left half-planes. To provide the obtained transfer function with physical reality we must extract only the terms with poles in the left half-plane, and the rest of the terms must be discarded.

The following technique is proposed for this purpose. In the first step the denominator of expression (VI.6.10) is replaced by a product of conjugate complex numbers. Thus:

$$S_{X_{01}} + S_{x_1} = \psi(j\omega)\psi(-j\omega) \tag{VI.6.15}$$

Then, in the second step, the component $1/\psi(j\omega)$ is extracted. The third step involves decomposition into partial terms:

$$\frac{S_{X_{01}}}{\psi(-j\omega)}\,\Phi(j\omega) = \frac{P_1(j\omega)}{\xi(j\omega)} + \frac{P_2(j\omega)}{\psi(-j\omega)} \tag{VI.6.16}$$

Omitting the second term (since its poles are located in right half-plane), we obtain in the fourth step the physically real transfer function in the following form:

$$\Phi_o(j\omega) = \frac{P_1(j\omega)}{\xi(j\omega)} \cdot \frac{1}{\psi(j\omega)} \tag{VI.6.17}$$

Fig. 154 illustrates this procedure.

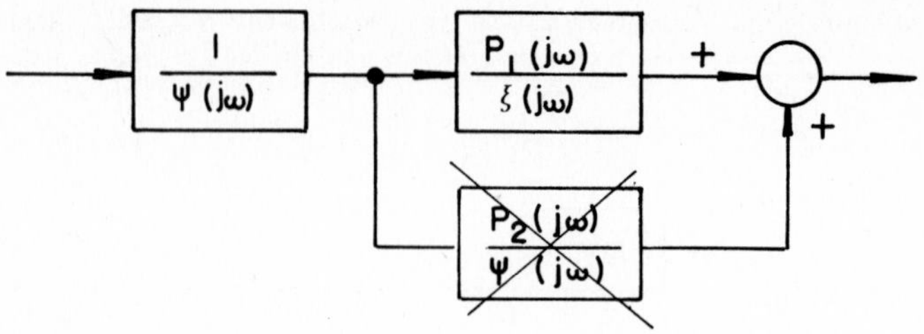

Fig. 154. Layout of the definition of the physically realizable part of the solution.

2. Another approach to the optimization problem is the use of calculus of variations. Analysis of expression (VI.6.5) permits minimization of the variance D_{x_2} by choosing an optimal form of S_{x_1} (in contrast to the above discussed method) for a given transfer function $\Phi(j\omega)$ and fixed value $D_{x_1} = D$. This approach is an attempt to improve the dynamic accuracy of a mechanism without increasing the accuracy of its links or of the manufacturing tools used in processing. It is assumed that this improvement of the accuracy of the output of the mechanism can be achieved by redistribution of the frequential content of the input disturbances x_1. We will now rewrite the functional in the following form:

$$D_{x_2} = \frac{1}{\pi}\int_0^\infty \theta(\omega)S_{x_1}(\omega)d\omega = \frac{1}{\pi}\int_0^\infty F(y,y',\omega)d\omega \qquad \text{(VI.6.18)}$$

where $\theta(\omega) = |\Phi(j\omega)|^2$

and y - optimal spectral density S_{x_1} of the random function x_i.
In addition, we use the obvious relationship:

$$D = \int_0^\infty S_{x_1}(\omega)d\omega \qquad \text{(VI.6.19)}$$

Let us seek the solution $y(\omega) = S_{x_1}(\omega)$ between functions which satisfy the following dependence:

$$y = \phi(\omega)y'\omega \qquad \text{(VI.6.20)}$$

Here $\phi(\omega)$ - unknown function which must be found.

This treatment gives the widely used exponential form for the spectral density. To illustrate this statement, we will solve the differential equation (VI.6.20). Thus:

$$\phi(\omega) \cdot \frac{dy}{d\omega} = y$$

which brings us to

$$\frac{dy}{y} = \frac{d\omega}{\phi(\omega)}$$

and then

$$\ln y = \int_{\omega_1}^{\omega} d\omega/\phi(\omega) \qquad \omega_1 \text{ - boundary conditions}$$

or

$$y = \exp[\int_{\omega_1}^{\omega} d\omega/\phi(\omega) \tag{VI.6.21}$$

Now let us apply Euler's equation. In the case under consideration we use the following general form of this equation:

$$\frac{\partial F}{\partial y} - \frac{\partial}{\partial \omega}(\partial F/\partial y'_{\omega}) = 0 \tag{VI.6.22}$$

Since we have from equations (VI.6.18) and (VI.6.20)

$$F = \theta(\omega)y'_{\omega}\cdot\phi(\omega) = \theta(\omega)y(\omega) \tag{VI.6.23}$$

we can rewrite Euler's equation (VI.6.22) in the form:

$$1 - \frac{\theta'(\omega)}{\theta(\omega)}\phi(\omega) - \phi'(\omega) = 0 \tag{VI.6.24}$$

or

$$\phi'(\omega) + \frac{\theta'}{\theta}\phi(\omega) = 1 \tag{VI.6.25}$$

By solving this differential equation with respect to $\phi(\omega)$ we obtain:

$$\phi(\omega) = \exp[-\int_{\omega_1}^{\omega} \frac{\theta'}{\theta} d\omega] \cdot \int_{\omega_1}^{\omega} \exp[\int_{\omega_1}^{\omega} \frac{\theta'}{\theta} d\omega]d\omega \tag{VI.6.26}$$

where ω_1 - a constant which must be defined by the boundary conditions.

Substituting expression (VI.6.26) into equation (VI.6.21), we obtain:

$$Ay(\omega) = S_{x_1}(\omega) \tag{VI.6.27}$$

To calculate the value A, we use the dependence (VI.6.19) in the following manner:

$$D \;=\; A \int_{\omega_1}^{\omega} y(\omega)d\omega$$

or (VI.6.28)

$$A \;=\; D \;/ \int_{\omega_1}^{\omega} y(\omega)d\omega$$

In practice, these calculations must be carried out by numerical techniques.

Trivial results for θ = const or θ'/θ = const can be achieved in an analytical way.

In chapter IV we discussed an application of the idea of optimization of the spectral density of the disturbances on the input of the mechanism without making the manufacturing accuracy requirements more rigid. The example given was that of a gear train optimized by choosing the right values for the number of teeth under different boundary conditions. It should be noted that the calculation technique used in chapter IV differs from that described in this section.

CHAPTER VII

AUTOMATIC VIBRATION CONTROL

1. INTRODUCTION

The investigation of the influence of random (and nonrandom) deviations of the excitation on the behavior of mechanisms brought us to a point in the thought process at which we considered the problem of the design of adaptive mechanisms. An adaptive mechanism is one which is able to change its parameters in an automatic way so as to optimize the response of the driven link despite a changing input.

Undesired vibration is often a serious problem in the construction of machinery. Fast rotating shafts, cam mechanisms, gear wheels, and linkages excite vibrations which impair the accuracy of machines, shorten their lives, and cause noise and operational failures. Lessening of vibrations is one of the main aspects of mechanisms research, and there are many theoretical techniques for the investigation of the dynamic behavior of mechanical systems and the dynamic optimization of mechanisms.

When a dynamic synthesis is carried out, the optimal values of the system's parameters are usually chosen so as to give minimum (or sometimes the maximum) vibration for given working conditions. Today, there are many ingeniously computed mechanisms and machines which do work optimally, but when working conditions change, the behavior of these mechanisms deteriorates, and then the engineer has to change the relevant parameters.

An example of a field in which adaptive mechanisms have still to be developed is tooling. Metal cutting on tooling machines, such as lathes and milling machines, is accompanied by vibrations of the work piece and the cutter. These vibrations depend on many parameters whose values change during the process. Although a great deal of attention has been devoted to this problem (see, for example, references [1-3]) and although special cutter designs and devices can minimize vibrations and thus improve the quality of the product, no attempt has yet been made to minimize vibrations continuously during processing.

Similarly, the technical literature contains a significant volume of work devoted to problems of cam dynamics and to the minimization of the deflections in the motion of the cam follower caused by the dynamics of the cam mechanism. Although there have been attempts to synthesize optimal profiles and to choose optimal detail stiffnesses, these optimized mechanisms are optimal only when the conditions correspond to the solution: a change in the conditions requires alteration of the system's parameters. As yet, no attempts have been made to find mechanical solutions which would match the parameters to a range of working conditions. Many other examples of this kind can be cited.

In principle, to minimize vibrations the engineer has to dissipate the energy by means of some damping device or to redistribute this energy in some other way so that the vibrating part under consideration will be deprived of energy (dynamic damping). This operation requires special choice of structure and parameter values. Sometimes increasing the manufacturing accuracy of the mechanism's details improves the dynamic properties of the mechanism, but this solution is often expensive.

This chapter deals with the means for providing an optimal (or close to optimal) working regime for a mechanism despite changes in the external conditions. Such a means of vibration control is known as automatic vibration control (AVC), and the mechanisms controlled in this way are called adaptive mechanisms (AM). The importance of adaptive mechanisms was eloquently described by Artobolevskii in his plenary lecture at the Fourth World Congress on the Theory of Machines and Mechanisms.

One approach that the designer can use to create self-optimizing (adaptive) mechanisms is the utilization of the dynamic damping principle for minimizing vibrations under continuously changing conditions. This approach may, in some cases, improve the quality of the machined product, increase the efficiency of tooling machines, and/or decrease expenses due to lower accuracy requirements for the machine parts. Although adaptive vibration control is usually concerned with the diminution of vibrations, it may also be applied for vibration enhancement. In both cases the solution includes the following steps: (1) measurement of the vibration situation; (2) design of a dynamic model of the system; and (3) choice and execution of a control strategy to obtain the desired results.

A number of examples will be presented to illustrate this concept. We can easily see that the problem of vibration reduction has a number of different levels of complexity. The following levels will be considered.

(1) On the first, and most simple, level we will consider automatic vibration control by a "relay type" control unit. The only measurement used here is the value of the variable input x. The control variable z is assigned one of a limited number of fixed values (Fig. 155a).

(2) The second level of complexity includes systems which automatically realize a constant continuous (or functional) dependence between the values of certain external factors and those of the internal parameters. The control unit which is introduced follows a previously calculated or measured function relating the

input x to the control variables z to provide the optimal action of the mechanism (Fig. 155b).

(3) The third, and highest, level comprises systems which have to calculate the functional dependence between the input x or ε and the control variables z and to then select the right values of the control variables to produce the optimal action of the mechanism. This case is, of course, the most interesting and important (Fig. 155c).

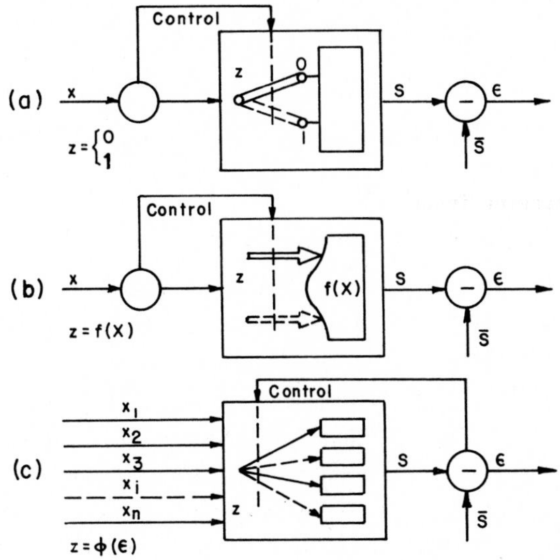

Fig. 155. a) Layout of a "relay type" adaptive control unit; b) layout of an adaptive control unit controlling a given functional dependence between the input and output; c) layout of adaptive control unit which automatically selects the optimal input-output dependence.

Thus, we can see a transition from a "relay" type control, through a fixed functional control, to a varying functional control computed while the mechanism is operating and upon which optimization is performed to yield the best setting of the control variables. In the following section, we present detailed descriptions of three examples illustrating these three levels of complexity: they are (1) a rapidly rotating shaft, (2) a cam follower, and (3) a vibrating bar device.

In some cases, the parameters of the excitation can be changed to cause vibrations in a particular direction. This technique is convenient for cases in which the vibrations serve a positive role, for instance, vibrofeeding, vibroscreening, and vibroselecting require that vibrations be kept at certain level. The optimal way of achieving these conditions would be by means of resonance (the coinciding of the frequency of the excitation with the natural frequency of the device). However, in conventionally built mechanisms of this sort, this means cannot be realized, because at the resonance frequency the device is very sensitive to changes in the load. As a result of this fact, machines of this type are especially designed so that their natural frequency during the work is maintained at a value differing by about 10-20% from the resonance value. In this way, a compromise is obtained between the desired optimum (resonance) and reality (high sensititivy). Automatic vibration control provides a means of avoiding the above described contradiction and thus creating devices that work permanently under optimal conditions. The third section of this chapter is devoted to the description of an adaptive vibrofeeders of this type.

2. EXAMPLES OF AUTOMATIC VIBRATION REDUCTION

Case 1. A rapidly rotating shaft

For a rapidly rotating shaft the problem is to ensure the minimum of vibrations of the shaft over a wide range of rotation velocities. The layout of such a mechanism is given in Fig. 156. A pneumatically driven shaft 1 is placed on two pneumatic bearings 2 and 3, of which the upper bearing 3 is movable. For this reason, the shaft is mounted on a holder 4 and connected to a pneumatic cylinder 5. A pneumatic rotating velocity pick-up 6 is included in the base 7. A mass 8 is fastened to the shaft. An automatic control system carries out the

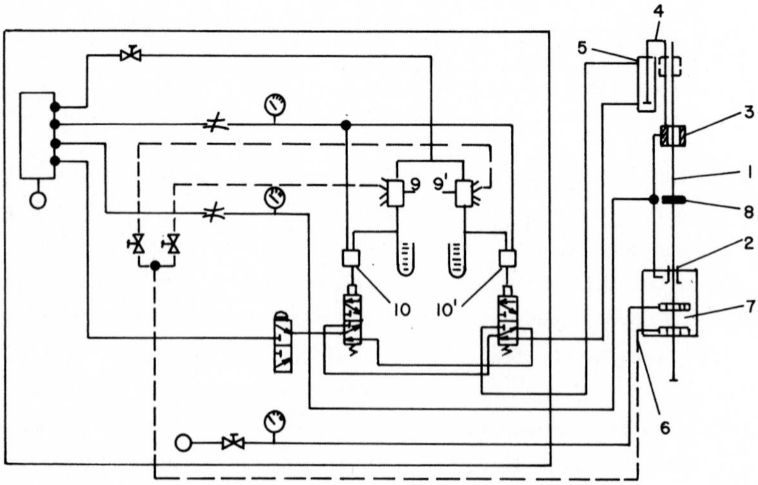

Fig. 156. Layout of "relay type" control of the support location of a rapidly rotating shaft.

optimization during variations of the rotation velocity. (It is, of course, possible to realize this idea in some other manner, e.g. electrical or pneumo-electrical.) The pick-up 6 produces a pressure which is related to the rotation velocity of the shaft. This pressure actuates the sensor 9 whose signal actuates pneumatic valve 10, which in turn controls the cylinder 5 moving the bearing 3 down. An analogous layout consisting of a sensor 9' and a valve 10' causes bearing 3 to rise. The two positions of bearing 3 correspond to the two critical velocities of the shaft 1. The most important point is that the automatic control system enables the upper bearing holder 4 to take one of two positions (the stroke is equal to 100 mm) and to change its position in agreement with the rotation velocity.

The dynamic properties of this system are shown in Fig. 157. The upper unbroken line represents the situation when the bearing holder is in its upper position, and the broken line that in which the bearing holder is in the lower position. If the changes of position take place at the points designated as ω_1, ω_{11} and ω_{111}, it is clear that the amplitudes of the vibrations of the shaft during acceleration or deceleration (as the unbroken lower line shows) will not be higher than some value A^*.

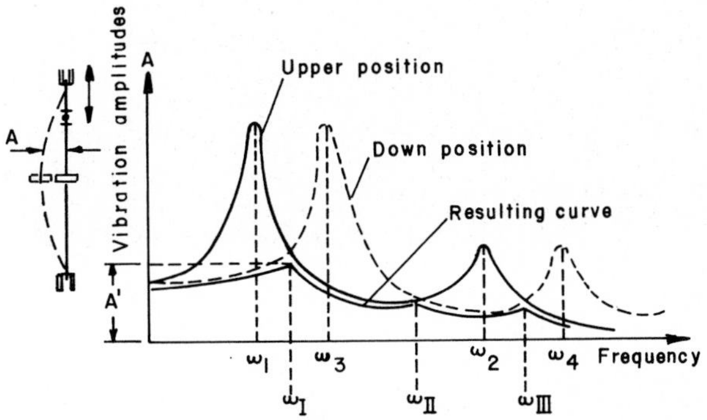

Fig. 157. Vibration amplitudes of the rotating shaft as a function of the rotation speed for different support positions.

A photograph of the device is presented in Fig. 158. The numbering of the main elements corresponds to that in Fig. 156.

Figure 159 gives a comparison of the vibration (acceleration) amplitudes of the base of the device during the acceleration of the shaft to approximately 12,000 rpm, and afterwards during its deceleration, both with (b) and without (a) the automatic control system. It is clear that the automatic control system improves the behavior of this mechanism.

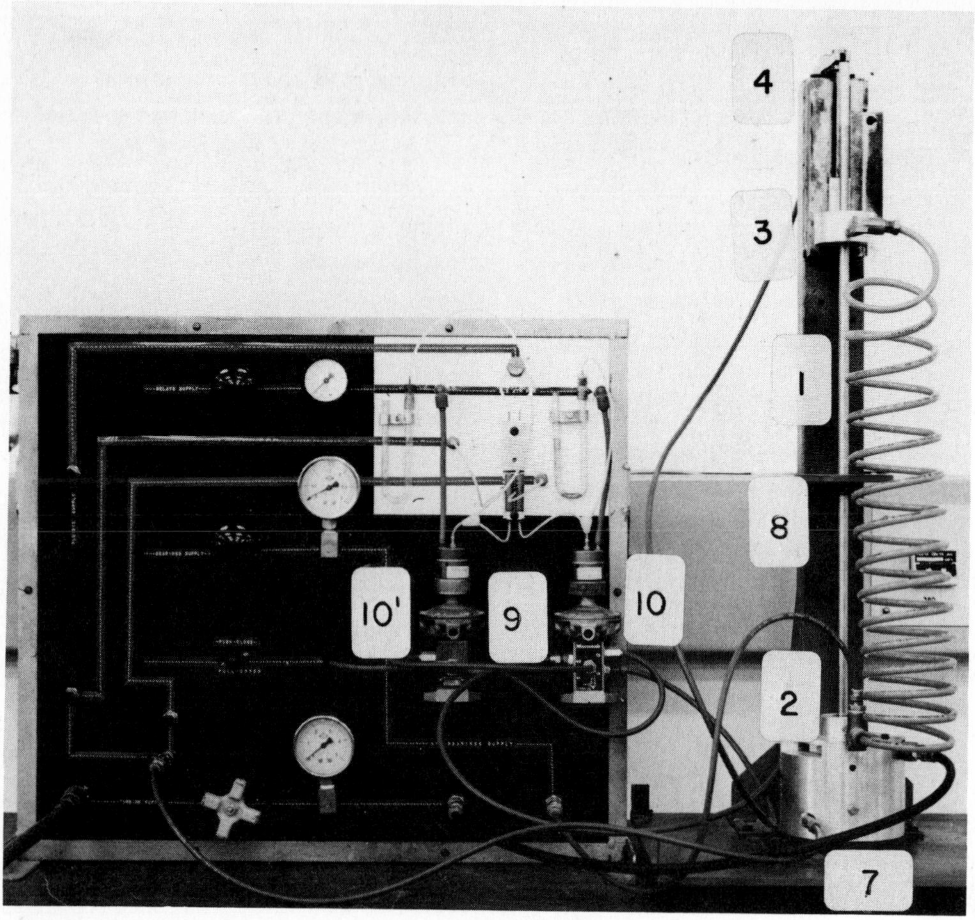

Fig. 158. Photograph of the device shown in Fig. 156.

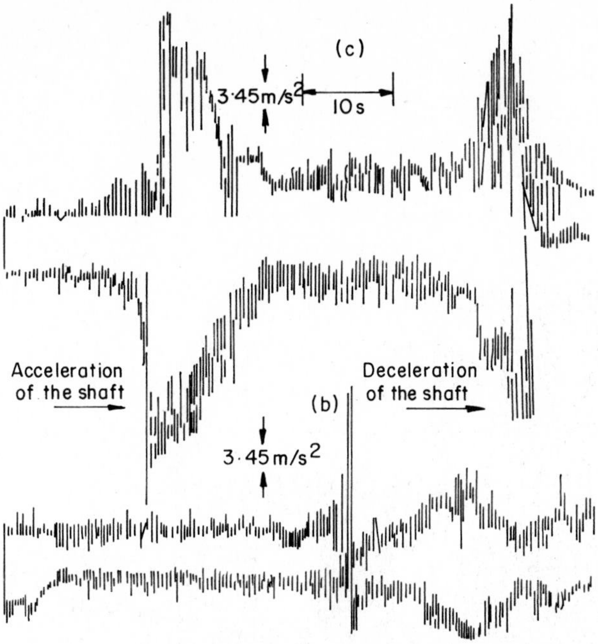

Fig. 159. Comparison of the vibrations of the shaft: a) without control; b) with adaptive control.

Case 2. A cam mechanism

For the cam mechanism the problem is to decrease the dynamic errors q of the motion of the follower. Here, $\varepsilon = s - s^*$ where s is the real follower motion and s* is the desired, or calculated, ideal follower motion. To solve this problem, the follower is divided into two parts so that the dynamic model of this mechanism has the form shown in Fig. 57 and 58 and so that the possibility of changing the stiffness c_2 is provided.

In Fig. 57 and 58, the mass 12 can be moved along the pivots 13 by means of pneumocylinder 15, thus changing the stiffness c_2. A set of strain gauges 14 is glued to the head of the shaft 11. A tachometer 16 measures the velocity of the camshaft 5. A variable resistor 17, connected to the mass 12, serves as the feedback. An electropneumatic control unit 18 compares the signal from the tachometer 16 with the feedback signal 17 and, in keeping with the results of this comparison, actuates the cylinder 14.

The stiffness c_2 is automatically changed when the camshaft velocity changes. In the case described here, the dependence between the velocity and stiffness is chosen to be linear, which approximates the experimental curve adequately enough. This approximation and the experimental curve are shown in Fig. 160.

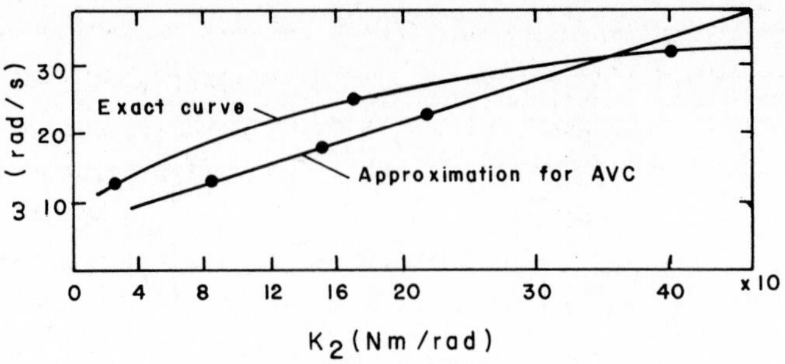

Fig. 160. Experimental and approximated curves of the optimal dependence between the cam shaft velocity ω and the stiffness K_2 of the follower.

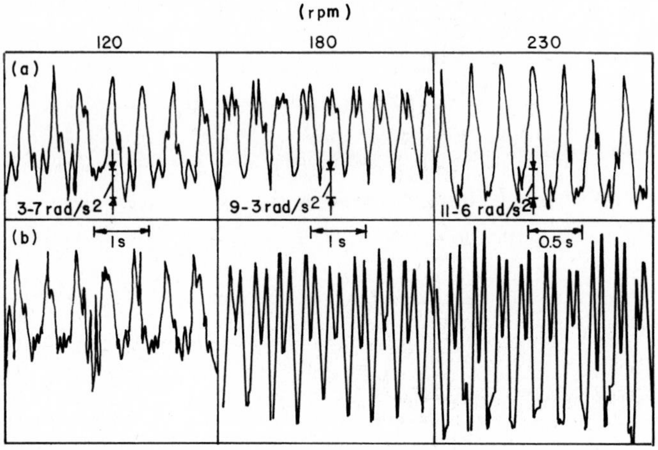

Fig. 161. Comparison of the measured acceleration of the follower for camshaft velocities of 120, 180 and 230 rpm for (a) automatic control and (b) in the usual case.

(The experimental curve shows the optimal value of c_2 for certain rotational velocities ω of the camshaft.) Fig. 161 shows the comparison between the acceleration amplitudes of the follower for certain camshaft velocities, (a) with and (b) without the automatic control system. (Each velocity is recorded on the oscillograph at a different amplification.) It is evident that the deviation of the acceleration in case (b) (without an automatic device) is considerably greater.

Case 3. A vibrating bar device

The multimass dynamic model discussed here is representative of a general vibrational situation, and the results obtained with this experimental model are applicable to a wide range of other devices. This model permits investigation of the behavior of a number of real, complicated mechanical systems which can be improved by the use of adaptive control. Fig. 162 presents (a) a photograph of the research equipment (with a PDP 11-40 computer being used to control the multimass model), and (b) the dynamic model itself. A schematic representation of the dynamic model is given in Fig. 163.

The device consists of a massive base 1; four bars 2, 3, 4 and 5; an oscillator 6, driven by a motor 7; three moving masses m_2, m_3 and m_4; and connecting rods 8 (which can be replaced by linear or nonlinear springs.) Oscillator 6 has two rotating debalanced masses m_6 and m_7 which can be adjusted to one of several different rotation ratios by means of a gear box. The velocities of m_6 and m_7 can be changed by manual control of the motor 7. The oscillator, whose mass is m_1, can be fastened manually to any place on the bar 2, thus defining the value x_1 (Fig. 163). The masses m_2, m_3 and m_4 (via motors 9, 10 and 11, respectively, which are controlled by the computer) are driven along the bars 3, 4 and 5, respectively, thus defining at any time the values x_2, x_3 and x_4. In this way, the stiffnesses of the free parts of the bars c_1 to c_8 can be defined for any point in time. Strain-gauge sets are glued close to the points of attachment of each bar. The strain-gauge signals serve as the inputs to the computer (of course, there are other ways of formulating the input.) The values x_2, x_3 and x_4 - through resistors connected to blocks 12, 13 and 14 - have feedbacks to the computer. The computer can thus determine the optimal positions (x_2, x_3 and x_4) of the masses m_2, m_3 and m_4 along the bars: for instance, the input vibration of the oscillator can be adjusted to minimize the vibrations of the mass m_3, or to minimize the relative motion between the masses. By changing the input parameters, such a system is able to react automatically in some approximate agreement (because of disturbances, noises, etc.) with a previously formulated problem. The above-described vibrating bar device makes it possible to carry out a series of investigations whose scope covers a range of definitions of the problem and a range of methods of solution.

These two aspects can be analyzed as follows. The definition of the problem includes such features as (1) the dynamic description of the model under consideration - whether it is linear or nonlinear, the number of degrees of freedom, etc.; (2) input and output - the criteria for optimization; the nature and number of the control variables; (3) time properties - the rate of change of the external conditions, the response time of the control system, the allowed calculation time; (4) the required accuracy of the final result.

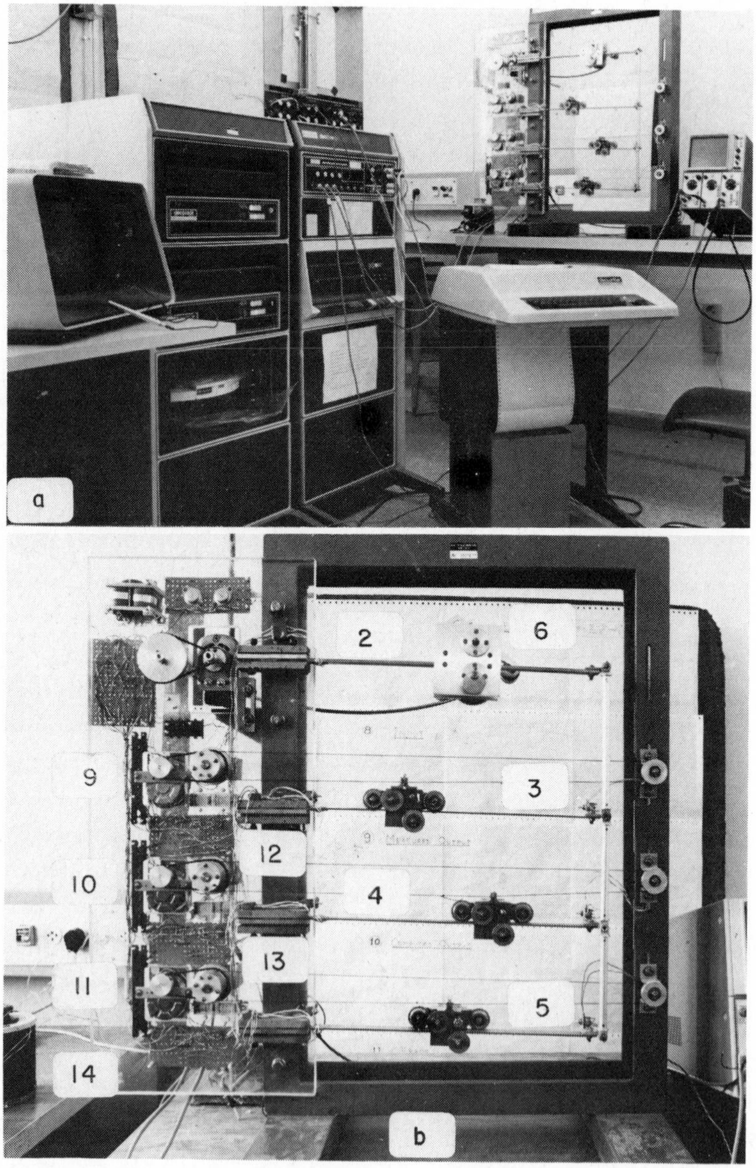

Fig. 162. Multimass experimental system (or vibrating bar device): (a) general view of the equipment; (b) general view of the multimass device.

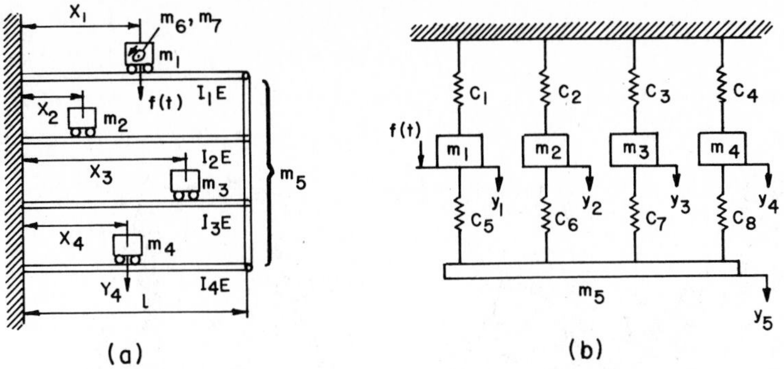

Fig. 163. Multimass dynamic system (vibrating bar device): (a) layout; (b) calculation model.

The method of solution includes the following features: (1) the kind of interference - the number, type, and sensitivity of the transducer, the range of the electrical parameters; (2) the mathematical approach to the problem - model or predetermined model based on physical properties, etc.; (3) use of a microcomputer for modelling and optimization, manner of optimization, etc.

In general, we may envisage a multidimensional problem/solution space, as is shown in Fig. 164. Measurement possibilities are given along one axis; properties of the models, along the second axis; optimization techniques, along the third axis; and realization of control possibilities, along the fourth axis.

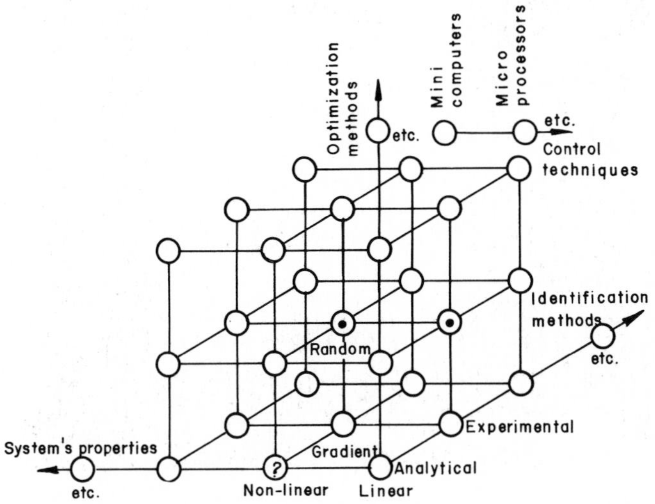

Fig. 164. Problem-solution space. ⊙ Solved possibilities; ? doubtful; O future possibilities.

This four-dimensional, noncontinuous space completely encloses the types of problems and solutions for the third level of complexity. The discussion that follows is limited to defining the problem, within its widest scope, with the vibrating bar device serving as an example of three points in the four-dimensional space.

As a simple starting point, let us take a linear model of the vibrating bar device. Consider, then, two masses, m_6 and m_7, rotating with velocities ω_1 and ω_2, so that the force of excitation is defined by:

$$F(t) = m_6\omega_1^2R_1\sin\omega_1 t + m_7\omega_2^2R_2\sin(\omega_2 t + \theta)$$

where R_1 and R_2 - the eccentricities of the rotating masses m_6 and m_7;
θ - the phase angle.

$$\text{Let}\quad A_1 = m_6\omega_1^2R_1;\quad A_2 = m_7\omega_2^2R_2 \tag{VII.2.1}$$

The mechanism may be described by a system of linear equations:

$$m_1\ddot{y}_1 + c_1y_1 + c_5(y_1 - y_5) = F(t),\quad m_2\ddot{y}_2 + c_2y_2 + c_6(y_2 - y_5) = 0$$

$$m_3\ddot{y}_3 + c_3y_3 + c_7(y_3 - y_5) = 0\quad,\quad m_4\ddot{y}_4 + c_4y_4 + c_8(y_4 - y_5) = 0 \tag{VII.2.2}$$

$$m_5\ddot{y}_5 + c_5(y_5 - y_1) + c_6(y_5 - y_2) + c_2(y_5 - y_3) + c_8(y_5 - y_4) = 0$$

where c_1 to c_8 are stiffnesses.

The goal of the optimization is defined as minimizing the vibrations of m_4. This criterion may be formulated as:

$$\min_{T\to\infty} \sigma_{y_4}^2 = \frac{1}{T}\int_0^T y_4^2 dt \tag{VII.2.3}$$

where T - time;
σ - the root mean square value.

The computer was used to calculate the values of $\sigma_{y_4}^2$ for several values of ω_1, ω_2 and for the following data:

$$\ell = 50\text{ cm}\qquad I_1 = I_2 = I_3 = I_4 = 0.00133\text{ cm}^4$$

$$m_1 = 0.8\text{ kg}\qquad m_2 = m_3 = m_4 = 0.5\text{ kg}\quad m_5 = 0.1\text{ kg} \tag{VII.2.3}$$

$$x_1 = x_2 = 2\text{ cm}\qquad E = 2.1\text{x}10^6\text{ kg/cm}^2\quad R_1 = R_2 = 1\text{ cm}$$

Fig. 165 presents a "map" of x_2 and x_3 combinations and the respective $\sigma^2_{y_4}$ value when ω_1 = 10 rad/s and ω_2 = 30 rad/s. The extreme positions of the mechanism are given in the following table:

	$\sigma^2_{y_4}$ (cm^2)	x_2(cm)	x_1 (cm)
max	60.99	15	45
min	0.025	18.8	18.8

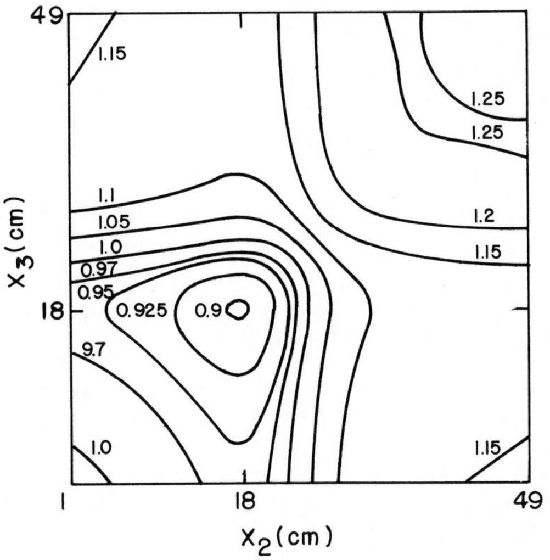

Fig. 165. Calculation "map" for values of x_2 and x_3 in the frequency range 30-90 Hz and for x_1 = 35 cm. This map can be used to control the vibrating bar device.

The computer contains information on the values of ω_1 and ω_2 from the strain-gauge set on the upper bar 2 and is able to determine the values of A_1 and A_2 from equation (VII.2.1). From equations (VII.2.2) and from the data (VII.2.3) in its memory, it calculates "maps" analogous with the map shown in Fig. 165. Finally, the optimal values of x_2 and x_3 values are worked out and sent to control units 9 and 10, which automatically move masses m_2 and m_3 to their optimal positions.

Of course, this idealized approach is based on a number of assumptions and on nonexact data, and its reliability is thus not very high. Instead of this preliminary predicted and very simplified mathematical description of the mechanism's behavior, based on rough theoretical assumptions, an identification method based on real measurements would be preferable.

For this more realistic case, some system identification (SI) techniques were used for defining the mathematical model. These techniques included deconvolution, the least squares method, and stored-response modelling (SRM) developed by Eichler [6]. Experiments revealed that deconvolution, although it is the simplest technique in terms of calculation, gave poor accuracy compared with both the least-squares method and SRM. This is due to noise effects. The least-squares method, the next most complex technique to calculate, gave reasonable accuracy for most samples and better accuracy for some than SRM. Finally, SRM gave moderate accuracy for most of the samples. An SRM model was built from 40 samples with a 0.5 millisecond time interval, and a plot of the results obtained with this SRM model vs. the real response of the vibrating bar device is shown in Fig. 166. It is thus evident that the least-squares method should be used wherever possible and SRM, for those cases where the least-squares technique is not appropriate.

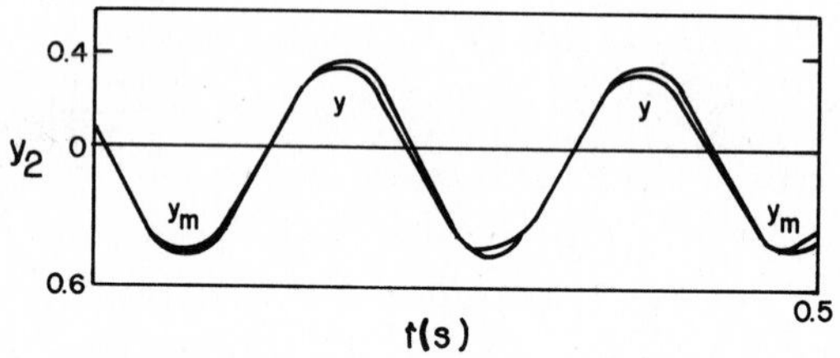

Fig. 166. Results calculated by the stored-response modelling (SRM) technique versus the real response of the vibrating bar device.

The calculated model and the simulation-derived resonance frequency as a function of x_2 are shown in Fig. 167. Fig. 168 shows the gain for 0 Hz (unit-step input) and for 4, 10, 40, and 60 Hz, as calculated from the model. The values calculated can be used as a calibration curve.

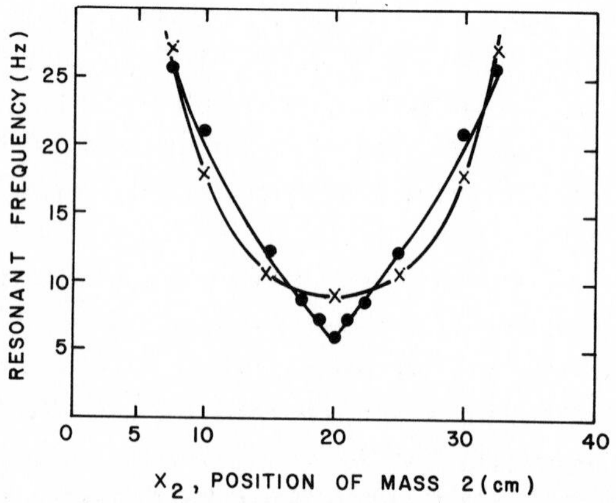

Fig. 167. Plot of the resonant frequency derived by the stored-response-modeling (SRM) technique as a function of $x_2(0)$ vs. the real results (x).

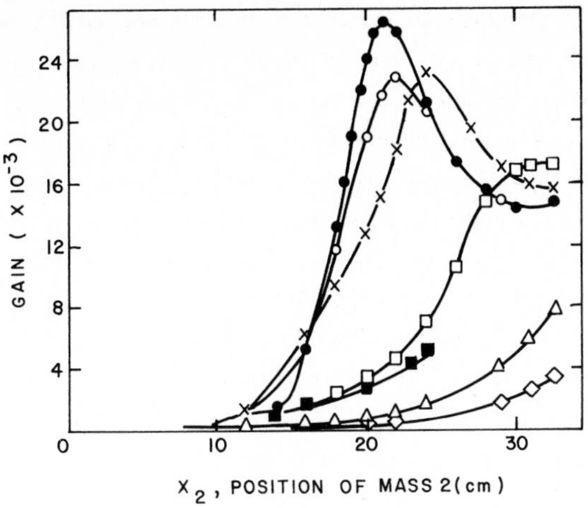

Fig. 168. Gain as a function of x_2 for several excitation frequencies; -●-, 0 Hz; -○-, 4 Hz; - x -, 10 Hz; -□- 20 Hz; -Δ-, 40 Hz; -■-, 40 Hz true; -◇-, 60 Hz.

Fig. 168 may now be used to solve the automatic vibration control problem as follows. Consider a measured input frequency of 4 Hz for which we wish to lessen the response at bar 2 as much as possible. For the entire range of movement of the mass, i.e. x_2 moving between 7.5 cm and 32.5 cm, we could choose 7.5 cm to yield the minimum output amplitude at bar 2 for a 4 Hz output. If, on the other hand, we consider restricted case in which the mass on bar 2 could be moved between x_2 = 19 cm and x_2 = 32.5 cm, then we could choose x_2 = 31 cm to yield the minimum amplitude response. In this manner, the curves shown in Fig. 168 can be used to obtain a "best" course of control action (in this case the position of the mass on bar 2) for any input in the area of the solution.

A third approach - physical experimentation - was used to obviate the necessity for developing a mathematical model of the system, which in many cases is a difficult or even impossible task, especially for essentially non-linear systems. The most important requirements that have to be met when seeking a computational method are: (i) an appropriate fit to the objective function being dealt with, (ii) simplicity of the algorithm which has to be realized by the microprocessor, and (iii) a reasonable time interval for execution of control. Accordingly, analog inputs and outputs of the PDP 11-40 computer were connected to the vibrating bar device yielding a closed loop control system. A randomized computing algorithm was selected, since these algorithms are sometimes superior to determined ones.

Among the criteria used in comparing different optimization techniques, the following points are worthy of mention.

If $\min_{x \in \chi} f(x) = f^*(x^*)$ and the minimization algorithm number r gives the minimized value of the objective function as $f_r(x_r)$, then $\Delta|f^*(x^*) - f_r(x_r)|$ can be taken as an optimization accuracy or quality criterion.

Now let us look at the execution time (in seconds). Suppose that there is an objective function $f(x_1,x_2,\ldots,x_n) = Y$ whose minimal value is desired, then we have to look for the best combination of parameters $x_1, x_2, \ldots, x_n$ which provides such a minimal value of the given function and to seek a technique which carries out this task in the shortest (or minimal) time. Here, we use the same random algorithm that was described in chapter IV section 5 for computation of optimal gear dynamics. To simplify matters for the reader, we will describe this algorithm once more, in brief, with some changes resulting from its application to the control system.

The limits of the parameter space can be expressed in any form:

$$x_{io} < x_i < x_{1*}\ , \quad i = 1,\ldots,n \tag{VII.2.4}$$

Here, the limits x_o and x_* can be functions or constant values. The first step comprises dividing the intervals by two. We will then have:

$$\bar{x}_i = (x_{io} + x_{i*})/2 \quad \text{and} \quad \Delta x_i = (x_{i*} - x_{io})/2 \tag{VII.2.5}$$

Obviously, $\bar{x}$ = the middle of the interval, and Δx = half of the interval. Let the number of each parametric "cube" be designated in binary code:

$$\alpha = (\alpha_1,\ldots,\alpha_q,\ldots,\alpha_n), \quad \alpha_q = \begin{cases} 0 \\ 1 \end{cases} \tag{VII.2.6}$$

Let "0" designate the left part of the interval and "1", the right one. For each fixed α take a series of n uniform $\overline{0.1}$ random numbers $h_1^{(j)},\ldots,h_n^{(j)}$, $j = 1,\ldots,k$. Now it is possible to calculate the values of the objective function f_j which agree with each j-th group of the randomized parameters:

$$f_j(x^{(j)}) = f_j(x_{10} + \Delta x_1[\alpha_1 + h_1^{(j)}],\ldots,x_{n0} + \Delta x[\alpha_n + h_n^{(j)}]) \tag{VII.2.7}$$

where k is the quantity of randomized parameter groups that have to be "thrown" to cover the space of one "cube" with sufficient density. For each of m cubes we have to compute k values of the objective function using each time n randomized parameters, according to equation (VII.2.6). Now we select the "cube" in which the minimal value of the objective function is obtained, and store the coordinates of that "cube". This reduced n-dimensional parametric "cube" defines the new parametric space. From here the procedure is repeated ℓ times until $\Delta x_i^{\ell} < \varepsilon_i$ is obtained. The value ε_i defines the permissible or desirable calculation accuracy for each i-th parameter. The calculation accuracy for parameter number i can be determined as $\varepsilon_i = (x_{i*} - x_{io})/2^{\ell}$. Obviously, we have to calculate $2^n k$ times the value of the objective function during one cycle, and $N = 2^{\ell+n} k$ times during the complete calculation. It should be noted that to arrive at some minima (or maxima) we have to repeat the same calculation q times.

The objective function of a real mechanical system changes relatively slowly, and even if the function has a number of extremes, the probability that these optimization results will not be "caught" by the wrong "pit" is high. Because of limited possibilities of the PDP 11-40 interface only two moving masses were controlled. Thus, their variable locations gave the parameter space. The root mean square value of the vibration amplitudes of the fourth mass m_4 served as the objective function. Hence, in this case n = 2. The goal of the optimization was to reach the minimum of $\sigma^2_{y_4}$. Here two "policies" were compared, as is described below.

In the first policy, random coordinates x_2 and x_3 of the masses were generated in a completely random way. The number of points in the "coordinate space" k was 25. The probability p of hitting in a "parameter area" $a = \Delta x_1 \Delta x_2$ can be expressed as $p_1 = 1 - [1 - a^n/A^n]^k$, where $A = (x_{1*} - x_{10})\cdot(x_{2*} - x_{20})$. The average control execution time T_1 can be described by $T_1 = k(x_{i*} - x_{i0})/nV$, where V is the average mass moving speed.

In the second policy, the random coordinates generated as in the previous case were listed in increasing order. Then the "first" mass was brought to the "first" random coordinate, and the "second" mass began to move from one point to the next (in increasing order). When the last point was reached, the "first" mass was brought to the second position, and then the "second" mass was moved backwards in "decreasing" order of its random coordinates. In this case the probability p_2 of "covering" an area a, defined as $p_2 = [1 - (1-a/A)^{\sqrt[n]{k}}]^n$, is worse, but the duration T_2 (in seconds) is much shorter: $T_2 = (\sqrt[n]{k} + 1)H/V$ where $H = x_{i*} - x_{i0}$. For instance for k - 100, n = 2, V = 1 cm/s, H = 24 cm and a/A = 0.2, we obtain $p_1 = 0.983$ and $T_1 = 1200$ s, whereas $p_2 = 0.796$ and $T_2 = 264$ s. If for the "second policy" we take k = 400, we obtain $p_2 = 0.977$, which is close to p_1, and $T_2 = 504$ s, which is still considerably less than T_1.

The results of automatic control executed by the vibrating bar device for a nonlinear case (backlashes between the bars and the masses) are presented in Fig. 169. The excitation includes two frequencies, ω_1 and ω_2, such that $\omega_1/\omega_2 = 0.9$ and $\omega_2 = 0.314$ rad/s. Fig. 169 also shows the locations of the vibrating masses before and after the optimization. Three steps were needed to reach the practical minimum root mean square value $\sigma^2_{y_4}$. The time required for this action was about 4.5 min, a time that can be reduced by increasing the valocity of the movement of the masses. The same effect can be achieved by

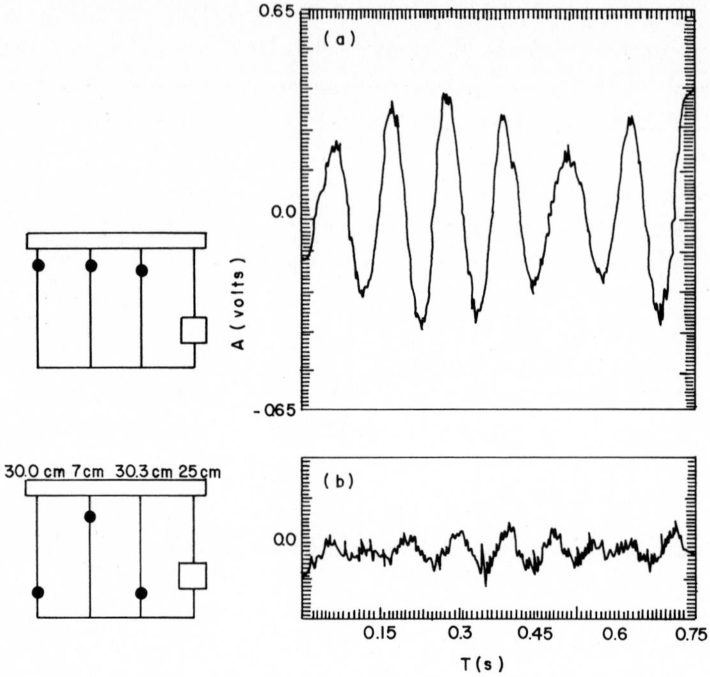

Fig. 169. Execution of automatic vibration control: a) vibrations of the mass 1 before control was instituted; b) vibrations of the mass 1 after the control was completed. The respective locations of masses 2, 3 and 4 are shown in the left.

reducing the sizes of the search areas, which must be reduced to reasonable values for each specific system. This technique does not require (1) any previous calculations or model assumptions, (2) any previous changes in the system, or (3) any knowledge about the parameters of the system. In addition, "noise" does not disturb the execution of control.

Conclusions

(1) Adaptive vibration control is of great importance in the optimal use of many practical working mechanisms in which the conditions of action of the mechanical system are variable.

(2) The complexity of the control unit depends on the amount of previous information about the structure of the system under consideration.

(3) For complicated, essentially nonlinear, mechanical systems, adaptive vibration based on "input-output" vibration measurements can be arranged. System identification techniques are sometimes useful for this purpose.

(4) In the author's opinion a very promising technique is that based on research tactics which provide the achievement of the optimal values of the objective function in a direct way: peculiarities of the mechanical structure and noises are automatically taken into account by this technique.

(5) The main disadvantage of this latter technique lies in the possibility of causing temporary high vibrations during the search. Special means have to be provided to avoid such situations.

BIBLIOGRAPHY

1. V.A. Kudinov, 1967, Dinamika Stankov. Moscow: Isdatelstvo "Mashinostre "Mashinostroenie". (In Russian" "Dynamics of Machine Tools".)
2. B.P. Barmin, 1972, Vibracii i Rezimy Rezania. Isdatelstvo "Mashinostroenie". (In Russian: Vibrations and Cutting Conditions".)
3. T.S. Sankar and M.O.M. Osman, 1975, Fourth World Congress on Theory of Machines and Mechanisms, Newcastle-upon-Tyne, England, 8-13 September 1975, On the effect of the dynamic characteristics of machine tools on the formation of surface profile.
4. I.I. Artobolevski, 1975, Fourth World Congress on Theory of Machines and Mechanisms, Newcastle-upon-Tyne, England, 8-13 September 1975. The past, present and future of the theory of machine and mechanisms.
5. B.Z. Sandler, 1977, ASME Winter Annual Meeting, Atlanta, 27 November-2 December 1977, ASME Publication 77 WA/DE 10. Cam Mechanism Accuracy.
6. J. Eichler, 1978, American Society of Mechanical Engineers Transactions 100 (June). Stored response modeling.
7. B.Z. Sandler, 1977, American Society of Mechanical Engineers Transactions 99, No. 1 (February). The use of a random algorithm for dynamic optimization of mechanisms.

3. ADAPTIVE VIBROFEEDERS

Vibrofeeding was introduced into the manufacturing industries in the early 1950s and since then has rapidly displaced mechanical feeding and orientation devices.

The principle of action of a vibrofeeder can be explained with the help of the diagram given in Fig. 170. Here, a tray 1 is fastened to two inclined springs 2 and to the armature 4 of an electromagnet 3. Thus, when a voltage is applied to the electromagnet, it pulls the tray towards itself, and when the voltage is cut off, the springs bring the tray back. The angle of inclination of the springs β forces the tray to move along an arc. For small displacements of the tray, it can be considered to be moving along a straight line a-a. If

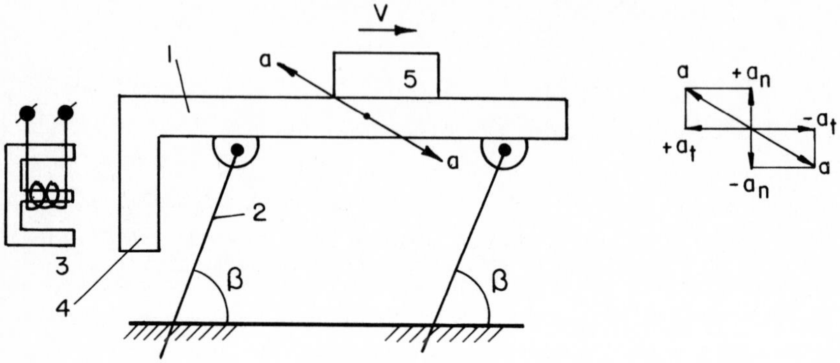

Fig. 170. Layout of a vibroconveying system.

an alternating current is applied to the electromagnet, the tray begins to oscillate. Thus, the tray experiences an acceleration a, which can be resolved into horizontal and vertical components, as is shown in Fig. 170. As a result of the action of the vertical component of the acceleration a_n, the body 5, which is situated on top of the tray, is pressed to the tray by an inertial force N:

$$N = m(g \pm a_n) \tag{VII.3.1}$$

This force causes friction force F

$$F = fN = fm(g \pm a_n) \tag{VII.3.2}$$

where f - friction coefficient.

The horizontal component of the acceleration a_t of the tray causes horizontal movement of the body 5 on the tray. To provide such a movement, the condition

$$ma_n \leq fN \tag{VII.3.3}$$

must be met. When this condition exists, the body does not move relative to the tray. Conversely, when

$$ma_n > fN \tag{VII.3.4}$$

the body slides relative to the tray. The arrow in Fig. 170 indicates the direction of movement of the body along the tray. The acceleration a changes harmonically, or nearly harmonically, as do its horizontal a_t and vertical a_n components. As a result, during part of the oscillation period the condition (VII.3.3) is fulfilled, and the body moves relative to the tray.

When high oscillation amplitudes are reached, the body can rebound from the tray: thus, the situation

$$a_n > g \tag{VII.3.5}$$

is usually undesirable in vibroconveying or vibrofeeding.

Obviously, the tray can be made in a spiral shape forming a bowl which oscillates angularly. Vibrofeeders of this type are very common, and a general view of a typical spiral vibrofeeder is given in Fig. 171.

Fig. 171. General view of a spiral vibrofeeder. (AA model-5 feeder built by Aylesbury Automation Ltd., England with the author's adapter.)

Vibrofeeders are widely used in automatic processing and assembly machines for feeding and orientation of the details with which the machine works. To provide the required productivity in feeding of the parts, the bowl of the device has to develop definite vibration amplitudes, which can be achieved by tuning the current source to certain amplitudes.

To guarantee minimal energy consumption, the vibrofeeder is designed and tuned to act close to its mechanical resonance point. At the same time, to guarantee stability of action, the excitation frequency is not chosen to be exactly equal to or too close to the resonance point, since the closer the frequency of the excitation force to the natural resonance frequency of the device, the more sensitive the whole device to small deviations in the conditions of action and the lower the stability.

Usually, an alternating voltage of 50 or 60 Hz is used to excite the vibrations (sometimes double those values - 100 or 120 Hz is preferred). Thus, the mechanical system is designed to have its natural resonance frequency close to one of these values. Because of the simplicity of obtaining of this excitation, a psychological taboo has developed in the design of vibrofeeders: in the overwhelming majority of cases the frequency of the voltage actuating the electromagnets will conform to one of the four above mentioned values. The stiffnesses of the springs, the masses and shapes of the bowl, and the location and number of electromagnets are, however, not subject to traditional restrictions.

The remainder of this section is devoted to the description of a vibrofeeder which is automatically kept in permanent resonance, regardless of continuously, randomly, or regularly changing working conditions (changes in mass, mechanical resistance, damping, or the current frequencies in the network). With such a vibrofeeder, stability of action is ensured , energy consumption from the network is minimal; and manual control by the operators is reduced to a minimum.

At this stage, we will not consider automatic control of the amplitude of the vibrations of the bowl, which depends, to a certain extent, on the mass changes as a result of the depletion of the feed material from the bowl. We should, however, bear in mind that there are certain technical measures which can help to avoid, or at least to minimize, the negative consequences of this variable.

Let us consider the model presented in Fig. 172. A vibrating mass m, which

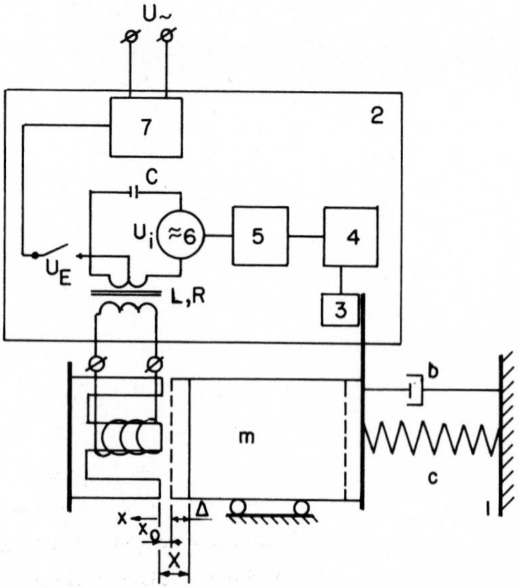

Fig. 172. Dynamic model of the vibrofeeder with the adaptive-control device.

which includes the bowl and its contents, is fastened to a base 1 by means of a spring whose stiffness c is given. The dissipative energy losses caused by friction of the parts in the bowl and by internal friction in the joints are taken into account by the use of a damping coefficient b. The vibrations of the mass are excited by an electromagnet, consisting of a core, an armature fixed to the bowl, and a coil with initial inductance L_o. Current is supplied to the coil from an electric circuit 2, which is connected to the network through a control unit. A sensor 3 provides information about the motion of the bowl to the circuit, and in this way a feedback is introduced into the automatic control system, thus closing the loop.

Displacement, speed, and/or acceleration of the vibrating bowl can serve as the feedback for the automatic control. On the basis of the reasons listed below, we prefer to use the acceleration measurement. In this case, only one element is attached to the bowl of the vibrofeeder since speed and displacement are relative to the immovable basis of the feeder. To obtain the required signal in the case of speed or displacement, two elements must be connected to the system, one to the bowl and the other to the base. The advantages of measuring acceleration are:

a) higher accuracy of the accelerometric feedback and a smaller possibility of introducing disturbances;
b) lower cost of fastening the sensor to the vibrofeeder.

In our experiments we used both speed and acceleration sensors. The former is based on the utilization of current induced in an immovable coil fixed to the base of the feeder by a vibrating magnet attached to the bowl.

The electronic circuit of our experimental vibrofeeder consists of a phase-shifter 4, which rotates the vector of the electromotive force generated by the sensor 3; a conventional amplifier 5 with negative feedback based on an RC741NB element; an invertor 6; and a rectifier 7 (Fig. 172).

We will continue our discussion with

(1) an analysis of the energy consumption of the adaptive vibrofeeder, as compared with that of convetional feeders.

(2) a presentation of the experimental results obtained with an adaptive vibrofeeder built at Ben-Gurion University of the Negev on the basis of an industrial AA model-5 vibrofeeder produced by Aylesbury Automation Ltd. (England).

The power N_o consumed by the system under consideration from the outer source can be defined as:

$$N_o = F\dot{x} \tag{VII.3.6}$$

The energy N used during half a period is:

$$N = \int_{0}^{T/2} F\dot{x}dt \qquad \text{(VII.3.7)}$$

(We specify half a period because the electromagnet is only able to pull the armature during half a period, while during the other half it does not influence the mechanical system.)

We will now describe analytically the model depicted in Fig. 172 and show the energy saving in comparison with a conventional vibrofeeder. According to the Figure:

X - the gap between the magnet and the armature when no electric current flows through the coil;

x_o - the initial gap between the magnet and the armature when the constant component of the corrent flows through the coil;

$|\Delta|=X-x_o$ - the deformation of the spring caused by the constant component of the electromagnetic force initiated by the constant component of the electric current.

Taking into account the directions of these sections, we can determine that:

$$-\Delta = X - x_o \qquad \text{(VII.3.8)}$$

The following equations describe the work of the system.

$$\begin{cases} m\ddot{x} + b\dot{x} + c(x + \Delta) = F_i + F_e \\ \frac{d(Li)}{dt} + Ri + \frac{1}{c}\int idt = U_i + U_e \end{cases} \qquad \text{(VII.3.9)}$$

where

b - lumped damping coefficient;

c - the lumped stiffness of the spring system;

C - lumped capacitance;

i - electric current;

L - lumped inductance;

m - the lumped moving mass (tray or bowl plus conveyed items);

R - lumped electric resistance;

t - time;

x - displacement of the bowl;

F_i - internal force developed by the magnet;

F_e - external component of control voltage;

U_i - internal component of control voltage;

U_e - external component of control voltage.

The force F_i can be expressed as

$$F_i = \partial W/\partial x \qquad \text{(VII.3.10)}$$

where W - magnetic flow equals $W = \frac{1}{2} Li^2$ (VII.3.11)

$$\text{while} \quad L = \frac{L_o}{\alpha}\left(1 + \frac{x}{x_o}\right)^{-1} \qquad \text{for } |x| << x_o \qquad \text{(VII.3.12)}$$

where

L_o - initial inductance of the coil;

α - lumped coefficient of the dissipation of the magnetic field.

Then

$$F_i = -\frac{L_o i^2}{2\alpha x_o}\left(1 + \frac{x}{x_o}\right)^{-2} \qquad \text{(VII.3.13)}$$

The voltage U_i, in our case, is generated by the circuit and is made proportional to the vibrating speed $\dot{x}$:

$$U_i = A_1\dot{x}$$

or to the acceleration $\ddot{x}$:

$$U_i = A_2\ddot{x}$$

where A_1 and A_2 are constants depending on the properties of the circuit. A constant magnetic field (generated by the constant current component) is used for the following reason. It is clear from equation (VII.2.13) that the electromagnetic force, which is the vibration exciter in the vibrofeeder under consideration, is proportional to the square of the electric current in the coil of the magnet. If the current is harmonic, i.e. if

$$i = i_o \cos\omega t \qquad \text{(VII.3.14)}$$

where i_o - the amplitude of the alternating current

ω - the frequency of the alternating current,

then the electromagnetic force will change with twice the frequency 2ω. To avoid this situation we have to ensure that the changing component of the current does not cross the zero axis (a negative value of the current is not allowed). By adding a constant current i^* which is not less than the amplitude i_o, we satisfy this condition.

On the basis of equation (VII.3.9) and our own experience, we assume that the motion law of the bowl actuated by the current in accordance with equation (VII.3.14) has the following harmonic form:

$$x = a\cos\omega t \tag{VII.3.15}$$

where a - the amplitude of the bowl's oscillations.

Let us denote:

q - electric charge;

q_o - amplitude of the charge;

$\omega_o^2 = c/m$ - natural frequency of the mechanical oscillator.

Now substituting equation (VII.3.13) into equation (VII.3.7) and remembering expression (VII.3.15), we obtain:

$$N = \frac{L_o x_o q_o^2 \omega^3 a}{2\alpha} \int_0^{T/2} \frac{\sin^3 \omega t dt}{(x_o + a\cos\omega t)^2} \tag{VII.3.16}$$

To simplify the analysis of expression (VII.3.16), we introduce a nondimensional value $B = x_o/a$. It then follows from equation (VII.3.16) that:

$$N = \frac{L_o \omega^2 q_o^2}{2} B[B\ln \frac{B+1}{B-1} - 2] \tag{VII.3.17}$$

On the other hand, considering the mechanical part of the vibrating bowl as a one-mass oscillator, we can express the oscillation amplitudes as follows:

$$a = F_o / m\sqrt{(\omega_o^2 - \omega^2)^2 + 4n^2\omega^2} \tag{VII.3.18}$$

where F_o - amplitude of the excitation force;

and $n = b/2m$

From equation (VII.3.13) we derive:

$$F_o = - \frac{L_o i_o^2}{2\alpha x_o} (1 + \frac{a}{x_o})^{-2} \tag{VII.3.19}$$

Remembering that $i = \dot{q}$, we obtain:

$$i_o = q_o \omega \tag{VII.3.20}$$

Substituting equations (VII.3.20) and (VII.3.19) into expression (VII.3.18), we obtain:

$$q_o^2 = \frac{2\alpha a(x_o + a)^2 m\sqrt{(\omega_o^2 - \omega^2)^2 + 4n^2\omega^2}}{L_o \omega^2 x_o} \tag{VII.3.21}$$

Substituting equation (VII.3.21) into equation (VII.3.17), we obtain an expression which describes the relationship between the power used and the excitation frequency in the following form:

$$N \simeq 2[B\ln\frac{B+1}{B-1} - 2](x_o + a)^2 m\sqrt{(\omega_o^2 - \omega^2)^2 + 4n^2\omega^2} \qquad \text{(VII.3.22)}$$

Let us define $\lambda = \omega/\omega_o$ and $\eta = n/\omega_o$, thus simplifying equation (VII.3.22), in the following way:

$$N \simeq 2[B\ln\frac{B+1}{B-1} - 2](x_o + a)^2 m\omega_o^2\sqrt{(1-\lambda^2)^2 + 4\eta^2\lambda^2} \qquad \text{(VII.3.23)}$$

It is now possible to show the dimensionless relationship of the required electric power for different λ while the value of B remains constant for the resonance regime $\lambda = 1$. Thus, the relationship of any power N_λ for any specific λ to the resonant power N_R (B is the same in both cases) is as follows:

$$N_\lambda/N_R = \sqrt{(1-\lambda^2)^2 + 4\eta^2\lambda^2}\ /\ 2\eta \qquad \text{(VII.3.24)}$$

Fig. 173 shows the dependence (VII.3.24) for different damping conditions.

Fig. 174 presents the experimental results obtained with a vibrofeeder manufactured by Aylesbury Automation Ltd. (England). Comparing the calculated and measured curves in these two Figures, we see that the damping parameter in the experimental device is about 0.006. The natural frequency of the conventional vibrofeeder differs from the excitation frequency (50 Hz) by about 14%. In our experiments, the absolute power values for the Aylesbury Automation vibrofeeder were:

I	N conventional	=	30 VA	without load
	N adaptive	=	4.22 VA	
II	N conventional	=	33.6 VA	with load
	N adaptive	=	10.8 VA	

Fig. 175 presents the dependence of the bowl's amplitude of vibration on the voltage change in the network. The Figure clearly indicates that the adaptive vibrofeeder is considerably more stable than the conventional model.

Fig. 176 gives additional information on amplitude dependences for different excitation and load conditions. The curve 1 represents the behavior of the vibration amplitude as a function of the load when the feeder is supplied with a constant frequency of 47.2 Hz which is close to the resonance of 450 g load. In this case the power consumption is 3.72 W. Curve 2 represents the behavior of the bowl's vibration under the same conditions for a network frequency of 50 Hz. The power consumption is considerably bigger, being about 9.95 W.

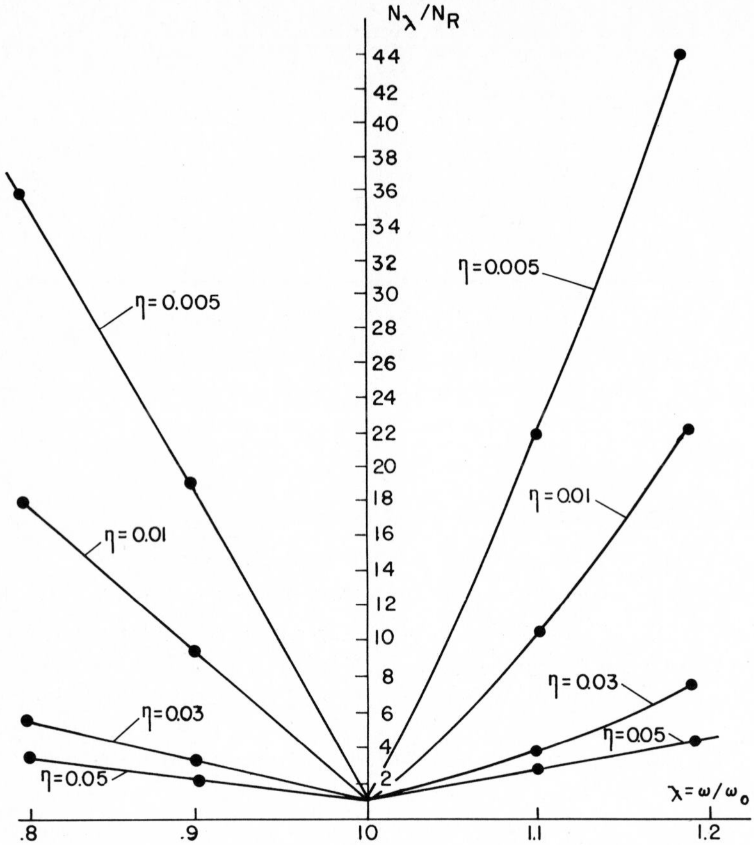

Fig. 173. Calculated dependence of the power consumption of the feeder as a function frequency of the voltage (for different friction conditions).

Curve 3 represents the behavior of the bowl of the adaptive vibrofeeder. The power consumption is again 3.72 W (but we can see that the same power facilitates bigger amplitudes).

Conclusions

(1) The energy consumed from the network by a vibrofeeder working permanently at its mechanical resonance frequency is considerably less than of that required by a conventional feeder, the energy saving being 60-80%.

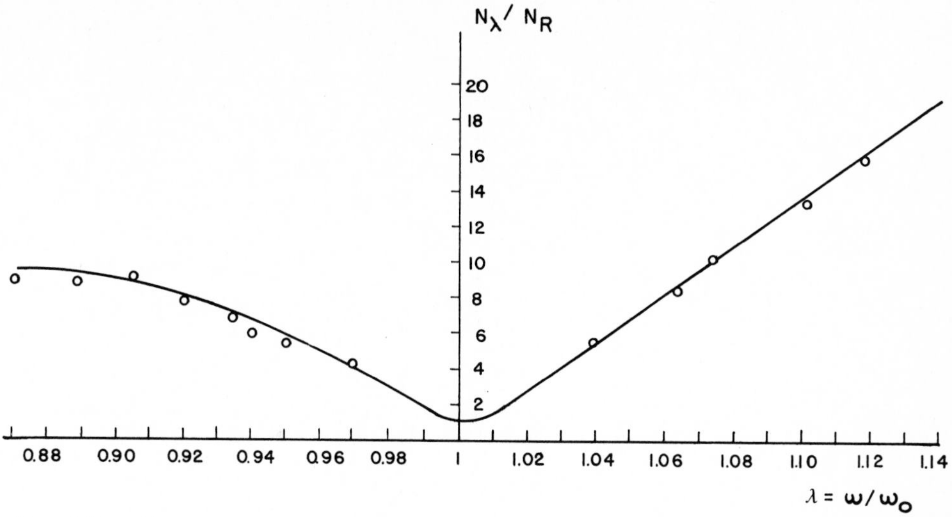

Fig. 174. Measured power consumption for the experimental feeder as a function of the voltage frequency.

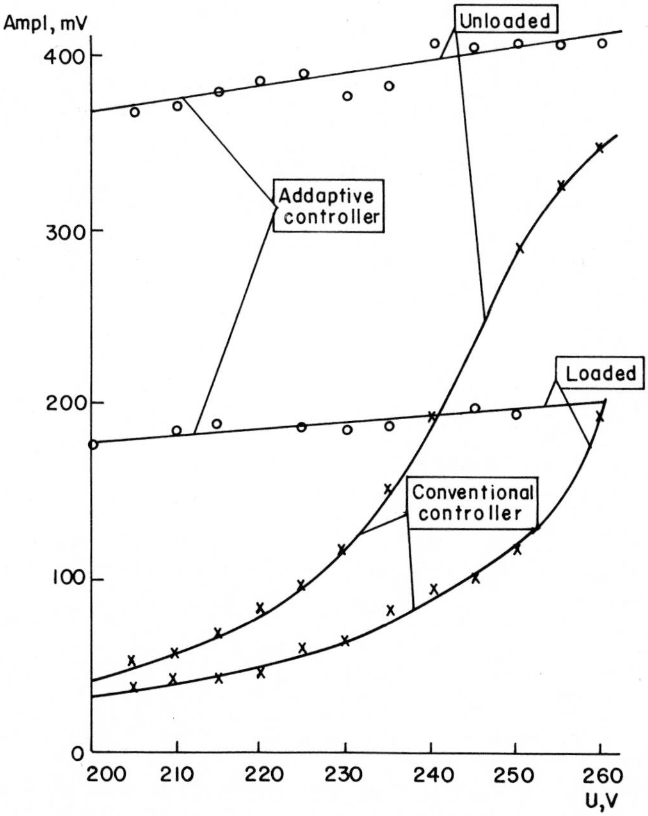

Fig. 175. Influence of changes in the network voltage on the bowl vibration amplitudes.

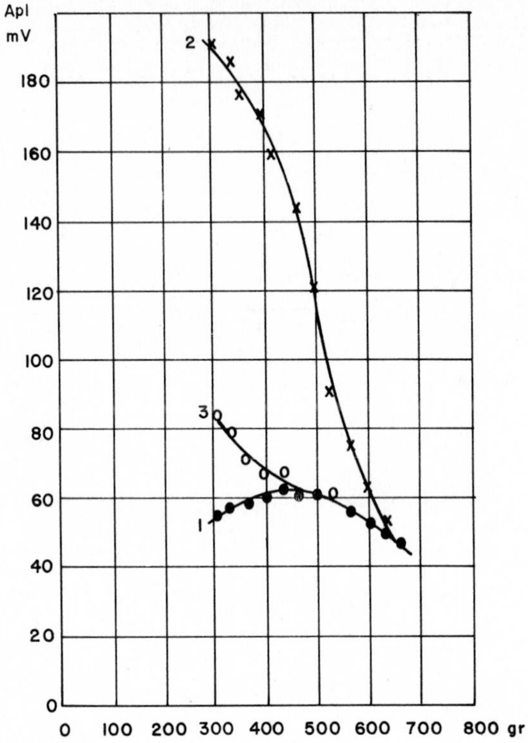

Fig. 176. 1. Bowl vibration amplitude as a function of the load at a voltage frequency of 47.2 Hz; 2. Bowl vibration amplitude as a function of the load of a voltage frequency of 50 Hz; 3. Automatically controlled feeder.

(2) The stability of vibrofeeding can be appreciably improved by the use of an adaptive self-tuning device, because the system constantly follows the "top" of the resonance curve even when the mass of the vibrating bowl is reduced to about 15-20% due to depletion of the feed material.

This section on vibrofeeding is written together with my colleague Dr. R. Mozniker to whom I express my deep appreciation.

SELECTED BIBLIOGRAPHY

1. H. Kettner, H. Ahrens and G.W. Stoevesandt. Zum Fordervorgang im Vibrations-Wendelforderer, VDI.Z 122, 1980.
2. S. Okabe and Y. Yokoyama. Study of vibratory feeders: Calculation of natural frequency of bowl-type feeders. ASME J. Mechanical Design

103/249: 249-256, 1981.

3. E.E. Lavendel. Syntez optimalnyh vibromashin, Izdatelstvo, "ZINATNE" Riga, 1970 (Synthesis of optimal vibromachines, in Russian).

4. B.Z. Sandler, USA patent 4114453, Sept. 19, 1978, Accelerometer Sensor.

AFTERWORD

The main concept of this book is the application of probabilistics to the investigation of mechanical systems. As far as we know, such an approach has been rarely used. Part of the material presented here is devoted to the direct application of random function theory to the investigation of random processes in, for example, the deflection of cam profiles, pitch of gear teeth, pressure in pipes, etc. The other part of the material raises some original ideas that can and must be further developed and deepened. They are:

1. The measuring technique (Chapter III, section 9 and Chapter IV, section 3) based on the comparison of two or more measured bodies, without a need for any kind of standard having a higher accuracy than that required for the measurements.
2. Adaptive mechanisms or automatic vibration control as means to control harmful or useful vibrations (Chapter VII).
3. The optimization of a mechanical system with the purpose of minimizing harm vibrations (or noise) by redistribution of the spectral density of the input noise (Chapter VI, section 6) instead of by the usual method of changing the structure of the system.
4. Estimation of the reliability of empirical formulas used for the calculation of some machine elements (Chapter IV, section 6). This permits answering the question of whether it is better to know many parameters describing specific properties of the element under consideration or to be very sure of a limited number of parameters.

I hope that this book will awaken an interest in investigating these areas further and will stimulate new ideas for the application of probabilities to mechanical systems analyses and syntheses.

INDEX

INDEX (cont'd)

INDEX (cont'd)

INDEX (cont'd)

INDEX (cont'd)